# Concept Learning

# Concept

## An Information

WESTERN MANAGEMENT SCIENCE INSTITUTE

UNIVERSITY OF CALIFORNIA AT LOS ANGELES

John Wiley and Sons, Inc.

*New York and London*

# Learning

## Processing Problem

**Earl B. Hunt**

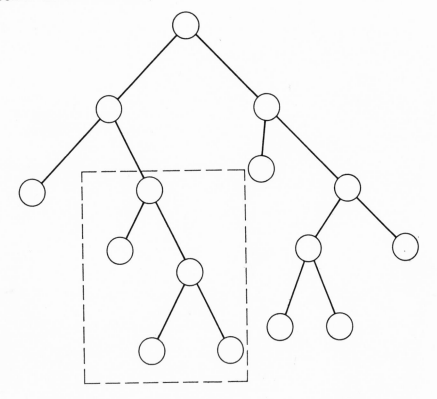

Library of Congress Catalog Card Number: 62-19147
Printed in the United States of America

7.50

TO CARL I. HOVLAND

# Preface

This book attempts to treat its topic, concept learning, from a "problem oriented" point of view. Concept learning is an important part of the organization of knowledge. Therefore it is worth treating in its own right; not solely as a topic in logic, a type of behavior to be derived from psychological theory, or a possible area of application for electronic computers. An attempt has been made to bring together some of the relevant material from all these fields.

To keep the book within a reasonable size, it was necessary to exercise considerable selection in including theoretical points of view and reports of particular research. Inevitably I had to use my own judgment. Therefore I had best state my own biases. I originally became interested in concept learning as a topic in psychology, somewhat later I became interested in the application of digital computer programs to inductive reasoning problems. My knowledge of symbolic logic is largely self-acquired, I can only hope that I have made an adequate presentation of the role of concepts, as conceived by some philosophers, in formal logic. With these limitations in mind, I hope that this report will be useful in correlating the efforts of many researchers who have approached the same topic in diverse ways.

This work was originally planned as a joint project with the late Sterling Professor Carl I. Hovland of Yale University. I was privileged to work with Professor Hovland, first as a student and later as a junior associate, from 1957 until his untimely death in April of 1961. He first introduced me to the study of concept learning and greatly influenced my approach to the problem. I have no doubt that, had he been able to work with me, his contribution would have been very valuable. Unfortunately, this was not to be. But my first acknowledgment must be to Carl Hovland, who, by example and direction, encouraged me to attempt a contribution of this nature.

I have been fortunate in having direct and indirect assistance from many colleagues and friends. Professor Donald Taylor of Yale University has continually supported and challenged my ideas. His support, criticisms, and encouragement have all been of great help to me.

vii

Dr. Herbert Wells devoted a great deal of his time to discussion of both the manuscript and the entire field. Professor George Miller of Harvard University made several valuable suggestions.

Specific chapters were discussed with different individuals. Professor Frank Logan has presented such cogent arguments for a "stimulus response" analysis of learning that I felt forced to devote a great deal of space to discussing the relation between concept learning and behavior theory of the type advocated by Hull, Spence, Logan, Neal Miller, and many other psychologists. My logical definition of concept learning is, in part, the result of helpful criticisms from Drs. James MacQueen, Leo Brieman, and Professor Masanao Toda. I was generously granted the opportunity to observe current research projects, either by visit, conversation, or correspondence, by S. Amarel, R. Banerji, Gordon Bower, Lyle Bourne, Edward Feigenbaum, M. Kochen, John McCarthy, J. Marschak, Allen Newell, Roger Shepard, Herbert Simon, and Douwe Yntema. Where the work of these gentlemen is referred to specifically I hope that they will not feel that I have misrepresented their efforts.

The responsibility for any errors of fact, omissions, or misinterpretations is, of course, mine.

Last, but certainly not least, I have received excellent administrative support. The work done in preparation of this manuscript was financed by a Ford Foundation grant for the study of concept learning which was originally made to Carl I. Hovland and later administered by Donald Taylor. The Western Management Science Institute, UCLA (James R. Jackson, Director), supported my work on the final draft, also under a grant from the Ford Foundation. The Psychology Department of Yale University, Professor Claude Buxton, Chairman, provided an excellent setting for the original preparation of a manuscript. At Yale Miss Sonya Dowrey typed the original paper, even learning to read my handwriting! Miss Jane Olejarcyzk at Yale and Miss Doris Isolini and Mrs. Marilyn Brown at UCLA handled countless secretarial tasks, which, had I had to do them, would probably have kept me from ever finishing the work. Miss Janet Kreuter read the final typescript for clarity and continuity, making several valuable suggestions.

EARL B. HUNT

*Los Angeles, California*
*August, 1962*

# Contents

# 1

# The nature of
# concept learning

## 1    *Some initial questions*

What is a "concept"? When we encounter grammatically permissible phrases such as the "concept of dogs," and the "concept of massive retaliation," we suspect that there is a duality of meaning not appropriate in scientific discourse. A glance at Webster's dictionary confirms our suspicions:

**concept** 1. A thought, an opinion. 2. *Philos.* A mental image of a thing formed by a generalization from particulars; also, an idea of what a thing in general is to be.

We shall be concerned with the second definition. The ability to think in terms of abstractions is one of the most powerful tools man possesses. It is literally true that we never step into the same river twice; every situation is in some sense unique. Yet we manage to order our experience into coherent categories by defining a given situation as a member of that collection of situations for which responses $x$, $y$, etc. are appropriate. We classify. Classification is not a passive process. Tests must be made to determine whether the present situation contains certain elements or whether it can be described in a particular way. The results of these tests provide the information we use to guide the classifying act. But how do we develop rules for testing? This is the question to which the present research has been addressed.

Understanding how humans learn abstractions is essential to the understanding of human thought. Even so, it is not the only reason for studying concept learning. The history of Western man suggests that soon after a person understands how he, a human being, performs a particular task, another human being will attempt to make a machine that will perform the task better. The second person may use, but is in no way limited to, the techniques discovered by the first. Hopefully, the machine that is produced will be a better performer. This sequence has occurred for most of the physical labor performed by man

1

in the last 3000 years. Should it be any different for mental labor? There may be a moral objection to artificial intelligence, but we cannot see any scientific reason why such automata could not be constructed. We shall go beyond a review of the evidence in human concept learning, therefore, and consider some of the principles that could be used in the design of an artificial classification mechanism. In doing so, we shall find that our understanding of the human action and, perhaps, the organization of knowledge may be enhanced.

If we are going to study abstracting ability we must be able to recognize its occurrence. How do you decide when a person has acquired a concept? Is it possible to define the "in general" in the phrase "what a thing in general should be"? It is, if we develop a notation which reflects our capacity to observe different aspects of the concept-learning process. We can only observe the stimuli to which an organism is exposed and the responses which it makes. We can operationally define concept learning by observing. A strong statement of the operational approach has appeared in a recent review of the relevant psychological evidence on concept formation (Kendler, 1961). Concept learning was defined as any situation that involves the "acquisition or utilization, or both, of a common response to dissimilar stimuli." Kendler cautioned that the definition was too broad. But she also pointed out, and quite correctly, that there must be an operational definition available which can be used to distinguish between concept formation and the situations that fit her general definition and are not concept formation. Can we develop such a definition?

As a start we need an almost trivial distinction. Acquisition of a response involves both the capacity to distinguish situations in which the response is appropriate *and* the capacity to make the response. Concept learning and use refers only to the identification step. The necessary distinction can be made by rewording Kendler's statement to read "acquisition, or utilization, or both, of a common *identifying* response to dissimilar stimuli."

If we think of utilization of a name as a response, such acts as learning to call particular animals "dogs" will be classified as concept learning. This seems appropriate. We certainly wish to include the learning of the use of names as an example of concept learning. There are other types of behavior, however, which fit the modified definition and may not be the sort of thing we mean, intuitively, when we speak of concept learning. Suppose a psychologist trains a rat to jump toward circles and away from triangles. Do we wish to say that the rat learns the concept of triangularity? Or do we wish to distinguish between two classes of behavior, discrimination and concept learning, under the same rubric of "common response to dissimilar stimuli"? The author feels that the distinction is important, and wishes to make it. But it must be made in a precise manner. To do so, three further restrictions will be placed on the general classification situation.

The first limitation can be stated as a question about the subject's capabilities. "If appropriately interrogated, could the subject instruct a human being in the use of the identifying response without using examples?" This question has a very interesting implication. At one fell swoop, we have reduced our concern to two types of subjects, humans and machines. Humans can talk to other humans; machines have their logic, which can be examined by means of wiring diagrams and blueprints. Even a randomly constructed machine can always be dismantled. At present, we cannot infer the internal logic of a non-human biological subject except by observing its classification behavior.

This restriction is somewhat unusual. We generally think of a "problem" as being defined by a state of the world facing the problem solver, and not by the characteristics of the problem solver. In fact, psychology has been defined as the scientific study of behavior, and behavior makes sense only in reference to particular stimuli. Yet we are limiting our study of "concept learning" to a particular class of subjects, one subclass of which is a set of nonliving entities. The restricted definition of concept learning to be used here can be justified only because we are concerned with the *process* by which concepts may be acquired. Concentration of our attention on processes useful in a particular task will force us to emphasize points different from those emphasized by investigators who see the task as an example of a general principle of behavior.[1]

The qualification also suggests, correctly, that we are interested in any situation in which a concept learner could, conceivably, have described his classification rule. It does not matter whether or not he actually made the description. If we feel reasonably sure that a symbol manipulation process is occurring, we can take as evidence about that process any response the subject makes, including verbal responses. But verbal responses may or may not be the best evidence. In particular, verbal responses must not be confused with the symbolic processes which underlie them. In our analysis, these processes assume the role of hypothetical constructs (in the sense used by MacCorquodale and Meehl, 1948). If we specify the process-response relation, any response may be used to infer a process. Conversely, the utility of an assumed process depends entirely on our ability to use it to predict observable responses.

A return to an introspectionist psychology is being neither assumed nor advocated. In fact, our limitation on the type of subject we shall study makes no statement whatsoever about the subject's ability to tell us *how* he formed a concept. We have only required that he be able to tell us what the concept is after it has been formed. Here the situation is similar to the sort of experimental problem encountered in perception; verbal report is one of the best ways the experimenter has of determining what the subject saw. On the other hand, the subject may be totally unable to state how or why he saw it. To deny total reliance on introspection is not the same as ignoring introspective reports. It is possible to create fairly elaborate models of cognitive action from essentially introspective and subjective data (Miller, Galanter, and Pribram, 1960). Completely ignoring such reports seems unreasonable. Again, we are in the same situation as those psychologists who wish to study the private phenomenon of perception. We cannot observe thinking directly. Perhaps the best course in the study of thought processes is the one that Dember (1960) has proposed for the study of perception: utilize introspective reports as heuristic guides, reserving the final test of models for situations in which they can be validated by observable responses.

We assume classification constancy. An object may be assigned to any number of classes but no object may sometimes be assigned to one class and sometimes not be assigned to the same class. For example, consider a particular animal. He may be a house pet, a collie, and a purebred dog. He may not be sometimes a purebred, sometimes a mongrel. This is not a trivial distinction. When we rule out changing classifications, we also rule out probabilistic concept learning, where infallible rules are not possible. We shall occasionally discuss non-deterministic categorization, and in particular the inferences that can be drawn by a concept learner when he cannot find a solution to a classification problem which he believes to be deterministic, but this will not be our primary concern.

By these definitions arbitrary categorization is not concept learning, yet it sometimes appears in the psychological literature under this name. A single response may be designated as appropriate for several arbitrarily selected stimuli. There is no way to state a classifying rule without using examples. Furthermore, the learner can use his classifying rule only for the stimuli he has previously experienced. This does not seem consistent with the dictionary definition of a concept; a concept should be generalizable beyond our immediate experience.

Learning to recognize perceptual patterns is a type of classification learning which poses a difficult logical problem. The act of categorizing sensory input is basic to our perception of the world about us. For instance, we separate geometric forms into "circles" and "not circles," colors into "red" and "not red." In speech recognition, we must be able to assign a variety of different sounds to the same previously learned category. Concept learning is certainly an example of pattern recognition. But is it legitimate to distinguish between this example and the pattern recognition behavior that occurs in perception?

Like Bruner (1957), we feel that a distinction between perception and conception does exist. Unfortunately, it is very difficult to make the distinction precise. The differences appear to be quantitative rather than qualitative, both in the perceptual and conceptual situations discussed by philosophers and those studied by experimental psychologists.

One of the major differences is in the process involved. The perceptual act of categorizing is immediate. We feel that "a rose is a rose is a rose" without further analysis of what a rose is. This is even more striking in the perception of "basic" organizations, such as figure and ground or even speech versus noise. During the learning of a perceptual classification a statable analytic rule is seldom developed. Instead, the categorizer appears to learn to make the appropriate response without analysis of the component parts of the stimulus. In a concept-learning situation, on the other hand, a *relatively* greater emphasis is placed on such an analysis. The concept learner is pictured as viewing a stimulus as an aggregate of examples of more molecular concepts and the relations between them. The classification rule being used at any one time should be statable in some language known to the learner. In the terms of Gestalt psychology, the "set" with which the subject approaches the task is different in perception from that with which he approaches the concept-learning task.

Another distinction can be made in terms of the properties of the task. In what we normally call perceptual pattern recognition, the information which is transmitted *directly* from the pattern to be categorized through the sensory receptors of the categorizer may not be sufficient to classify the pattern. Consider the example of "circles." Most of the circles which we see (for instance, coins on a desk) reach our eyes as signals that cannot be distinguished from the signal received from an ellipse. Yet we make the classification "circle," usually without hesitation. How?

In perceptual identification, information is transmitted by the object and the context in which it occurs. This can easily be demonstrated by situations in which the cues from the object to be categorized and its context are in conflict, for example, the spoken phrase "Parson Jones was a God sneering man." Certain perceptual constancy phenomena, in which objects are assigned to a particular category largely on the basis of the context in which they occur instead of the information which they transmit to the receptors, also illustrate this principle. In both cases objects are misidentified (relative to their projection of energy on sensory receptors) because of the simultaneous presence of certain other objects. Since concept learning refers to the learning of what a thing *in general* should be, it seems reasonable that we demand that conceptual classifications be based only on information contained in the object to be categorized.

Neither the process nor situational differences between perception and conception are "all or none" distinctions. The degree to which a person is able to specify an analytic classification rule varies, and so may his "set" to develop one. Context may be an all important determiner of class membership, it may be trivially relevant, or it may be somewhere in between. Any distinction will have some degree of arbitrariness. Nevertheless, the distinction should be made. It may be quite important in the design of artificial pattern recognizers or in the construction of simulation of human processes. A "perceiving" automaton should perhaps rely on a large number of error-prone tests. Its discriminations would be rapid and essentially statistical. A concept-learning pattern recognizer, on the other hand, would handle a formally identical problem in quite a different way. It would seek to build up a few, highly accurate tests based on a restricted portion of its environment. On a priori grounds, we cannot maintain that biological problem solvers, and especially human beings who have available the analytic power of speech, do not shift their categorizing processes from perception to cognition, or vice versa, depending on the demands of the situation. Thus pattern recognition problems which, at a certain level of formal description, are only quantitatively different from concept learning, may be solved in qualitatively different ways. Since we are concerned with the conceptual task, we shall normally be most interested in the problem-solving processes appropriate to it.

As it is used in this monograph, concept learning is defined as a term which applies to any situation in which a subject learns to make an identifying response to members of a set of not completely identical stimuli, subject to the following restrictions:

1. The subject must, conceivably, be able to instruct a human to apply the classification rule. The subject is not allowed to use examples during the course of this instruction.

2. The rule to be learned must be one that can be applied to any appropriate stimulus regardless of the context in which the stimulus appears.

3. The rule must be deterministic; once a given stimulus is completely described it must be uniquely classifiable.

Rule 1 eliminated the study of infrahuman organisms. Rule 2 eliminated almost all the so-called perceptual learning phenomena. Rule 3 eliminated the learning of many rules (e.g., weather prediction) by which we lead our stochastically categorized lives. Is there anything left?

A large class of very interesting phenomena remains. To point to a few examples, medical diagnosis, decoding, and taxonomy are all cases of concept learning. All forms of behavior in which the use of a name is learned will be included under the rubric "concept learning." In fact, for a brief definition of our topic, we can use the phrase "learning the use of names."

This definition of concept learning differs from some definitions found in the current psychological literature. Bruner, Goodnow, and Austin (1956) distinguished between concept *acquisition* and concept *formation*. According to them, the former process is generally what we have defined as concept learning. Although their definition is not explicit, most of their examples of concept acquisition (and certainly their experimental situations) are cases of concept learning. They do, however, treat categorizing from probabilistic cues as a special case of concept learning whereas we specifically exclude it. Bruner et al. also distinguish the learning of a pre-established classification rule from concept formation, in which the learner discovers a previously unknown rule for the application of a name. A concept former discovers a new way of ordering objects into sets so that a meaningful classification rule can be found. Such a reordering of objects into new equivalence classes may be thought of as a basic operation in the psychological processes of creativity. Fascinating as this problem is, we shall not discuss it here.

Piaget, in his monumental research on the development of thought in children, has attempted to develop a logic system suited to the description of human mental processes (Piaget, 1957). He uses the term *concept* within this system. But he appears to mean something quite different from the meaning implied by the studies of concept learning in American experimental psychology. For Piaget, a "concept" is an explanatory rule, or law, by which a relation between two or more events may be described (e.g., the concept of causation). Such explanatory statements need not be classification rules.[2] In particular, they may say nothing about the assignment of a name to a particular object. The learning of Piaget's "concepts" is another fascinating topic about which we shall have little to say.


## 2    *Plan of the book*

This monograph has been organized with a definite view in mind. We wished to present a unified picture of current research and thought on the topic of concept learning. It was felt that workers in several disciplines, proceeding quite independently of each other, have made substantial contributions to the field. The psychological study of concept learning has undergone a resurgence in the past few years. At the same time, workers interested in the design of artificial intelligence systems have faced the problem of how concepts ought to be learned. A major purpose of this text is to present a synthesis of the work in these separate but related areas.

Concepts are essentially definitions in symbolic logic. Therefore, their role in logic should be considered. In the psychological literature especially, very little attention has been given to a formal definition of concepts and concept learning. Several authors in mathematical logic, however, have considered the role of concepts and names at length. At a less abstract level, others have considered the problem of recovering the definition of a particular concept from examples of objects to which a name can be applied. In Chapter 2, a notation for describing concepts and concept learning will be presented and related to the role of concepts in formal logic. This will require an explicit notation for description of stimuli and classification rules. In part, the discussion repeats the definition of concept learning presented in this chapter. It will be a much more concise discussion. Even so, the discussion of Chapter 2 is not an axiomatization of concept learning, nor does it contain formal proofs of theorems about concept learning. The verbal definitions offered in this chapter will be made sufficiently precise to permit efficient scientific study of the empirical facts concerning human and artificial concept learners. It is hoped that the system of definitions presented will aid researchers in relating their experimental findings and theoretical arguments to each other in a more orderly fashion than has been possible to date.

The next four chapters are concerned with the performance of a notoriously flexible and imprecise "computer" which can learn concepts, *homo sapiens*. Chapter 3 discusses various attempts to derive concept-learning phenomenon from theories of learning. Considering the dominant position of learning theory in psychology today, we felt justified in devoting so much space to these attempts. Presentation of an exhaustive literature search was not our goal. Several such searches are available (notably Kendler, 1961, and Vinacke, 1951). We wished to marshal and discuss in depth the key evidence on which currently active theories rest and, in some cases, the evidence which seems most embarrassing to them. Since there seems to be a fairly large body of the latter type of evidence, our conclusion will be that present learning theories are inadequate to account for our empirical knowledge of concept learning.

Chapters 4, 5, and 6 discuss concept learning from the point of view of psychology outside of learning theory. In Chapter 4, the relation between concept learning and stimulus complexity is explored. In particular, variables relating to perception and identification of stimuli are considered as they might affect concept learning. In Chapter 5, problems of information retention during concept learning are reviewed. In Chapter 6, some behavioral "strategies" which humans may use to avoid overtaxing their stimulus identification and memory capacities are described.

Armed with a logical analysis of and psychological evidence about concept learning, we shall then be in a position to ask how concepts should be learned. In the last few years, several ingenious answers have been suggested. These "answers" have been designs for automata capable of inductive inference. The automata have, for the most part, been realized by programming digital computers. They vary in design and in the generality of the concept-learning problem to which they are addressed. Although the field is still in a state of flux, certain general design principles are beginning to emerge. These have importance both for their own sake and as suggestions for a possible theory of human concept learning.

Chapter 7 is a brief discussion of the techniques used to design concept-learning automata. In particular, we shall be concerned with the programming of digital computers and the logic underlying different programming methods. In Chapter 8, an information-processing simulation of human concept learning is discussed. In Chapter 9, we analyze some artificial intelligence systems of concept learning. Unfortunately, we have no way of making a simple distinction between the two. Our best advice to the reader is to examine the chapters.

Finally, a summary of current research activity and problems, together with some suggestions for future approaches, is presented. Such a summary with predictions is always risky, since neither psychology nor artificial intelligence systems have been exhaustively reviewed. We have tried to present a few projects. We have always sought research illustrative of principles that appear to have a "growth potential" rather than automata or theories which are, in 1962, practical aids in solving classification problems.

REFERENCES

Amarel, S., 1960. An approach to automatic theory formation. *Proceeding of Illinois Symposium on Principles of Self Organizaiton.* Urbana: University of Illinois Press.

Bruner, J. S., 1957. Going beyond the information given. In *Contemporary approaches to cognition.* Cambridge, Mass.: Harvard University Press.

Bruner, J. S., J. J. Goodnow, and G. A. Austin, 1956. *A study of thinking.* New York: Wiley.

Dember, W. N., 1960. *The psychology of perception.* New York: Holt.

Kendler, Tracy S., 1961. Concept formation. *Annu. Rev. Psychol.,* **13,** 447–472.

MacCorquodale, K. and P. E. Meehl, 1948. On a distinction between hypothetical constructs and intervening variables. *Psychol. Rev.,* **55,** 95–107.

Miller, G. A., E. Galanter, and K. Pribram, 1960. *Plans and the structure of behavior.* New York: Holt.

Piaget, J., 1957. *Logic and psychology.* New York: Basic Books.

Vinacke, W. E., 1951. The investigation of concept formation. *Psychol. Bull.,* **48,** 1–13.

FOOTNOTES

1. Parenthetically, the author should confess that he doubts that a single set of laws can be found which will describe the classification behavior of verbal and nonverbal animals. The assertion that such laws do or do not exist is a statement of faith.

2. It would be possible to represent a concept, in Piaget's terms, by mapping the set of arguments onto the set of values of the function. If only the two sets were known, the induction of the function relating them might be exceedingly difficult. On the other hand, it might not be impossible. Working in a more conventional logic system than Piaget's, Amarel (1960) has proposed machine methods for the inductive definition of a function relating two sets. This work is discussed further in Chapter 9.

# 2

# Analysis of the problem

## 1    *General remarks*

As we conceive it, the scientific study of a problem consists of (*a*) a description of a particular phenomenon in a precise, unambiguous, and perhaps abstract manner, and (*b*) certain statements about the relations between different aspects of the phenomenon of interest. The description must be precise enough to be given empirical reference so that the truth or falsity of the relational statements can be determined. Such a conception of science assumes the existence of a language, on which we can place certain requirements. The language must be unambiguous, so that it is clear what a particular statement implies concerning the relation between different entities. No natural language adequately satisfies this criterion, although it might be possible to construct a spoken language that would (Brown, 1960). At the same time, the language must be suitable for describing the problem at hand. The scientist usually, if not always, begins work on a problem with a vague desire to "understand something" about a real world problem. If he cannot describe his interests, the precision of his language is irrelevant.

The search for a suitable language for all science has a long history. At one time, great effort was devoted to stating problems in natural language. The development of an adequate mathematical notation during the seventeenth century was a major step in the development of the physical sciences. A similar introduction of mathematics into the behavioral sciences has been attempted, beginning with economics and, in the last few decades, gathering emphasis in psychology and sociology. The idea of stating theories as mathematical equations has long been present in psychophysics. In the 1930s, this idea was extended to the study of learning, largely through the influence of Clark Hull and his co-workers (Hull, et al., 1940).[1] Since then the use of mathematics has become important in psychological theorizing. Mathematical psychology is clearly here to stay.

Until quite recently, the trend toward mathematical statement of theories made little practical impression on the study of the higher mental processes. The difficulties encountered in applying mathematical techniques in this field typify some of the objections that are made to the application of mathematics throughout the behavioral sciences. If the unambiguous language is so restrictive that interesting empirical problems cannot be described, of what use is it? May not the language of mathematics restrict the thinking of its users, so that the psychologist will be forced to study simpler and simpler situations in order to apply mathematically convenient approximations? When critics of mathematical psychology wish to be particularly caustic, they can object that it has resulted only in the elaborate analysis of rats running down straight alleys, or in the prediction of trivial binary choices. The higher mental processes seem to have been lost in the process of describing and analyzing them.

The issue is not easily settled. An excellent argument can be made for restricting research effort to prototypical situations which can be analyzed in an unambiguous manner (Spence, 1957). If the situations are known to be prototypical (e.g., if we knew that the understanding of the behavior of a rat in an alley was basic to the understanding of behavior), this argument would be unanswerable. Since there is no clear proof, however, that we have isolated prototypical situations, the argument that scientific description should be relevant to interesting empirical phenomena is pertinent. There is certainly a need for a better understanding of the higher processes. A president of the American Psychological Association has pointed out to his colleagues that the analysis is overdue (Hebb, 1960).

We must be careful not to overstate the alternatives. We do not have to accept the ambiguous language of, say, psychoanalysis. Neither do we have to adopt an unambiguous terminology which, having been developed for a different situation, cannot be applied to the data at hand. We can state the question better by asking whether a language exists that provides us with a higher degree of precision than we now have without imposing intolerable abstractions on the basic phenomena. There have been several recent attempts to find such a language.

For the most part, these attempts still operate within the framework of mathematics. Luce (1959) and Restle (1961b) have attempted to develop axiomatic descriptions of individual choice behavior. Bourne and Restle (1959) adapted Restle's (1955) stimulus-sampling theory of discrimination to a restricted form of concept-learning experiments. More recently, Restle (1961a) and, in a less extensive treatment, Suppes and Atkinson (1960) have shown that the cognitive notions of hypothesis testing can be expressed mathematically. (Parenthetically, both Restle and Suppes and Atkinson restrict consideration to simple hypotheses. This is certainly a start, however, toward the rigorous development of cognitive theories of behavior.) Paralleling this work in time, but intellectually independent of it, Newell, Shaw, and Simon (1958) have proposed the use of computer programs as models of human behavior when mathematical or logical descriptions of the same phenomena lead to unmanageable statements. In part because of their work, the highly general notations of symbolic logic and set theory are now practical tools in the construction of theories of complex mental behavior.

But before we can have a theory complete with axioms and derivations, we must have the language in which the theory is expressed. In this chapter an attempt is made to show that concept learning can be described, with precision and without excessive abstraction, using symbolic logic and set theory. A system of notation is to be developed, not a theory. Our goal is to describe the problem of concept learning, not to propose a solution.

The description which follows is an elaboration of Hovland's (1952) "communications analysis" of concept learning. The principle departure from Hovland's analysis is in the introduction of a more general notation.

To keep the chapter self-contained, an intuitive description of some aspects of symbolic logic and set theory will be presented. This description is intended neither as a text nor as an axiomatic presentation of these complex topics. Rather, it is intended as a guide for the general reader, and particularly for the research worker in concept learning who has not studied symbolic logic.

The author confesses that, at least for him, a detailed analysis of any scientific problem presents a peculiar hazard. It becomes very easy to lose sight of the forest because of the trees. To avoid this, let us step back and take a look at the "big picture" before presenting a detailed analysis of its many aspects.

We feel intuitively that concepts are things used in thoughts. To avoid metaphysics, let us define a thought as a statement in some language. Further assume, since this is not a discussion of pathological thinking, that the person who makes the statement knows the meaning he wishes to convey when he utters it. He can only be sure of success if he has an unambiguous language. Unfortunately, no natural (i.e., spoken) language is completely unambiguous. The closest approximation to an unambiguous language is the notation of symbolic logic. Although no presently speakable language is based on formal logic, we can conceive of thoughts as statements in symbolic logic.

Our questions become "What is the role of concepts in logic?" and "What does it mean to learn a concept in a symbolic logic system?"

## 2   Symbolic logic

Before answering the foregoing questions, we must examine the statement of ideas in symbolic logic. Since this is a complex topic in itself, only a brief presentation will be made. The intent is to give the "flavor" of the language, rather than a detailed examination. The interested reader is referred to Suppes' (1957) text for a more complete discussion.

Logic is concerned with the truth or falsity of sentences. Sentences refer to symbols and connections between symbols. For instance, if there are two symbols, $p$ and $q$, then $p$ is a sentence, $q$ is a sentence, and a sentence consisting of $p$, $q$, and a connective between them is a sentence. Either $p$ or $q$, or both, may be a symbol which stands for a complex sentence about some other symbols, $a,b,c$, etc. Thus, the notation is quite general. The idea of negation is also basic. Negation or "not" will be represented by the symbol $\sim$, so $\sim p$ can be read as "not $p$" or, "if $p$ is true, $\sim p$ is false and vice versa."

Negation refers to an operation on one symbol, or a unary operation. Connections between two symbols are also possible. These connections are similar to, but more precise than, some of the connectives of spoken English. The five connectives which we shall have occasion to use in this text are conjunction, inclusive and exclusive disjunction, implication, and biconditional (or double implication).

The conjunction of two statements will be symbolized by &. The sentence $p$ & $q$ is true only if the sentences $p$ and $q$ are true.

The inclusive disjunction of two statements will be symbolized by $\vee$. The sentence $p \vee q$ is true if either $p$, $q$, or both are true.

The exclusive disjunction of two statements will be symbolized by $\underline{\vee}$. The exclusive disjunction $p \underline{\vee} q$ is true if $p$, or $q$, but not both, is true.

Implication, that is, $p$ implies $q$, will be denoted by an arrow, $p \to q$. This relation of "implication" is roughly equivalent, in English, to the statement "If $p$ is true, then $q$ is true." Although it is psychologically difficult to realize (Vinacke, 1952), the statement $p \to q$ is *not* contradictory to the statement "$q$ is true but $p$ is not." In analysis of causal relations $p \to q$ means that $p$ is sufficient but not necessary evidence for the truth of $q$.

On the other hand, our last binary relation, "double implication" or biconditional, symbolized by $p \leftrightarrow q$, is a statement that the truth of $p$ is sufficient to establish the truth of $q$ and vice versa. Therefore, we can say that $p$ is sufficient and necessary to establish $q$.

Finally, we shall introduce the equality sign, $=$. The relation $p = q$ means that, by substituting the definitions of symbols in terms of statements and connectives in terms of other connectives, $q$ can be derived from $p$ and vice versa. The equality symbol is not a connective of formal logic and is introduced for convenience.

The relation between the truth (T) and falsity (F) of a statement and the truth or falsity of its component parts (the statements represented by $p$, $q$, etc.) is expressed in Table 2-1. The truth or falsity of the statement is given by the entry in the appropriate right-hand column, the truth or falsity of the components in the entry in the two left-hand columns. The right-hand entries are best interpreted as statements of the consistency of the appropriate compound statement with the conditions expressed on the left. For instance, it would be inconsistent to aver that the statement ($p$ and $q$) is true if we know that $p$ is false. Therefore the entry in the first right-hand column of Table 2-1 is F whenever the first left-hand column is F. On the other hand, the statement ($p$ and/or $q$) would be consistent with the condition that $p$ is false and $q$ is true. This is shown in the table.

Actually, Table 2-1 represents five truth tables, one for each of the five binary connectives. A truth table can be defined for any statement, no matter how many components it contains. If the statement has $n$ elements, there will be $2^n$ possible conditions involving just these components. One line of the truth table will correspond to each of these conditions.

*Table 2-1   Truth table for binary connectives*

| State of Symbols | | State of the Entire Statement Based on Symbols | | | | |
|---|---|---|---|---|---|---|
| $p$ | $q$ | $p \ \& \ q$ | $p \lor q$ | $p \ \overline{\lor} \ q$ | $p \rightarrow q$ | $p \leftrightarrow q$ |
| T | T | T | T | F | T | T |
| T | F | F | T | T | F | F |
| F | T | F | T | T | T | F |
| F | F | F | F | F | T | T |

As practice in understanding how this notation can be applied to actual thoughts, let us translate the following sentence into symbolic logic form:

"If the Yankees or the White Sox win the pennant, they will win the World's Series; otherwise the Cardinals will win the series."

Let $a1$ be the statement "The Yankees win the pennant" and $a2$ the statement "The Yankees win the World's Series." Similarly, define $b1$ and $b2$ for the White Sox, then $c2$ for the Cardinals. The statement can be translated as follows:

(2.2.1)     $(a1 \rightarrow a2)$ & $(b1 \rightarrow b2)$ &

$(a1 \rightarrow \smile b1)$ & $(b1 \rightarrow \smile a1)$ & $[\frown(a1 \vee b1) \rightarrow c2]$

or, equally well,

$$[(a1 \; \& \; a2) \; \overline{\vee} \; (b1 \; \& \; b2)] \; \overline{\vee} \; c2$$

In general, there are several equivalent ways of stating a sentence using different connectives. As a matter of fact, we can define the other operations in terms of negation and inclusive disjunction. The fact that inclusive disjunction is required has, as we shall see, important consequences.

In our example the symbols of the logical statement were used to refer to English sentences which included nouns, verbs, etc. We could generalize somewhat by saying that a symbol referred to all events which could be described by a particular English sentence. There may, of course, be one or no such events.

The notation of symbolic logic is a particularly appropriate language for describing complex mental processes. We can assign symbols to represent all our primitive undefined ideas. Once this is done for a particular problem, we have clear and unambiguous rules concerning the manipulation of these symbols into grammatically correct sentences. Furthermore, we can examine the relations between different sentences to determine which sentences are consistent with each other. Unfortunately, the statement of an interesting problem may lead to grammatically correct but unmanageable sentences. At least the strings of symbols and connectives will be difficult for a human being to handle. As we shall see in Chapter 7, recent advances in computer technology have provided us with an automatic device for manipulating the formulas of symbolic logic. This has changed the status of symbolic logic from a theoretically possible to a practically feasible tool for theory construction.

If a consistent thought can be expressed as a statement in symbolic logic, what role does a concept play? Suppose the symbol $q$ is equivalent to the phrase "Concept $A$ is applicable to Object $B$" (e.g., "Dobbin is a horse"). If $q$ is true, then by implication some other sentence is also true. But the implied sentence is of a special type; it must contain symbols which refer to descriptive statements about object $B$. The concept is defined in terms of the description of objects to which the concept is applicable. The idea of description is not a primitive notion of symbolic logic. It must be defined. This requires the still more general notation of set theory to which we now turn.


## 3    Set theory

The classic definition of a set is "a collection into a whole of definite, well-distinguished objects (called the elements of the set) of our perception or of our thought" (Cantor, cited by Kamke, 1950). Sets are determined by their elements and not, unless explicitly stated, by the structure of the elements within a set. For instance, the set of all letters is the set $\{a, x, b, d,$ etc.$\}$ in any order. The alphabet, on the other hand, is an ordered set, $\{a, b, c,$ etc.$\}$. Its elements obey a particular ordering relation with respect to each other. Symbolically, we shall refer to a set by a capital letter, for example the set $U$. On occasion we shall wish to define a set by its elements. The elements will then be denoted by small letters and will be subscripted and enclosed in special brackets. For example, the set $\{a_i\}$, $i = 1 \ldots n$ consists of $n$ elements represented by the symbols $a_1, a_2$, etc. On occasion the elements of a set will themselves be sets. We shall then use subscripted small letters when the symbol is understood to refer to an element of a set and the same letter subscripted and capitalized when the symbol is to refer to the name of a set.

The basic operations which we shall use to manipulate sets are identity, inclusion, complementarity, intersection, and union. Two sets, $A$ and $B$, are identical $(A = B)$ if all elements of $A$ are elements of $B$ and vice versa. The complement of a set is always taken with respect to some universe of elements and is the set of all elements in the universe but not in a particular set. The complement of $A$ is written $\overline{A}$. The set $A$ is included in a set $B$ if all members of $A$ are also elements of $B$. This is written $A \subset B$. Identity is a special case in which $A \subset B$ and $B \subset A$. We shall sometimes not wish to distinguish between the possibilities that $A$ is included in or is identical to $B$; in this case the connection will be written $A \subseteq B$. The intersection of two sets is the set of elements which are members of both sets, and is written $A \cap B$. The union of two sets is the set of elements which belong to either of the sets, and is written $A \cup B$. Each element is counted only once in the union of two sets, even though it may appear in each set. Thus, William Howard Taft appears only once in the set defined by the union of the set of presidents and chief justices of the United States, although he was a president and a chief justice.

A set can be an element of another set; that is, sets of sets are possible. For this reason we introduced our special notation for symbols as sets and as elements of sets. In particular, in describing objects it will be necessary to take sets, sets of sets, and occasionally sets of sets of sets.

A partition of a set exists when there are mutually exclusive subsets within the set such that the union of all the subsets is equivalent to the original set. In a partition, every element of the original set is assigned to one and only one subset. For instance, the set of purebred dogs can be partitioned into collies, spaniels, poodles, etc. Different partitions of the same set may be useful for other purposes.

From time to time we shall have occasion to refer to the number of elements in a set $S$. This will be written as $\eta(S)$.

The universe $U$ is defined as the set of all objects which might conceivably be of interest. For instance, if we are learning the concepts for the names of breeds of dogs, the universe is the set of all dogs. With reference to any set $S$ included in a universe, the universe is equivalent to the union of the set $S$ and its complement $\overline{S}$;

(2.3.1)                                  $U = S \cup \overline{S}$

Finally, set theory postulates exactly one set with no elements, the empty set $\Lambda$.

A connection between set theoretical and sentential formulas may be established. If $p$ is a descriptive statement (e.g., "It is red"), let $P$ be the set of objects in $U$ to which $p$ may be applied. Treat any other descriptive statement $q$ in the same way. Suppose that some compound sentential statement involving $p$, $q$, and a connective has been made. It is alleged that the compound statement is a statement that holds for all objects in a given subset of the universe. In other words, there exists a set $T$, $T \subseteq U$, in which there is no element such that its description contradicts the compound statement. Alternately, the set $T$ consists of only those objects whose descriptions are consistent with some line, with value $T$, of the truth table of the compound sentential statement.

For negation and the binary connectives, $T$ is defined as

| (2.3.2) | Conjunction | $T = P \cap Q$ |
|---|---|---|
| (2.3.3) | Inclusive disjunction | $T = P \cup Q$ |
| (2.3.4) | Exclusive disjunction | $T = (P \cap \overline{Q}) \cup (\overline{P} \cap Q)$ |
| (2.3.5) | Implication | $T = Q \cup (\overline{P} \cap \overline{Q})$ |
| (2.3.6) | Biconditional | $T = (\overline{P} \cap \overline{Q}) \cup (P \cap Q)$ |
| (2.3.7) | Negation | $T = \overline{P}$ |

It may be alleged that a particular compound statement is an adequate description of the entire universe of objects, which is equivalent to the set theoretical statement

$$(2.3.8) \qquad \overline{T} = \Lambda$$

To disprove the allegation, it is only necessary to produce a single object, a counterexample, that is an element of $\overline{T}$. From a consideration of the definition of $T$ for any sentential statement, we can construct a hypothetical $\overline{T}$ (or a set of sets of types of $\overline{T}$, a partition on $\overline{T}$ which depends on unions and intersections of the sets $P$, $Q$, $\overline{P}$, and $\overline{Q}$) and search $U$ to see whether there is any element of $\overline{T}$ in $U$.

As an example of this procedure, let us construct a set theoretic translation of a statement which defines a universe and makes assertions about it:

"All Russian women are either scientists or mother heroines." [2] The universe is the set of all Russian women. The statement avers that this universe is equivalent to the set $T$, defined by the exclusive disjunction of the statements "is a scientist" and "is a mother heroine." Let $S$ be the set of all scientists and $M$ the set of mother heroines. Then, according to the allegation,

$$(2.3.9) \qquad U = T = (S \cap \overline{M}) \cup (\overline{S} \cap M)$$

and,

$$(2.3.10) \qquad \overline{T} = (S \cap M) \cup (\overline{S} \cap \overline{M}) = \Lambda$$

To disprove the statement, all we have to do is to find at least one Russian woman who is a scientist and a mother heroine *or* who is neither a scientist nor a mother heroine. In a reasonable universe the first woman would be rather difficult to find, but the second woman would represent a common type.

Suppose that the statement is true in fact, but that we are not certain of its truth. The only way we can establish our certainty is to observe different Russian women. Since only one counterexample is needed to disprove the statement, we could never state absolutely that the rule was true until we had observed every existing Russian woman. On the other hand, we might be able to increase our inductive faith in the rule under certain circumstances. Suppose we knew that Russian women were a subset of the class of all women, and that the statement was not correct for all women. Furthermore, for all women, suppose we knew (or had an estimate of) the percentage of scientists, the percentage of mother heroines, and the correlation between these traits. We could take a sample of Russian women to determine whether or not the statements 2.3.9 and 2.3.10 held true in the sample. We could then ask whether the sample was large enough so that, assuming that Russian women are actually a random sample of all women, we should have expected a member of $T$ in the sample. If the answer is "Yes, the probability is very small that a member of $T$ would not be obtained from a random sample of all women," we suspect that the rules for describing Russian women are different from the rules for describing women in general.

We still cannot state, however, that this particular statement about Russian women is true. There may be several statements consistent with a particular $T$. Statistical proof that a $T$ is empty does not discriminate between statements consistent with that particular $T$'s being empty. In the universe of all women, the set of people who are both scientists and mother heroines is probably small. We might accept (tentatively) the hypothesis that $T$ is empty on the basis of a sample of Russian women which, if Russian women are no different from other women, would have been expected to include at least one member of the set $(\overline{S} \cap \overline{M})$. It might be quite reasonable to expect that a sample of the same size, drawn from the universe of all women, would not have contained a member of the set $(S \cap M)$. Therefore, this sample is consistent with the statement originally given, or with the statement

"All Russian women are scientists and/or mother heroines."

A general rule which we must follow in the study of concept learning by inductive inference is that before we can accept (at an arbitrary level of confidence) the statement that a particular $T$ is empty, we must convince ourselves at an appropriate level of confidence that each of the sets used to define this $T$ is empty. How this may be done will be considered later, because it belongs to our discussion of concept learning rather than to a discussion of set theory.

## 4   Descriptions

Objects are distinguished from each other by their descriptions. Hovland (1952) pointed out that concept learning must be based on the information transmitted by the descriptions of the objects which are used to illustrate the concept to the learner. It is impossible to understand the responses a concept learner makes unless we know how he describes the objects he observes. To have a clear idea of what this description was, Hovland developed a system of notation in which objects were characterized by values on dimensions (e.g., color-red). Hovland's system was promptly adopted for experiments in concept learning. (After Bruner, Goodnow, and Austin (1956), the term *at-*

*tribute* is often substituted for dimension.) In this section, Hovland's notation will be redefined, starting from a set-theoretic definition of the subject's ability to observe.[3] This will show the relation of the experimental psychologist's operational definition of concept learning to the role of concepts in symbolic logic. The set-theoretic definition of description can be used to extend Hovland's discussion of concept learning beyond the topics covered in the original paper. A similar definition of description has been developed, independently, by Banerji (1960).[4]

Consider a concept learner who is observing objects $u$ in a universe $U$. We assume that the learner has the primitive capacity to distinguish variation of the objects along some dimensions. The familiar psychophysical dimensions of color, size, weight, etc., are examples. The analysis is not limited to such dimensions, however. We might speak of the dimension "place of birth." The important point is that a set of possible types of distinctions which any learner can make is assumed to exist. Each of these can be made independently of the other. Any object can, then, have associated with it a descriptive statement which locates it on a particular dimension $\Omega_i$ in the set of possible dimensions, $\{\Omega_i\}$, $i = 1 \ldots n$. We can think of each dimension as being one of the dimensions of the $n$-dimensional description space $\Omega$. Any point in $\Omega$ can be specified by stating its coordinates in terms of positions on each of the $\Omega_i$. Formally, $\Omega$ is the product space.

$$(2.4.1) \qquad \Omega = \Omega_1 \times \Omega_2 \times \Omega_3 \times \ldots \times \Omega_j \times \ldots \times \Omega_n$$

To take a concrete example, suppose an athletic coach is describing five of his players. Assume that he can discriminate only height and weight. The situation is depicted in Figure 2-1, where the area of the square corresponds to the space $\Omega$. Although any object (in this case the players) can be represented by a (not necessarily unique) point in the square, there is no requirement that each point in the square actually represents an object. We are not required to have a man who is 6 feet and 7 inches tall and weighs 120 pounds. But we do want to be able to say that a person is 6 feet 7 inches tall, or that he weighs 120 pounds.

The space $\Omega$ will be called the description space. It can be thought of as a representation of all conceivable descriptions. All dimensions that the learner can distinguish are present in $\Omega$, and discriminations along any one dimension are assumed to be as fine as can be made. To specify an actual description, we replace the set of dimensions $\{\Omega_i\}$ with a set of partitions of dimensions $\{D_i\}$. Each $D_i$ represents a partition of possible positions along the corresponding $\Omega_i$ into equiva-

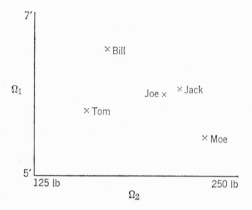

Figure 2-1. The space $\Omega$ (see text).

lence categories. For instance, the continuum "weight" would be replaced by the three categories "light, medium, and heavy." Any object
which falls into category $v$ of partition $D_i$ will be said to have value $v$
on dimension $i$. Combining the newly defined partitioned dimensions
into a product set $E$, such that

$$(2.4.2) \qquad E = (D_1 \times D_2 \times \ldots \times D_i \ldots \times D_j), \qquad j \le n$$

we create a set of combinations of values on partitioned dimensions.
[A product set "of the second kind" of the two sets $D_i$ and $D_j$ is the

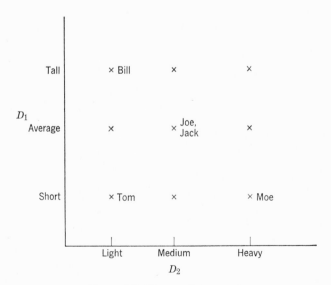

Figure 2-2. The set $E$ (see text).

set of all sets that can be formed by combining an element of $D_i$ with an element of $D_j$ (Kamke, 1950).] Each of the elements of $E$ is a conceivable description of an object within the partition of the $\Omega_i$ used to establish the $D_i$. This situation is shown in Figure 2-2, where the players' descriptions are given in terms of nine possible combinations of categories of height and weight.

Establishment of $E$ may involve selection as well as partition of the basic dimensions $\{\Omega_i\}$. This is shown in 2.4.2. Each $E$ is defined as the product space produced by a partition of some $j$ dimensions, and $j$ may be less than $n$. A basketball coach might use only three categories of height, whereas a wrestling coach might be interested in three categories of weight.

As in the description space $\Omega$, we assume that any object $u$, $u \in U$, has a description which is an element of $E$. But not all elements of $E$ need to represent the description of an object in $U$. To avoid confusion, we can think of $E$ as the set of possible ways of describing an object. Since we wish to distinguish between the description of objects and the objects themselves, we shall say that any $E$ implies the existence of a set $C$ of types of describable objects. Every element in $C$ represents a set of objects, each of which have the same element in $E$ as their description. Each element in $C$, however, need not have as members of its set any actual object (i.e., an object $u \in U$). On the other hand, an element in $C$ may represent a set which contains more than one object $u \in U$. For instance, in Figures 2-1 and 2-2 "Joe" and "Jack" are objects that are distinct in the description space $\Omega$ but are indistinguishable in $E$ and hence are members of a set represented by a single element in $C$.

Obviously, there is no unique $E$ for any $\Omega$. The partitions and selections used to establish the set $\{D_i\}$ may be altered. As a matter of fact, the set $\{D_i\}$ may and usually will be chosen on the basis of some theoretical rationale. A basketball coach has a reason for making fine distinctions between individuals who are over 6 feet tall but considering all persons under 6 feet as "short." For some purposes the dimensions and values may themselves be considered objects, and there may be concepts formed about the elements of $E$. Still more generally, functions may exist which utilize as their arguments values of specified dimensions of the same object. These functions can be used to define the value of a new (derived) dimension of an object. A description in terms of relations between the values of other dimensions (e.g., "squat," "skinny") can be generated. We shall return to this point shortly.

A somewhat frivolous example can illustrate our analysis. Take as the universe the set of young women competing for the Miss Universe title. Each contestant is an object. The contestants from countries located in Asia form a set within this universe. So do the contestants who do (or do not) reach the final competition. Furthermore, any set of objects is distinct from the objects in it. Logically at least, the Irish contestant can be considered as an object or as the set of contestants from Ireland.

A set of contestants may be specified by referring to the descriptive statements that apply to the elements of the set. We can form a set of descriptive statements by establishing appropriate partitions and selections of the types of variations which we shall observe, given all ways by which we can discriminate between subjects. This discrimination need not be based on sensory capacity. Any knowledge about contestants may be used. For instance, "geographic origin" is a possible dimension. "Continent of origin" is a partition of this dimension into five values, the names of the continents.

What $E$ is actually used is largely a matter of convenience. Although it is generally desirable to have a small $E$, for most situations of which we can think, there is no unique $E$ of arbitrarily small size. Furthermore, $E$ may contain many more elements than are actually needed to describe all the elements of $U$. From our previous definitions, it follows that for any stated $E$ based on partitions into dimensions $D_i$, $E$ generates a set of conceivable objects $C$ defined by all possible combinations of one value from each dimension. Set $C$ does not have to be identical to $U$, and in general it will not be. For instance, a reasonable $E$ for our beauty contest competitors will generate a $C$ which contains a hypothetical object described as a "tall, blue-eyed, redhead from Japan." We are not required to have such a young lady among the contestants.

A "good" $E$ will depend on the discriminations between objects that we wish to make. To continue our example, it is possible to describe women in terms of such dimensions as blood type and presence or absence of tonsils! If our interest is in dividing contestants into sets defined by their success in the beauty pageant, however, we suspect that the dimensions given in the last example are not needed. To give a definition of an adequate $E$ we must ask "Adequate for what purpose?" Although we have not yet defined the terms *concept* and *concept learning*, we suspect, from the sense of the last chapter, that adequacy will involve discrimination between objects that are and are not members of some sets which constitute a partition of $U$.

The establishment of the various sets, $\{D_i\}$, $E$, and $C$, will be called a description process. The symbol $\phi$ will be used to refer to a particular description process; the symbol will be superscripted (e.g. $\phi^{(1)}$), as will the associated sets, when necessary. We may summarize the steps involved in a description process as follows.

DEFINITION 1. A description process $\phi$ creates a set $E$ of conceivable descriptions. Each conceivable description is applicable to a (possibly empty) set of objects, $\{u_j\}$, $\{u_j\} \subseteq U$. The description is said to be applicable to these objects. Set $E$, itself is the product set of the elements of a selected set $\{D_i\}$, of $j$ partitions $j \leq n$) of the $n$ dimensions of variation by which a concept learner can distinguish between objects.

DEFINITION 2. Every $\phi$ creates a set $C$ of describable types of objects. The $i$th element of $C$, $c_i$ is the name of the set of objects in $U$ to which the $i$th element of $E$, $e_i$ is applicable.

To describe the concept-learning process, two additional definitions are needed.

DEFINITION 3. A description process $\phi$ is complete if every element $c_i \in C$ names a set containing one or no objects, $u_i \in U$. If $\phi$ is complete, the elements of $E$ provide unique descriptions for every object in the universe.

DEFINITION 4. Consider an arbitrary partition $\{P_i\}$ of $U$ into the sets $P$ and $\overline{P}$. A description process $\phi$ is relevant to $P$ if the elements of $E$ can be used to specify, by combinations of different types of objects, $(c_i \in C)$, a set that is equivalent to $P$.

The idea of relevance is particularly important in concept learning. The requirement that a particular description process $\phi^{(1)}$ be relevant to a partition $\{P|\overline{P}\}$ is equivalent to stating the requirement that $C^{(1)}$ contain elements $c_1 \ldots c_j$ such that

$$(2.4.3) \qquad P = \{c_1 \cup c_2 \cup \ldots \cup c_j\}$$

If this condition is not satisfied, the elements of $E^{(1)}$ and/or the values of the partitions $\{D_i^{(1)}\}$ cannot be used to state a rule for deciding, from its description, whether or not an object is an element of $P$. A complete description will always be relevant, since in a complete description there is at most one object in each $c_i$. A relevant description need not be complete, however; in fact, the concept-learning problem will be computationally simpler if we work with the smallest, least complete, relevant description.

Imagine a hunter walking through a forest and encountering bears. He may find that he can describe bears by their color (black, brown, and white) and by their size (large, medium, and small). Suppose that he encounters just one of each of the nine possible types of bear. The description process just given will be complete. As a zoologist, the hunter may find that an incomplete description based on color is relevant when he wishes to distinguish polar bears from other bears. The more cumbersome complete description would also be relevant. If white bears are polar bears, then large white bears, medium white bears, and small white bears are also polar bears. Clearly, the smaller relevant description is preferable. On the other hand, this incomplete description might not be relevant to a discrimination between, say, friendly bears and hungry bears. (Notice that the complete description would still be relevant, since friendly bears could be enumerated.)

A description must also be defined, at least in part, by the capacity of the observer to apply a descriptive statement. The determination of this capacity (the space $\Omega$) is an empirical question. It will, of course, be quite important in any specific concept-learning example. For the purpose of logical analysis, we can postulate the existence of a formal description process $\phi$ of the objects in a given universe. This is the set of descriptive statements that will be made by an observer when he is attempting to discriminate between two particular sets, $P$ and $\overline{P}$, which represent partitions of $U$. We assume that such a description exists and is known. In practice, a formal description process amounts to either an agreement between a subject and an experimenter that a particular description contains the information sufficient to solve a concept-learning problem (in a psychological experiment) or a catalogue of sensory capacities of a particular concept-learning machine (in artificial intelligence experiments).

It was indicated earlier that descriptions could be derived from descriptions. A derived description will be defined as one whose dimensions have values which are established by computing a function of values of dimensions of the object in the original description. This is equivalent to saying that a derivation is a function which uniquely defines a new set of values on the derived dimensions, once an object's values on the original dimensions are stated. For instance, the function "square root" defines the value 2 when the argument 4 is stated. A description could be derived from a description which was itself derived.

Let the set $\{D_i{}^*\}$ be the set of derived dimensions where the derivation is obtained by the set of functions $\{f_i\}$. The argument of each function $f_i$ is the set of values of dimensions which corresponded to a representation of the object in the original description (i.e., the appropriate element of $e_j \subset E$). A derived set of descriptive statements, $E^*$, can be constructed from the derived dimensions,

(2.4.4)     $E^* = (D_1^* \times D_2^* \times \ldots \times D_i^* \times \ldots \times D_k^*)$,     $k \leq j$

Denote the simultaneous application of all functions in the set $\{f_i\}$ by $F$. Then

(2.4.5)                          $F(E) = E^*$

establishes either a one-one or a many-one mapping of possible object descriptions from the original to the derived description. A comparable mapping from $C$ to $C^*$ is implied. Because of the one-one or many-one nature of this mapping, it follows that $\eta(C^*) \leq \eta(C)$. Of particular importance is the fact that although each element of $E$ may correspond to one or no descriptions of objects in $U$, each element of $E^*$ may correspond to the description (defined by $\phi$) of one or more objects in $U$. Thus $\phi$ must be complete if $\phi^*$ is, but $\phi$ may be complete when $\phi^*$ is not.

A description of items in terms of relations between the values which they have on different dimensions is an example of a derived description. In an experiment, Hunt and Hovland (1960) used a series of geometric patterns which had as a complete description the set $E$ specified in Table 2-2. Using the relation of inequality and equality, we could also apply the derived description $E^*$ of Table 2-3 to the same stimuli.

Table 2-2    Complete description of Hunt-Hovland stimuli

| Dimensions | Values |
|---|---|
| Color at top of pattern | Red, black, green, brown |
| Type of figure at top | Star, cross, triangle, fleur-de-lis |
| Number of figures at top | 1, 2, 3, 4 |
| Color at bottom of pattern | Red, black, green, brown |
| Type of figure at bottom | Star, cross, triangle, fleur-de-lis |
| Number of figures at bottom | 1, 2, 3, 4 |

Table 2-3    Derived descriptions of Hunt-Hovland stimuli

| Dimensions | Values |
|---|---|
| Colors | Same on top or bottom, different |
| Type of figures | Same on top or bottom, different |
| Number of figures | Same on top or bottom, different |

A new definition is needed for derived descriptions.

DEFINITION 5. A description $\phi^{(2)}$ is derived from a description $\phi^{(1)}$

if (a) an $E^{(2)}$ is defined as the product space of a set of dimensions $\{D_i^{(2)}\}$, (b) all the elements of the set $C^{(2)}$ of types of objects define sets of possible objects which include as subsets one or more of the sets of object types defined as elements of $C^{(1)}$ and (c) every subset of objects defined by an element of $C^{(1)}$ is included in or equal to an element of $C^{(2)}$.

There are three ways in which such derivations could occur. A dimension which was present in $\phi^{(1)}$ could be dropped in $\phi^{(2)}$, so that $E^{(2)}$ would consist of statement about $n-1$ descriptive statements. The corresponding element of $C$ would define a set of objects without regard to the value of the $n$th dimension with respect to $\phi^{(1)}$. Within one of the dimensions of $\phi^{(1)}$, two or more values could be combined into a single value. Finally, new elements could be defined by the relation between values of different dimensions, as in the Hunt and Hovland experiment. Elements of $E^{(2)}$ would then be defined by the joint occurrence of some set of $k$ values in different dimensions defined with respect to $\phi^{(1)}$. Another example of such a derivation is patterning (Estes, 1959). Here the presence of a particular subset of values becomes a cue for the observer, but the separate existence of the individual values no longer is a cue.

If a derived description is relevant, its source description is also relevant. This follows from the transitivity of the inclusion relation,

(2.4.6)                    $$C_i^{(1)} \subseteq C_j^{(2)} \subseteq P$$

A nonrelevant description may be derived from a relevant one, however.

Any discrimination involves two steps. First a relevant description small enough to be manageable (i.e., computationally feasible) must be found. The discrimination must be made within this description by reconstructing the required partition on $U$ in terms of the elements of the $C$ established by the description. As we have seen, the logical connectives for conjunction or disjunction are basic in this second step. Relations are particular types of derivations of descriptions and as such enter in the first step, establishing the appropriate description. Logical connections between relationally defined elements still must be determined.

How does a concept learner decide whether to spend his time searching for a particular set of logical connectives between the elements of the present description or searching for another, more appropriate description? It is clear that if the description space $\Omega$ is not relevant, no relevant description can be computed from it; that is, the problem is not solvable within the limits of the learner's descriptive ability. Even if we assume that $\Omega$ is relevant, the question remains whether to alter the present description to a simpler form or to search for logical connectives within it.

This question cannot be answered without reference to the data-processing capability of individual concept learners. Every new computation of a description increases the chance of deriving a non-relevant description. On the other hand, complex descriptions may be unmanageable. Some heuristic guide for making use of maximum data-processing capability must be available. From quite different evidence, Berlyne (1960) has suggested that biological organisms seek an optimal amount of stimulus complexity. This can be regarded as a best estimate, based on past experience, of an environment in which information can be obtained without excessive computation cost. Depending on the similarity of the present and previously encountered situations, the estimate might or might not be helpful.

## 5    *Concepts*

In Chapter 1, concept learning was equated to the learning of names. A name is a symbol which refers to an object or entity. In the terminology of the previous sections, a name is a symbol used to refer to a set. In a natural language such as English it is easiest to equate names with nouns. But the idea of a name is more general than this. Any phrase or descriptive sentence could also be assigned a symbol, and this would be its name. For instance, in telegraphy there is a single symbol for the phrase "I have made an error and will repeat the previous transmission." This symbol may be used whenever the sentence would be appropriate.

Church (1958) reasoned that a name has two properties, its meaning or *concept* and its denotation. The denotation is the set of objects to which the name can be applied. The concept is a statement of structure in the description of the objects to which the name applies. In a concrete example, to say that an object is a dog means that the object belongs to a set, any one of whose elements may be referred to as a dog. This set is the denotation of the name "dog." The concept of "dog" is a rule by which we decide, from the description of an object, whether or not it can be called a dog. Such a decision rule may be expressed as a series of questions about the description of the object, for example "does it bark?"

Church's definition of concept and denotation can be expressed using the set-theoretic definition of description. The denotation of a name relates it to particular elements in the universe of objects; the concept of a name relates it to a description of the objects. Specifically, the denotation of the name is the subset of the universe consisting of all objects to which the name can be applied. The concept is a classification rule by which the appropriateness of applying a name may be determined. The classification rule has as its argument the element of $E$ which corresponds to the description of the object. If this element belongs to a subset of $E$ such that all members of the subset are descriptions of members of the denotation of the name, the name may be applied to the object. A subset of $E$ may be established without enumerating its elements. All that is needed to define any subset is a statement of the values of particular dimensions which are common to all members of the subset. For instance, in the universe of human beings, we can speak of the subset of redheaded men without specifically writing down the names of each redheaded man in the world. We may also have a classification rule which asks whether a particular man, whose existence may not have been realized before he was encountered, belongs to the set of redheaded men.

The somewhat ambiguous use of the term "concept" in natural language and, more particularly, in the psychological literature may lead to confusion. In the terminology we are adopting, it is proper to speak of the concept of a name. Experimental descriptions and colloquial English are more likely to refer to the "name of a concept." In colloquial English the phrase "concept of a name" might be taken to refer to the idea of naming. On the other hand, "the name of a concept" is sensible only if "concept" refers to a set of objects. Here the "concept" would refer to what we have called the denotation of the name.[5] Using "concept" to refer to a set of objects may have unfortunate logical consequences. It would be difficult to distinguish between an object and a concept which refers only to that object. This would violate the basic rule of set theory that a set is distinct from the elements of the set. Furthermore, this use of the term "concept" leads to confusion between sets of actual objects and sets of conceivable objects. For instance, if we use the symbol $A$ for the name with the concept "men who have returned from Mars" and the symbol $B$ for the name with the concept "female presidents of the United States," we might like to have some way of distinguishing $A$ and $B$. Church's terminology permits such a distinction.

The example given is part of a larger class of situations in which two different concepts may refer to the same set of objects (in the preceding example, the empty set). This is a formal way of saying that one object may have more than one name. The two names are not equivalent because each, although they refer to the same objects in $U$ (equivalent denotation), may refer to a different description of $U$ (nonequivalent concepts). If two names have the same denotation and are understood to be used with the same description, however, they must be equivalent. As an example, Church considered the names "the author of 'Waverly'" and "Sir Walter Scott." Both have the same denotation—a particular English author. The first name has as its concept the set of objects which have a dimension "did or did not write 'Waverly'" and a value "yes." The second name refers to a set of objects defined by a description of humans by their first and last names and their titles in the English heraldry system.

In the example, as in our discussion of descriptions, a name has its concept defined in terms of other names. The denotation is defined in terms of the intersections and unions of the denotations of the other names. Thus, eventually a denotation defined by a concept will be a set of concrete objects. Ultimately, we are assured that we will remove the vagueness from "what a thing in general shall be."

Does our definition of concepts permit us to use names in a reasonable way? To answer this, we must consider how we use symbols in sentences. Suppes (1957) suggested two reasonable criteria for naming: eliminability and noncreativity.[6] A name is eliminable if in any sentence in which it appears it can be replaced by its concept without altering the meaning of the sentence. For instance, the meaning of the sentence "President Kennedy spoke to Khrushchev" is not altered if it is changed to the clumsier statement "An object that won the presidential election in 1960 spoke to Khrushchev." A name is noncreative if any object to which the name may be applied can be substituted for the name, without altering the meaning of the sentence. To understand this, consider an example (Hunt and Hovland, 1960) of a concept which did not meet this criterion. The baseball term "strike" was defined as "a ball which passes through the strike zone without being hit by the batter or at which the batter swings and fails to hit into fair territory." This permitted the sentence, "After letting two good pitches go by, Mantle *hit a grounder foul down the third base line* and was out." Because of the baseball rule that a foul ball is not a strike after the batter has two strikes, this sentence is false. On the other hand, the sentence is consistent with the rules of baseball if *made a third strike* is substituted for the italicized section of the sentence.

Suppes' criterion of eliminability and noncreativity will be met if the concept of a name defines the same set of objects in $U$ as its denotation. There is an advantage in distinguishing between the concept and denotation. When asked how a name is to be used, we may require a statement of the concept and not the denotation. If we asked a human his concept of the even numbers between one and one hundred, would we care to listen while he said "two, four, six, eight, . . ."?

We can also define an efficient concept. Within a given description, the sentence which defines the concept of a name with use of a minimum number of subsets of $E$ is the most efficient. The rationale of this definition is that the cost of utilizing a concept should be monotonically related to the number of questions which must be asked about the description of an object that is to be categorized. An efficient concept should minimize the number of discriminations which must be made before a name can be applied. The most efficient concept is one that can be applied to a rough description of the objects to be categorized. The cost of obtaining such a concept will vary with the cost of deriving particular descriptions, the cost of determining a concept within a particular description, and the method of scanning objects to determine their description. At present, we cannot state a general rule for calculating the relative efficiency of two concepts or for determining the most efficient concept in a given learning situation.


6    *Inductive definition of concepts*

The original purpose of Hovland's system of notation was to aid the experimental psychologist in understanding the information-processing requirements of concept-learning experiments. Concept learning requires that a subject discover inductively the form of a concept by observing objects that are or are not members of the denotation of the name. If the process the subject uses is to be analyzed, the experimenter must know exactly which possible statements of a concept are consistent with the examples presented up to any given time. This requirement can always be satisfied if the experimenter and the subject agree on their description of the objects. Once the description is established, there is a finite set of possible statements of the concept. This set can be specified before any examples are shown to the subject. During the learning phase, there is a progressive elimination of members of this set on the grounds that they are inconsistent with the evidence presented. Obviously, the concepts that might be correct (i.e., consistent with previously presented evidence and possibly consistent with evidence to be presented) also form a finite set.

Hovland (1952) showed that these statements were true if the subject knew the logical structure of the statement which defined the concept, but not the elements (dimensions and values) which were involved. It is true even if the structure is not known. Suppose that the correct concept can be stated in the logical form $a$ $(c)$ $b$, where $a$ and $b$ are unknown values of unspecified dimensions and $(c)$ is some logical connective. The concept-learning task reduces to the discovery of the identity of $a$ and $b$. Within a given description there are only a finite number of possible identities. The situation is not radically changed if $(c)$ is unknown. There are only a finite number of connectives, associated with each connective is a finite set of possible values of $a$ and $b$, so even if the connective $(c)$ is not known, there are still a finite number of hypotheses.

We can also view the problem in terms of the number of possible denotations. Once a $\phi$ is agreed on, we know from the definition of a description that the greatest number of types of objects that could be distinguished in the universe is

$$(2.6.1) \qquad \eta_{\max}(U) = \prod_{i=1}^{n} v_i = \eta(E)$$

the number of unique descriptions possible when there are $n$ dimensions with $v_i$ values on the $i$th dimension. A name may be assigned to any subset of the universe, and this name will have as its concept a statement of subsets of $E$ which, taken together, correspond to the denotation of the name. The question "How many concepts are there *within a given description?*" can be reworded as "How many subsets $S$ are there in $E$?" Any object type $c$ must be described or not described by an element of $S$, that is, either $c \in S$ or $c \in \bar{S}$. We can construct a binary number of $\eta(E)$ digits such that the $j$th digit is one if the $j$th object type in $C$ is a member of $S$, zero otherwise. We can reword the question, again, to "What is the value of the largest such number?" It is $2^{\eta(E)}$. (We take the largest such number, since we **must** find the size of the set of such numbers with leading zeroes included.) This set is obviously of size, in binary numbers 111 . . . 1. However, this size includes the empty set, which corresponds to binary zero, 000 . . . 000. We do not usually consider no description as a concept of a name. If we omit this empty set, we find that we have $2^{\eta(E)} - 1$ possible denotations, and hence, $2^{\eta(E)} - 1$ possible concepts. Once the description is fixed, so is the number of possible concepts. The problem of choosing the correct concept remains.

Hovland's original analysis based choice entirely on logical refutation of hypotheses by counterexample. Suppose a concept learner had an immense memory bank available. Given the description of the universe, he could store in this memory bank each and every possible concept (hypotheses) and the denotation associated with it. During concept learning, the learner would encounter particular objects together with the names applied to them. Each denotation of a concept would define a particular partition of $U$ into two sets, $S_i$ and $\overline{S}_i$. The assignment of an object to $S$ or $\overline{S}$ as observed in the universe would be evidence whether or not a particular partition $\{S_i\}$ actually existed. Every time an object was presented whose name was not consistent with the existence of a partition, the concept that generated this partition could be removed from the memory bank. Eventually only one concept would remain; this would be the correct concept. If the concept learner observed only part of $U$, there might or might not be only one concept remaining in memory after he made his observations. If there should be more than one concept in the bank, experimental definition of the correct concept would be equivocal.

If the experimenter states, in advance, the number of dimensions and values involved and the logical connective between the elements of the answer, it is possible to specify the minimum number of positive instances (i.e., number of objects in the denotation of the name) which are required to define the concept unequivocally. It is also possible to estimate the required number of negative instances. We can consider concept learning as an example of decoding, in which positive and negative instances transmit information which can be used to reduce the number of hypotheses remaining in the memory bank.

There are two important aspects of Hovland's analysis. He showed that given a formal description the information requirements of concept learning can be defined. The idea of a memory bank with varying degrees of fullness provided a model which distinguished between complete ignorance of a concept, the accomplished learning of a concept, and varying degrees of progress toward complete learning. There is no recourse to more or less vaguely defined notions of the psychology of the concept learner.

Hovland's analysis is not and was never intended to be a model for a machine designed to learn concepts, nor for the human psychological process involved in concept learning. The most obvious reason why it cannot be so used is that it requires an impossibly large memory bank. Very simple problems would require storage capacity beyond that of the largest computer available or planned today.[7] Empirically, it has been demonstrated that humans who attempt to handle problems of only moderate complexity in this fashion will become confused and be unable to proceed (Bruner, Goodnow, and Austin, 1956).

## 7    Probabilistic induction

Hovland's "memory bank" model proceeds entirely by counter-example. An hypothesis is removed from the bank whenever it is demonstrated to be false. There is no way to distinguish among hypotheses that are still in the bank. All hypotheses not known to be false are assumed to have an equal probability of being true. As a psychological assumption, this is clearly in error. Conceivable answers may be favored differentially. In fact, Polya (1954a) has argued that "guessing" is at the heart of creativity and inductive reasoning. We should like to have a measure that distinguished between hypotheses which imply that, if they are true, the available data is very likely and hypotheses which imply that the available data, although possible, are somewhat unusual. We gave one such example when we discussed Russian women. If all the Russian women we encounter are either scientists or mother heroines but not both, our observations are not impossible if in actuality either the statement "Russian women either are scientists or mother heroines" or the statement "Russian women are scientists and/or mother heroines" is true. If we never encounter a mother heroine who is a scientist, we begin to suspect that the former statement is closer to the truth.

In other words, a statement of the induction problem should distinguish between likely and unlikely as well as between possible and impossible hypotheses. Hovland's analysis should be included as a special case. At this point, we do not require a model that actually describes the inductive behavior of a given concept learner. Such a model would be an analysis of behavioral strategies. It would consist of a set of (perhaps mathematical) rules for generating good guesses rather than a set of rules for describing the inductive reasoner's progress toward his goal. Rules for generating guesses could involve heuristic principles with less than universal application. Rules for describing induction should be algorithmic and universally applicable.

Watanabe (1960) has developed a mathematical description of induction that is analogically similar to information theory.[8] This description is a statement of the general induction problem and clearly includes concept learning as a special case. Carnap (1960) has presented a similar analysis in inductive logic.

Watanabe's results were derived by generalizing Bayes' theorem of inverse probability. The theorem can be used to express the relationship between an observed outcome and all events which could have produced it. As such, Bayes' theorem is simply an algebraic manipulation of the definition of conditional probability (Feller, 1957).

Let $p(a)$ and $p(b)$ be the probability that statements $a$ and $b$ are true. Let $p(a|b)$ be the probability that $a$ is true if $b$ is true. For the case at hand we shall assume that $b$ is a statement which, among other things, specifies a probability of $a$'s being true. Thus, $p(a|b)$ can be defined without reference to the truth of $b$. The definition of conditional probability is

$$(2.7.1) \qquad\qquad p(a \;\&\; b) = p(b) \cdot p(a|b)$$

Bayes' theorem rearranges this,

$$(2.7.2) \qquad\qquad p(b) = \frac{p(a \;\&\; b)}{p(a|b)}$$

Watanabe considered a situation in which we must choose one statement (hypothesis) $b_i$ from a set $B$ of statements about the true state of nature. "State of nature" is to be understood as the actual probability of observing a given sequence of events, using a particular technique of observation. Each hypothesis $b_i \in B$ can be considered a conjecture about the true probabilities. There is no requirement that a completely accurate conjecture be included in $B$. We wish to select the best approximation to the true state of nature by observing a sequence of events $a^{(t)}$ from $t = 1$ until $t = \infty$. Our belief at time $t$ that a particular hypothesis is the best approximation in $B$ should reflect the information in the observations to that time.

Concept learning is such a situation. A possible statement of a concept is an hypothesis (again, "All Russian women are scientists or mother heroines"). The observations that can be made are pairings of names with objects that have certain descriptions[9] (e.g., Olga, who is a Russian woman, is a mother heroine). These observations provide the data $a^{(t)}$. We can consider more complex hypotheses, such as the statement that "All Russian women are scientists or mother heroines, and mother heroines are fifteen times more common than scientists," and we can extract information from more complex observations, such as "Of thirty-five Russian women, twelve were scientists and twenty-three were mother heroines."

Before making an observation at time $t$, we could calculate the a priori probability of obtaining a particular data point $a$. Consider the case in which there is just one hypothesis $b_i$ which either is or is not true. We have

(2.7.3)   $p(a)^{(t)} = p(b_i)^{(t-1)} \cdot p(a|b_i) + p[1 - p(b_i)^{(t-1)}] \cdot p(a|\overline{b}_i)$

If we know that the set B contains all possible hypotheses about the true state of nature, then 2.6.3 becomes

(2.7.4)     $p(a) = p(b_i)^{(t-1)} \cdot p(a|b_i) + \sum_{\substack{b \in B \\ j \neq i}} [p(b_j)^{(t-1)} \cdot p(a|b_j)]$

The basic argument of Bayesian induction is that when event $a$ is observed at time $t$, the probability of a particular hypothesis $b_i$ being true should be made proportional to the extent to which $b_i$ caused the a priori prediction of $a$. The appropriate equation for a posteriori probability is

(2.7.5)                $p(b_i)^{(t)} = \dfrac{p(b_i)^{(t-1)} \cdot p(a|b_i)}{\sum_{b_i \in B} p(b_j)^{(t-1)} \cdot p(a|b_j)}$

In many induction problems we do not know whether or not the set $B$ contains all possible hypotheses about the true state of nature. To allow for this, Watanabe substituted for $p(b_i)$ the term $q(b_i)$, which he interpreted as a statement of the probability at time $t$ that $b_i$ will be selected as the closest approximation to the true state of nature if observations are repeated, using the same technique, until $t = \infty$.

The definition $q^{(t)}(b_i)$ can be written

(2.7.6)   $q^{(t)}(b_i) = \dfrac{q^o(b_i)[p(a^{(1)}|b_i) \cdot p(a^{(2)}|b_i) \ldots p(a^{(t)}|b_i)]}{\sum_{b_i \in B} q^o(b_j)[p(a^{(1)}|b_j) \cdot p(a^{(2)}|b_j) \ldots p(a^{(t)}|b_j)]}$

in which $q^o(b_i)$ is interpreted to be the a priori credibility of hypothesis $b_i$ before any data is collected. Thus we can reflect initial bias, including the bias toward regarding particular hypotheses as equally probable. Here, for all $b_i$, $q^o(b_i) = 1/N$, assuming $N$ hypotheses.

By analogy to information theory, we can measure the uncertainty at time $t$ concerning the correct hypothesis

(2.7.7)                $H(q^{(t)}) = -\sum_{b_i \in B} q^{(t)}(b_i) \log_2 q^{(t)}(b_i)$

At any point $t$,

(2.7.8)                          $\sum q^{(t)}(b_i) = 1$

and

(2.7.9)                          $0 \leq q^{(t)}(b_i)$

so the measure of credibility has the mathematical features of a statement of probability. Refutation of an hypothesis by counterexample is included in the measure. Refutation of $b_i$ is equivalent to the equality

$$(2.7.10) \qquad\qquad q^{(t)}(b_i) = 0$$

occurring at some point. This can occur on a priori grounds, if $q^o(b_i)$ is zero, or if $p(a^{(t)}|b_i)$ is zero for any $t$. The a priori case is an example of a situation in which a hypothesis is known to be false as the result of previous induction or prejudice. (We include prejudice because we wish to include the case in which the concept learner refuses to consider a particular hypothesis.) If $p(a^{(t)}|b_i)$ is zero, the event $a^{(t)}$ must have been impossible according to some hypothesis $b_i$. Hence, $a^{(t)}$ was a counterexample, and the credibility of $b_i$ should go to and remain at zero. A glance at 2.7.5 shows that this will in fact occur.

The measure $H(q^{(v)})$ varies between zero and $\log_2 N$, where $N$ is the total number of hypotheses being considered. It reaches its maximum at

$$(2.7.11) \qquad\qquad q^{(t)}(b_i) = 1/N$$

for all $b_i$. This is the situation in which all hypotheses being considered are equally likely. Intuitively, this is the point of greatest confusion about the correctness of any particular answer. The measure reaches a stable minimum, zero, when one and only one $q^{(t)}(b_i)$ reaches one. Reaching this minimum means that the concept learner is convinced, beyond the shadow of a doubt, that a particular hypothesis is the closest approximation to truth that is contained in $B$.

In a concept-learning situation, the data $\{a^{(t)}\}$ consist of the set of pairs defined by the objects of the universe and the name to whose denotation each object is assigned. Hypotheses can be translated into statements about the probability of encountering any pairing of an object and a particular name. Hypotheses may vary greatly in amount of complexity. Any hypothesis partitions the data set $A$ into two sets $B_i$ and $\overline{B}_i$ of possible and impossible data points. For instance, in the example we have been using, the existence of a Russian woman who was neither a scientist nor a mother heroine would be impossible. Watanabe's measures could also be used to distinguish between hypotheses which specified the relative frequency of scientists and mother heroines, as in our previous example. As we have shown, this is a deficiency of Hovland's model.

The distribution of object types in the obtained sample is (after allowing for sampling bias) the best estimate of the actual frequency of object types in the universe. It will not necessarily correspond to the exact form of the true distribution. The true form is approached as a limit if sampling is continued.

The set of hypotheses under consideration may not contain any hypothesis which correctly states the name and frequency of all object types in the universe. Bayesian induction will therefore select the hypothesis that maximizes the likelihood that the obtained sample would have been obtained if the hypothesis was, in fact, correct. [This is approximately equivalent to minimizing the chi-square distance between the obtained frequency distribution and the various frequency distributions specified by the different hypotheses (Hunt, 1961).] There is no assurance that such a hypothesis will be unique. There may be a set of hypothesis $B' \subset B$ such that for all pairs of hypotheses $b_i$, $b_j$ included in $B'$, when the data collected to time $t$ is regarded as a single datum $A$.

$$(2.7.12) \qquad p(A|b_i) = p(A|b_j), \qquad b_i, b_j \in B'$$

and

$$(2.7.13) \qquad p(A|b_i) > p(A|b_k), \qquad b_i \in B', b_k \in \bar{B}'$$

For all hypotheses in $B'$, the relative credibilities at time $t$ will be determined by their relative a priori credibilities since the sample did not distinguish between them.

The a priori credibilities can never be completely "overwhelmed" by any data sample of finite size unless the sample contains a logical refutation of a particular hypothesis. This becomes something of a problem in evaluating the potential usefulness of Watanabe's analysis. Watanabe suggested that if the $q^o$'s were unreasonably distributed in the light of the evidence, a new set of $q^o$'s could be applied. But this does not settle the problem, since "unreasonable" is not defined. In any case, it seems that the problem of predicting the $q^o$'s is a problem for psychology rather than mathematics or logic. Recent investigations of the ability of subjects to make reliable estimates of how sure they are that a particular event will occur (Adams and Adams, 1961) suggest that an empirical solution is possible. An artificial intelligence system may capitalize on rather vague initial preferences for hypotheses (Hunt, 1961). Watanabe's analysis can be regarded as a general proof that inductive reasoning is possible (and therefore that concept learning is possible). The progress of an inductive reasoner can be measured by $H(q)$. It can be proven (although we shall not do so) that:

1. For finite $t$ (i.e., a terminating sample of data), $q(b_i)$ is equal to zero if and only if the data sample contains a logical refutation, and $q(b_i)$ is equal to 1 only if all other hypotheses $b_j$ are refuted by counterexample. This is Hovland's case.

2. On the other hand, in infinite experimentation $(t \to \infty)$, $q^{\infty}$ $(b_i)$ approaches a limit. If $B'$ is defined as the set of hypotheses which assign a greater likelihood to the actual distribution than any hypotheses not in $B'$, the limit is

$$(2.7.14) \qquad \lim_{t \to \infty} q^{(t)}(b_i) = \frac{q^o(b_i)}{\sum_{b_j \in B'} q^o(b_j)}, \qquad b_i \in B'$$

for all hypotheses in $B'$. For any $b_k$ not in $B'$ the limit is zero independent of the a priori credibilities.

3. If all probabilistically equivalent hypotheses are regarded as a single hypothesis, there is a finite stage $t$ beyond which the expectation of $H(q^{(t)})$ always remains constant or decreases. The limit of $H(q^{(t)})$ is zero.

4. Since the $q^{(t)}$'s are based on a sample, $H(q^{(t)})$ will fluctuate about its expected value. Beyond a certain stage $v'$, however, the expected size of the fluctuation decreases.

Watanabe's measures reflect differences between plausible hypotheses, disproven hypotheses, and possible but unlikely hypotheses. His analysis should have widespread application in the analysis of concept learning by humans and artificial intelligence devices.


8    *Definitions in psychological studies of concept learning*

The discussion of the role of the "learner" and the "experimenter" has been rather glib, in the hopes that the meaning would be clear from the text. Actually, several different procedures have been used by psychologists interested in concept learning. All have been called studies of "concept learning" or "concept formation." Within the logical framework that has been presented in this chapter, three different types of concept-learning experiments can be distinguished. The problem presented to the subject is not the same in the different experiments.

The first and perhaps the most common situation is an experiment in which the subject learns the concept of a name. The experimenter shows the subject all, or some subset, of the denotation of the name. The subject's task is to state the concept adequately, efficiently, and without redundancy if possible. In a second type of experiment, denotation learning (which may be combined with the first), the subject is shown a subset of the denotation. This is often accompanied by a subset of the complement of the denotation. The subject is then shown a test set which contains some members of the denotation. The task is to select these. Presumably a correct use of a name (in denotation learning) reflects the subject's ability to use the correct concept. At times this may be an unwarranted assumption. Hull (1920) observed that the criteria for denotation learning may be satisfied before the criteria for concept learning are. Two different concepts may imply identical partitions of a particular test set into examples of things to which a name can or cannot be applied.

Explicit use of denotation learning may be made to infer the concept that the subject has derived from the training objects. In the training phase, the subject is shown a subset of the universe. He is told which names can be assigned to each of the objects in the subset. This information may not define a unique concept for each name. (In the terms of Hovland's (1952) model, the memory bank contains more than one entry at the end of the training phase.) In the test phase, the subject is asked to assign names to each element of a new set of objects. From his assignments, the experimenter may be able to infer the concept which the subject has learned.

As an example, consider a problem in which the objects to be categorized are four-letter nonsense syllables. In training, the subject is shown the following items as examples of the arbitrary class, $\pi$; {NPVN, RPVR, ZPVZ}. He is also shown another set of items which are examples of syllables not in class $\pi$, {XPRY, ZMVT, XYXN}. In a concept-learning experiment, the subject is then asked "What is the rule that can be used to assign an object to the set $\pi$?" In a denotation-learning experiment he could be shown the following set of objects, {NPVR, XPVY, ZRMZ, YZXY}, and asked which of these belonged to the set $\pi$. Since there are at least two possible categorizing rules which reproduce the sorting shown in the training phase "All members of $\pi$ have the letters PV in the middle" and "All members of $\pi$ have the same first and last letter," the way in which the subject sorts the test set can be used to infer the concept he has learned. Experiments using this procedure have been conducted by Buss (1950) and Hunt and Hovland (1960).

Data from denotation and concept-learning experiments are susceptible to different types of errors. Unless the subjects are highly verbal, they may not be able to state their concept of a name. In particular, they may be handicapped by ambiguities in their natural language. For instance, we have found that American undergraduates frequently use the word "and" to refer to a disjunction, although the dictionary meaning of "and" is conjunction. In denotation learning, the subjects' sorting may not be completely consistent with any concept. The best the experimenter can do in such cases is to establish trends by using statistical averages. Such aggregated data may not reveal the nature of the learning process in individual subjects.

A situation could arise in which the subject had to learn the name of a concept. The subject would have already used a particular categorizing rule to sort objects into a set (the denotation) and its complement. His task would be to discover what name the experimenter used for objects in that set. In this case, the experimenter is more of a tutor and the subject a learner. Although we know of no psychological studies that have been conducted in this way, something very much like name learning takes place when anthropologists study the language of a foreign society. As a simple example, the anthropologist will already have divided humans into two groups, men and women. He can safely assume that any other society also uses this categorization. He can only find out what a particular society's term for "man" and "woman" is by pointing to appropriate people and asking an informant what the native's term is. This procedure is valid, since the anthropologist can be reasonably sure that he and the informant will both know different names for which they have an identical concept. Brown (1956) has pointed out that this assumption is not always correct. Two languages may not have the same concepts, even about such commonplace physical things as colors. In our terms there is a chance for confusion if the learner does not present a denotation that corresponds to the denotation of some concept known to the tutor. The learner may present a denotation which intersects, includes, or is a subset of one of the tutor's denotations. Imagine that an anthropologist is trying to learn the Lapland word for "snow." In fact, the Laplanders (as do other Arctic and subArctic peoples) have several words for snow, depending upon the characteristics of the snow. If the anthropologist pointed to only a few examples, he might conclude that a particular Lapland word had the same meaning as the English word "snow" when it actually meant "loosely packed, deep snow through which a man cannot travel without snowshoes."

Some types of concept-learning studies performed by psychologists are hard to fit into our classifications. One is the study of categorization based on probabilistically correct cues (e.g., Bruner, Goodnow, and Austin, 1956, Chapter 7). We have assumed that there is a concept for every name, and that the concept defines the entire set of the denotation (the criteria of eliminability and noncreativity). We did not admit the possibility that a particular operation on the information presented can develop only a partially correct answer. When this happens it is assumed that either (a) the correct concept is so complex that the concept learner attempting to discover it must accept a simpler approximation, or (*b*) the concept is based on information not represented in the description space, and therefore the problem is unsolvable. In the probabilistically correct cue experiments an object is assigned to a particular denotation, with probability $p, p < 1$, if it is described by some specified combination of dimensions and values. Thus, we might have two identical objects, one in and one out of the denotation of a given name. A complete description of objects would not be relevant, and our system of notation would be inappropriate.

Chomsky and Miller (1958) devised *finite-state grammars* as a technique for experimentation in psycholinguistics. Miller (personal communication) pointed out that a finite-state grammar provides a possible concept-learning problem which does not fit into any scheme of notation that presupposes a finite universe. Such problems can be handled in our notation.

A finite-state grammar consists of a set of symbols to be combined into strings and a set of rules specifying the probability with which one symbol (or group of symbols) follows another. Consider a very simple example in which each alternative is equally probable. Let all strings begin with *A*. An *A* is always to be followed by either a *B* or a *C*. A *B* may be followed by itself or the string may stop. A *C* may be followed by an *A* or the string may stop. There are an infinite number of strings of symbols which can be generated by these rules. For instance, the strings *AB, AC, ACACACAB* are all allowable. So is any string *A* followed by an arbitrary number of *B*'s. But not all strings of *A*'s, *B*'s, and *C*'s are allowable. *ABC* is not, for if *B* is followed by anything it must be followed by another *B*. If humans were to observe a large number of allowable and not allowable strings, they would learn to distinguish the two. We ought to call this learning "concept learning," so our notation should fit it.

Strings of symbols can be described by a process $\phi$ which establishes a finite set $E$ of descriptions. The infinite universe of possible strings can be partitioned into a finite number of sets $\{c_i\}$ of types of strings. A description process which does this may be relevant in the sense described earlier. Concept learning can thus take place using as objects the strings generated by a finite-state grammar. What a description process cannot do is to establish a set of descriptive statements $E$ such that any conceivable string generatable by a given grammar would have a unique description. In terms of description processes, relevant processes $\phi^{(1)} \ldots \phi^{(j)}$ might exist, but no description process could possibly be complete.

Werner and Kaplan (1950) used an experimental technique in which the concept of a name was defined solely by the context in which the name was used. Suppose a subject is to develop a concept for the name GELF. In fact, the experimenter has decided that GELF will have the same meaning as the English word tomato. The experimenter shows the subject sentences in which GELF is used as a synonym for tomato (e.g., "A GELF is round, red, and juicy." "GELF soup is very good."). Strictly speaking, Werner and Kaplan's subjects never observed any object to which the name applied. This task is not "concept learning" within the narrow, precise meaning used here. Although Werner and Kaplan's experiments are certainly interesting examples of induction, they will not be discussed further.

REFERENCES

Adams, J. and P. A. Adams, 1961. Realism of confidence judgments. *Psychol. Rev.,* **68,** 33–45.

Banerji, R. B., 1960. An information processing program for object recognition. *Proc. General Systems,* 117–127.

Berlyne, D. E., 1960. *Stimulus selection and conflict.* New York: McGraw-Hill.

Bourne, L. E. and F. Restle, 1959. Mathematical theory of concept identification. *Psychol. Rev.,* **66,** 278–296.

Brown, J., 1960. Loglan. *Scientific American,* **202,** 53–63.

Brown, R., 1956. Language and categories. In Bruner, Goodnow, and Austin (1956).

Bruner, J. S., J. J. Goodnow, and G. A. Austin, 1956. *A study of thinking.* New York: Wiley.

Buss, A. H., 1950. A study of concept formation as a function of reinforcement and stimulus generalization. *J. exp. Psychol.,* **40,** 494–503.

Carnap, R., 1960. The aim of inductive logic. *Proceedings of the International Congress for Logic and Methodology of Science.* Stanford: Stanford University Press.

Chomsky, N. and G. A. Miller, 1958. Finite state languages. *Inform. Control,* **1,** 91–112.

Church, A. A., 1958. *Introduction to mathematical logic.* Princeton: Princeton University Press.

Dember, W., 1960. *The psychology of perception.* New York: Holt.

Feller, W., 1957. *An introduction to probability theory and its applications.* Vol. 1 (2nd ed.), New York: Wiley.

Hebb, D. O., 1960. The American revolution. *Amer. Psychologist,* **15,** 735–745.

Hovland, C. I., 1952. A "communication analysis" of concept learning. *Psychol. Rev.,* **59,** 461–472.

Hull, C. L., 1920. Quantitative aspects of the evolution of concepts. *Psychol. Monogr.,* **28,** whole No. 23.

Hull, C. L., C. I. Hovland, R. T. Ross, M. Hall, D. T. Perkins, and F. G. Fitch, 1940. *Mathematico-deductive theory of rote learning.* New Haven: Yale University Press.

Hunt, E. B., 1961. The evaluation of somewhat parallel models. Working Paper No. 1. Western Management Science Institute, University of California at Los Angeles.

Hunt, E. B. and C. I. Hovland, 1960. Order of consideration of different types of concepts. *J. exp. Psychol.*, **59**, 220–225.

Kamke, E., 1950. *Theory of sets* (Bacemihl translation). New York: Dover.

Kochen, M., 1960. Experimental study of 'hypothesis-formation' by computer. Paper read at 1960 London Symposium on Information Theory.

Luce, R. D., 1961. A choice theory analysis of similarity judgments. *Psychometrika*, **26**, 151–164.

Luce, R. D., 1959. *Individual choice behavior*. New York: Wiley.

Newell, A., J. C. Shaw, and H. A. Simon, 1958. Elements of a theory of human problem solving. *Psychol. Rev.*, **65**, 151–166.

Organski, A. F. K., 1961. Population and politics in Europe. *Science*, **133**, 1803–1807.

Polya, G., 1954a. *Induction and analogy in mathematics*. Princeton: Princeton University Press.

Polya, G., 1954b. *Patterns of plausible inference*. Princeton: Princeton University Press.

Restle, F., 1955. A theory of discrimination learning. *Psychol. Rev.*, **62**, 11–19.

Restle, F., 1961a. Statistical methods for a theory of cue learning. *Psychometrika*, **26**, 291–306.

Restle, F., 1961b. *Psychology of Judgment and Choice*. New York: Wiley.

Shannon, C. and W. Weaver, 1949. *The mathematical theory of communication*. Urbana: University of Illinois Press.

Spence, K., 1957. *Behavior theory and conditioning*. New Haven: Yale University Press.

Stevens, S. S., 1960. The psychophysics of sensory functions. *Amer. Scientist*, **48**, 226–253.

Suppes, P., 1957. *Introduction to logic*. Princeton, N.J.: Van Nostrand.

Suppes, P. and R. Atkinson, 1960. *Markov learning models for multi-person interaction*. Stanford: Stanford University Press.

Vinacke, E., 1952. *The psychology of thinking*. New York: McGraw-Hill.

Watanabe, S., 1960. Information-theoretical aspects of inductive and deductive inference. *IBM J. Res. Develpm.*, 208–231.

Werner, H. and E. Kaplan, 1950. Development of word meaning through verbal context: An Experimental Study. *J. Psychol.*, **29**, 251–257.

FOOTNOTES

1. The use of mathematical notation for theory construction is a separate topic from the use of statistical and mathematical techniques to evaluate data. Sophisticated data evaluation techniques appeared in the social sciences independently of and earlier than the work of Hull and his students.

2. A mother heroine of the Soviet Union has at least ten grown children (Organski, 1961).

3. Hovland originally developed his system as an analogy to the mathematical theory of communication (Shannon and Weaver, 1949). He did not use Shannon's theorems, and his analysis is independent of information theory.

4. The idea of defining dimensions and values by sets occurred to the author after reading a research report by Kochen (1960). The idea that a descriptive statement names a set of objects is a common notion in set theory and is explicitly stated in Suppes' (1957) elementary text. It has been suggested that the idea of ordered sets can be applied to all psychophysical descriptions (Dember, 1960). If this were true, it would follow that our description is sufficient to depict formally all human perception. The evidence on this is not clear, however. It has also been maintained, both experimentally and logically, that psychophysical discriminations are based on a ratio scale (Luce, 1959, 1961; Stevens, 1960).

   A somewhat different approach to description has been taken by Restle (1961b). He regards a dimension (variable in his terms) as a partition of the universe of objects. A value is defined by one of the subsets in this partition, the set of objects having that value on that variable. This is compatible with the notion of description presented here.

5. Banerji (1960) uses "concept" in this sense. He shows that a meaningful set theoretic definition is possible.

6. His argument has been paraphrased to fit the terminology being used.

7. If there are $v$ values for each dimension $v \geq 2$, the number of possible concepts is $2^{v^n}$, a superexponential function of $n$. Even if we suppose that only one storage register is needed to store all the information associated with a concept, the number of storage registers needed will, for $n \geq 40$, exceed the number of neurones in the human brain.

8. Polya (1954b) presented an outline of inductive reasoning similar to Watanabe's.

9. Watanabe suggested (1960, p. 230), by an example taken from Kochen's (1960) computer program for learning concepts, that his analysis was appropriate only for objects which bore the name of the concept to be learned. Our definition of a set of data points suggests that the analysis is more general.

# 3

# Concept learning
# and basic learning

## 1    *General remarks*

Most modern experiments on the psychology of learning test models of the process by which a molecular stimulus evokes a molecular response. The original hope of the creators of such models was that all learned experience, including problem solving and concept learning, would be derived from a theory of the learning of simple stimulus-response (S-R) connections. Emphasis has now shifted to construction of more concise models for miniature situations, but the basic statement of faith in the power of the learning analysis has not been abandoned. Rather, it is now admitted that an adequate analysis of simple situations is a more difficult task than had been imagined.

In its most general form, the S-R theory states that, as a result of continued association under certain conditions, a stimulus acquires an increasing power to evoke a response. This statement is probably impossible to disprove. Indeed, Luce (1959) has presented an axiomatic argument that the idea of "habit strength," or a steadily developing response potential for a given stimulus, is implicit in any reasonable measurement of monotonically changing choice behavior on repeated presentation of the same cues. His argument does not depend on empirical proof. Whether or not a basic learning theory approach is the most fruitful in understanding a complex phenomenon such as concept learning is another question.

No single universally accepted "basic" learning theory exists. There is considerable experimental and theoretical controversy about how S-R connections are developed. In fact, experiments in learning probably account for half of the literature in experimental psychology. Learning theory is also the field in which psychologists have developed some of their most systematic analyses. Rigorous criteria are used to evaluate learning models, largely because of the example of Hull (1943).[1] The theoretical literature alone has been the topic of a review volume (Hilgard, 1956), and many reviews of subfields have appeared.

We shall deal only with specific attempts to extend learning theories to concept learning.

Theories of the conditioning of responses fall into two broad classes, depending on how they depict the connection between a stimulus and a response. One school, exemplified by the work of Hull (1943), Spence (1957), and Logan (1960), postulates a continually strengthening bond between the stimulus trace of an object (the object's internal representation in the subject) and a response. Since several responses may be conditioned, with varying degrees of strength, to a particular stimulus, responses compete for evocation. Changes in their relative strength are the result of changes in the habit strength, or the connection between the stimulus and the response.

Another approach conceives of the stimulus as being equivalent to an abstract set of elements. Each element is conditioned to one of the possible responses; the probability of occurrence of a particular response is equal to the proportion of elements conditioned to it. A second assumption is that on each stimulus presentation some proportion $\theta$ of the total population of stimulus elements is sampled (i.e., chosen at random). All elements in the sample are then conditioned to the response that is actually made. This sampling process places learning into the model via "all-or-none" conditioning of responses to basic stimulus elements, an idea first proposed by Guthrie (1935). The current work on stimulus sampling models derives largely from Estes' (1950) formalization of the idea. Although conditioning of each element is on an all-or-none basis, if the sample size is small relative to the number of elements in the set representing the stimulus, the probability of a particular response will change slowly. This change will give the appearance of a continuously increasing learning curve, especially if data from several subjects are averaged (Estes, 1960a).

Early theoretical formulations of the stimulus sampling theory assumed that practically any conceivable stimulus should be represented by a large set of basic stimulus elements. This assumption has now been questioned, however. In several simple learning situations it may be useful to assume that the effective stimulus is represented by one or two elements. This assumption has been shown to lead to accurate prediction of response probabilities in paired associates learning (Estes, 1960a, Bower, 1961) and to the prediction of some response patterns in two choice discrimination tasks (Suppes and Atkinson, 1960).

Many theorems concerning observable behavior can be developed from the assumptions of stimulus sampling. Stimulus sampling is not the most general form of a theory, however. The stimulus sampling model is one of a larger class of models in which the probability of response at trial $n$ is a linear function of the probability of response at trial $n - 1$. The more general theory, which was introduced to psychology largely by Bush and Mosteller (1955), stresses abstract algebraic manipulation to derive testable predictions. The stimulus situation as such is not introduced. Restle (1959) has pointed out that this lack of conceptual structure makes it difficult to apply the abstract models to experimental situations more complex than the acquisition of a response in a fixed situation. Although models of the linear operator type have generated a great deal of experimental activity in the analysis of such simple learning situations, they have not had great use in the analysis of concept learning.

Tests of different models of response conditioning require simple situations. Because the indivisible responses and stimuli should be defined with as little oversimplification as possible, learning theorists have concentrated their efforts on the analysis of simple learning problems. One situation that has been studied extensively with animals and humans as subjects is the discrimination experiment. In this experiment the subject is rewarded for making one of two motor responses depending on which of two binary stimuli (e.g., triangles or circles) is presented. Even in this simple situation there has been controversy over the ability of a stimulus-response theory to handle the data. Krechevsky (1932) maintained that some form of hypothesis testing had to be introduced into the model in addition to response conditioning. It appears, however, that a stimulus-response theory (including the cue-conditioning argument which, when large numbers of stimulus elements are allowed, amounts to the same thing) can account for the results of animal discrimination experiments (Spence, 1936; parenthetical conclusion mine).

Concept learning can be studied without reference to a basic learning theory. Indeed, it may be impossible to explain human behavior without a species-specific theory. Hull (1952, p. 41) warned that the analysis of speech and symbol manipulation may require new elementary laws of behavior. Spence (1957) has cautioned that stimulus-response theories are models constructed for a particular ideal environment. On a strictly logical basis, they cannot be generalized beyond the laboratory situations in which they have been tested. In the study of concept learning we must keep these cautions in mind. It is also a good idea to consider two, unequally important, criteria for a theory of behavior in any environment. First and foremost, the theory must demonstrate its ability in handling the facts of its own problem area. Second, it should be compatible with theories used in related areas.

In studying the higher mental processes, we find ourselves in a position envisioned by Spence (1957) when he asked what would have happened if Galileo had had to explain the workings of modern machinery. Spence concluded that Galileo would have repeated his studies of gravity, rolling balls down inclined planes in an attempt to derive principles for the operation of complex machinery from experiments in an idealized environment. By analogy, Spence argued that psychologists should study simple organisms (e.g., the white rat) in simple stimulus-response situations (e.g., speed in running a straight alley). But what is the distinction between "simple" and "complex" situations? Do we really know the pertinent stimuli and responses when we study rats running down straight alleys? Logan (1960) has found it useful to separate responses in a straight alley into responses in parts of the alley (a fractionation of the stimulus) and to refer to different speeds of running as different responses (a fractionation of the response). We could go further. Although learning theorists [possibly excepting Hebb (1949)] have disavowed interest in the neurophysiological changes involved in learning, we wonder why. At what point is behavior simple or complex? The rat is physiologically complex. Should we confine ourselves to the study of learning in the amoeba?

Not necessarily. The direct study of a complex mechanism is a scientifically legitimate method of analyzing its behavior. It is not the only method, and what is the best procedure in a particular case is an empirical question. The answer will depend in part on the mechanisms in question and in part on the caliber of the personnel who use each method. There is no a priori method of specifying which line of scientific inquiry will be the most useful for any general class of problems.

It would be nice, however, in terms of scientific parsimony, if the laws for complex situations such as concept learning were derivable from any more molecular learning theory approach. Such a derivation has been attempted by several investigators.


2    *Stimulus trace and generalization models*

Hull (1920) introduced to the study of concept learning the methods of modern experimental psychology. His study has been a prototype for many similar experiments, which, as we shall see, is in some ways unfortunate since it contained certain restrictive elements. Hull had human subjects view twelve series of Chinese pictographic symbols paired with nonsense syllables. Chinese symbols are constructed from radicals, which are the identification elements of a given pictographic character. They correspond somewhat to word stems in English, although only one symbol is used. Unknown to the subject, Hull paired certain radicals with selected nonsense syllables. The subject had to anticipate the nonsense syllable paired with the stimulus at each presentation. In addition to the presence or absence of the crucial radical, stimuli varied in other, irrelevant, ways. Hull found that simpler concepts (i.e., series in which only a few irrelevant elements were included in the stimuli) were easier to learn. This effect was emphasized if the relevant radical was made more noticeable (e.g., by writing it in one color and the remaining symbols in another). Hull's subjects could usually state what syllable was paired with a symbol before they could explain the rule for classifying a symbol. In the terminology of Chapter 2, subjects could identify the denotation of a name before they could state the concept.

The first finding is consistent with Hull's later theorizing (Hull, 1943, 1952). He assumed that each pairing of the nonsense syllable and any element of the stimulus continuously increased the strength of association between the response and that element. Since the radical was most frequently paired with the correct naming response, it eventually gained sufficient strength to elicit the response by itself. Other elements were paired, presumably at random, with other nonsense syllables so they would not acquire a similar habit strength. This argument is particularly clear when the subject is allowed to give only one response to each instance. The connections between the various responses and each stimulus element can be considered to be competing within an element and/or summating over elements. Since only the critical element (in this case, the radical) has a bias toward connection with the naming response, its presence alone will eventually become sufficient to evoke the appropriate response.

Recent findings (Estes, 1960a; Estes, Hopkins, and Crothers, 1961; Rock, 1957; Bower, 1961) have cast doubt on the assumption that habit strength increases continuously. Even if the establishment of a connection between a response and a stimulus is an all-or-none event, Hull's results can be explained in terms of a molecular learning theory approach. Complex pictographs would, presumably, give rise to a large population of elementary stimulus cues. In Hull's experiment stimulus cues were sampled and conditioned on each learning trial. Some of the stimulus elements were associated with presence or absence of the radical. Since their presence correlated perfectly with the naming response, all elements so associated would eventually be conditioned to the appropriate naming response. No other cue would have acquired and maintained this (or any other) connection, so eventually the presence of a population of "radical" cues, all highly biased toward being conditioned to the appropriate response, was sufficient to insure a stimulus sample in which the preponderance of stimulus elements were conditioned to the naming response. At each learning trial a small number of cues, relative to the size of the total population, were involved in the conditioning process. The probability of a given sample of cues containing a plurality of elements conditioned to the correct response increased by a series of discontinuous steps. Each step was so small, however, that an observer could not distinguish this from a gradual, continuous rise in the probability of a correct response. This was doubly true if, as in Hull's experiment, the probability of a correct response was determined by averaging data over subjects. When the complexity of the figure was reduced, the percentage of relevant cues in the stimulus universe was increased. When the relevant radical was outlined, either the number of cues from the shape of the radical was increased or (and ?) the probability of obtaining radical cues in a given sample was increased. Either alteration of the stimulus should lead to faster learning, in agreement with Hull's results.

For several years after Hull's paper, there was little further development of a S-R theory of concept learning. Hull and his students instead turned their attention to the analysis of simpler learning situations. (Hilgard (1956) has speculated that Hull came to the conclusion that a more rigorous theory of the learning of a single stimulus-response connection was needed before complex mental processes could be analyzed.) Several important theoretical papers appeared in the 1930s, a "miniature theory" of rote learning (Hull et al., 1940) followed, and the work culminated in publication of two attempts (Hull, 1943, 1952) to construct an axiomatic theory of learning. Compared to recent mathematical models, Hull's system may seem cumbersome and unsophisticated, but it was the first important attempt to develop such a theory. One of Hull's students, Eleanor Gibson, published a paper (Gibson, 1940) which was to influence greatly the study of concept learning. Gibson was concerned with the role of stimulus and response generalization during the learning of paired associates. For nearly 20 years the ideas she introduced have influenced theoretical and empirical studies of human learning. Although the original paper may no longer be a source of new research ideas, it was certainly a major step toward the understanding of human thought processes [for further amplification, see the review by Underwood (1961)].

Like Hull, Gibson saw the complex phenomenon of verbal learning as a thing to be understood by understanding its component parts. The problem for the experimenter was to isolate the molecular stimulus and learn how it was paired with the molecular response. To do this, Gibson concentrated on the learning of paired associates lists. (Her analysis is not logically restricted to this situation.) In the paired associate experiment the subjects observe a sequence of stimuli. These may be nonsense syllables, English words, or pictures. When a particular stimulus is presented, the subject is supposed to make a designated response. The subject may be required to recite the letters VEK whenever the letters RUZ are presented. If he fails to do this or recites an incorrect response, he is corrected. Within a given experiment, several such pairings are learned. The entire set of pairings constitutes a list. A trial occurs when a list is presented to the subject. Normally the order of items within a trial is changed at random. The experiment continues until either a given degree of performance is reached (e.g., $x$ successive trials without an error) or until a fixed number of trials have occurred. The time between trials may be varied. Trials on one list may be interspersed with or followed by trials on a second list.

Gibson claimed that the basic problem facing the subject is to learn to make a discrimination between different items on the same and different lists. Difficulty in discrimination is due to stimulus generalization between different items, which may or may not be on the same list. The result of stimulus generalization is that the act of conditioning a particular response to stimulus $A$ increases the probability that it will be given upon presentation of some similar stimulus $A'$. This tendency is decreased if $A$ and $A'$ appear in markedly different lists, thus permitting discrimination between them on the basis of cues from the overall stimulus context. Gibson referred to the tendency of a particular response to generalize to a different stimulus as the gradient of (stimulus) generalization. This gradient was assumed to arise from some underlying continuum of stimulus similarity. Actually, the continuum of stimulus similarity is applicable to the stimulus trace, or internal representation of the stimulus within the learner, and not to the stimulus itself. After all, any reasonable theory of learning must refer to conditioning of a response to a stimulus trace and not to the stimulus itself. Underwood (1961) has remarked that although it is clearly more in the spirit of the Gibson and Hull analysis of learning to refer to a physical similarity between stimuli, the fact that conditioning and generalization actually refer to the stimulus trace makes it possible to apply the same analysis in a more vaguely defined space. We shall encounter this idea again in our discussion of mediated generalization.

Empirically, it has been shown that the learning of two lists in a paired associates experiment results in poorer performance on the individual lists. Several experiments have shown that there is a positive relation between the similarity of the lists to be learned and the amount of interference (McGeoch and Irion, 1952). This result is in accord with Gibson's theory; she deduced that interference arose from the learning of an identical response to dissimilar stimuli or from learning of dissimilar responses to identical stimuli. For instance, if the members of a set $A$ of stimuli are paired with the members of a set $B$ of responses, learning the $A$-$B$ pairing should interfere with subsequent learning of a second pairing, $A$-$C$ or $C$-$B$. In either pairing, the second learning task imposes a requirement that is counter to the response tendencies generalizing from the first.

In concept learning, all members of a denotation must be paired with the same response, the name whose concept is to be learned. Suppose we think of the denotation as a paired associates list of stimuli. If the stimuli within this list have similar stimulus traces, the concept-learning problem should be easy. But if (some of) the stimuli on the list are similar to the stimuli on a second list (the denotation of another name), learning will be difficult. The same effect can be seen if we start with a stimulus sampling model. Similarity can be interpreted as the presence of overlapping sets of stimulus cues. When a concept is learned, the cues whose presence is relevant to a particular naming response will be conditioned to the response. Irrelevant cues will be randomly paired with this response.

This random pairing may cause interference if two concepts are to be learned. Every time a member of the denotation of the first concept is presented, some of the relevant cues will be conditioned to the appropriate name. These cues will, eventually, be biased toward being conditioned to the required naming response. Irrelevant cues will not be so biased. But, if there are a large number of cues which are shared with stimuli in the denotation of a second name, and if the shared cues are relevant in the second concept-learning situation, the supposedly irrelevant cues will be conditioned to an inappropriate naming response, the second name. The probability of the correct name's being given will be a joint function of the size of the set of relevant and of the set of shared cues. This is simply a rewording of Gibson's analysis into the language of the stimulus sampling theory.

The reader may be convinced of this by a heuristic argument. A cue-conditioning model can be represented by assigning each cue to the intersection of lines on an $n$-dimensional grid. By making finer and finer measures on each dimension, the grid, and any stimulus trace represented in it, can be made arbitrarily close to a continuous stimulus trace. Since the interference argument does not depend on the fineness of the grid, it is valid for any approximation of a continuous trace.

Baum (1954) extended Gibson's argument to concept learning. Baum reasoned that the denotation of each concept was a list, to each member of which the same response was appropriate. High intralist (intradenotation) similarity should facilitate concept learning; high interlist (interdenotation) similarity should inhibit it.

In Baum's experiment the subjects were required to learn lists of nine stimuli, with nine separate responses. As in the usual paired associates procedure, the subject would offer a response and then be told whether or not it was correct. On the next trial, a new list would be presented in which the stimuli were different but the responses were the same. What made this different from the usual paired-associates experiment was that the responses represented names and had concepts associated with them. For instance, each list might contain a picture of a face, and the response VEL would be appropriate for the face on each list. Another response (say, ZOG) would be appropriate for any stimulus which was a picture of four objects.

This procedure was originally developed by Heidbreder (1946) to test some hypotheses concerning the relation between object perception and concept learning. In Baum's experiment (and in most of Heidbreder's), the stimuli on each list, in addition to representing examples of a particular concept, fell into three broad classes. These were drawings of concrete objects, drawings of abstract patterns, and drawings of a specific number of things. Both Baum and Heidbreder and her associates found that subjects first learned concepts based on the presence of concrete objects of a given type, then the concepts based on the presence of abstract forms, and finally the concepts of number. Heidbreder (1949; Heidbreder, Bensley, and Ivy, 1948) concluded that this was because of the greater perceptual accessibility of concrete objects. Heidbreder felt that concept learning was to be seen as a special example of perception. This conclusion was in accord with the Gestalt psychologist's stress on the importance of perceptual phenomenon. Baum, looking at the concept-learning problem as a learning theorist, maintained that the data could better be explained by Gibson's generalization hypothesis. Baum analyzed errors made by subjects and found that the denotations of the concepts most dif-

ficult to learn contained stimuli which subjects frequently inter-
changed. For instance, the responses appropriate to form *a* were more
likely to be given to form *b*, and vice versa, than were similar confusions between concepts based on concrete objects. In the latter stages
of learning, after the "objects" responses were learned, this interchange would be uninteresting. The differential frequency of exchange
of responses appeared on early learning trials, as would be expected
by the generalization hypothesis.

By considering the form of the generalization gradient postulated
in Hull's work (a "bell-shaped" curve), Spence (1936) deduced that the
effect of negative instances (examples which were not members of a
concept set) was to restrict the range of values to which an animal
would respond along crucial stimulus dimensions. Buss (1950) showed
that this principle also applied to human concept learning. In a
pretest series, Buss taught his subjects to respond by categorizing as
"positive" either all members of a set of tall wooden blocks or the
tall blocks in a set of tall and short blocks, or by categorizing as "not
positive" all of a set of short wooden blocks. (In a control condition,
the "positive" response was assigned to short blocks.) Subjects were
then asked to give the "appropriate" response to a series of inter-
mediate-sized blocks. The number of intermediate blocks categorized
as "positive" was greatest when only positive instances had been
presented, least when only negative instances were presented.

Welch (1947) also presented a concept-learning model based on
the idea of direct conditioning of a response to a stimulus trace. He
assumed that any stimulus object was represented, inside the subject,
by a neural condition which was isomorphic with the stimulus. This
neural trace, which Welch made equivalent to *s*—the stimulus trace
in Hull's (1943, 1952) theory—was assumed to change progressively
with time. Welch was not clear as to the nature of this change; he
evidently meant some sort of fading procedure. This would be consistent with the exponential decay of *s* in Hull's system. Welch postulated that when a naming response was made it was conditioned to
all elements of all previously presented stimulus compounds[2] which
were present inside the subject at the time of the response. Since
criterial elements (i.e., those elements which defined instances as members of a concept) would be present on all occurrences of a naming
response, they would eventually acquire sufficient response strength
to evoke the naming response.

Welch used this model in studies of the learning of hierarchal concepts. Hierarchal concepts define sets whose elements are also concepts
(e.g., collie-dog-animal). Since a higher-order concept is further re-

moved from the direct "stimulus trace" of its instances, and since the instances of higher-order concepts on the average have less common elements, they should be more difficult to learn. This hypothesis was confirmed in a series of experiments on children's concept learning (Welch, 1940). The fact that all subjects were children temporizes the conclusion. Several investigators have suggested that the conceptual abilities of young children, brain-injured humans, and animals are particularly tied to the physical elements of the stimuli (T. S. Kendler, 1961). If the basic instance elicits a well-learned response, which in turn produces stimulus elements which are criterial for another response (a higher-order concept), learning of higher-order concepts should be easier. This hypothesis has been supported by a study by Kendler and Vinberg (1954), in which young children practiced naming possible stimulus elements (e.g., triangle, yellow, etc.) before they learned a concept based on the stimulus elements which they had named. That concept learning was facilitated by the naming procedure suggests a need for a "mediational response" S-R analysis of concept learning. Both the Welch and Gibson analyses consider only direct connections between stimulus elements and responses.

Welch's assumption of a neurological correlate for $s$ is unnecessary and probably not advisable. As Spence has pointed out (1957), $s$ is a mathematical variable in a system of equations; it does not require a physical analogue.

An analysis which considers only conditioning to stimulus elements does not seem suited for explanation of concept-learning situations in which no element of the stimulus is perfectly correlated with the presence or absence of a particular name. This situation can occur if the concept to be learned is a conjunction or a disjunction of two stimulus elements (e.g., red *and* triangle). A stimulus trace theory can handle this situation by introducing a postulate concerning cues which result from a particular combination of stimulus elements. Unless the rules for forming such patterns are specified, this amplification of the basic theory destroys much of its attractive simplicity.[3] It would seem also that such a postulate would have to predict rather slow learning. If the element combinations involve conjunctions, and therefore imperfect stimulus element-response correlations, concept learning is certainly neither impossible nor difficult (Bruner, Goodnow, and Austin, 1956; Hunt and Hovland, 1960). A series of experiments by Bourne and Haygood (1959, 1961) have, however, shown more rapid learning when the criterial values of each relevant dimension are perfectly correlated with the naming response. Even though significantly harder, a true conjunctive concept is not extremely difficult to learn. It will be shown (Chapter 8) that an information-processing theory can be used to explain the differential difficulty of learning various logical types of concepts.

## 3    A cue-conditioning model

Restle (1955, 1957, 1958; Bourne and Restle, 1959) has presented a comprehensive model of discrimination learning based on the "all-or-none" stimulus sampling model of conditioning. Bourne and Restle's (1959) article dealt explicitly with concept-learning. Their analysis is the most complete derivation of concept learning from a theory of stimulus sampling and conditioning to elementary cues. Attention is focused on a rather limited concept-learning problem. Stimuli are specified by binary dimensions, each dimension indicating the presence or absence of a particular set of cues. In a two-choice problem, each dimension is either relevant (in the sense that one of its values is *always* associated with the appropriate name) or irrelevant. Thus the discovery of any one of the relevant dimensions transmits sufficient information for the subject to make the appropriate discrimination. In a four-choice problem (described in detail by Bourne, 1957), the more conventional conjunctive concept analysis is used. Four names are used. Each is associated with one of the four combinations of values of two binary dimensions. In this problem it is possible to add redundancy by introducing a new dimension which may be substituted for one of the two original relevant dimensions.[4]

Each dimension is assumed to give rise to a set of cues. By this, Restle apparently means that certain subsets of cues represent the appearance of a specific value on each dimension. When a correct response is reinforced on trial $n$ the probability of a relevant cue $k$ being conditioned to that response $F(k, n)$ is changed by the linear operator.

$$(3.3.1) \qquad F(k, n + 1) = F(k, n)(1 - \theta) + \theta$$

If no reinforcement is given, the probability of a relevant cue's being conditioned by the next trial remains at

$$(3.3.2) \qquad F(k, n + 1) = F(k, n)$$

This model is similar to those proposed by Estes (1950) and Estes and Burke (1953). Bourne and Restle added the further assumption (consistent with Restle's earlier work) that irrelevant cues become adapted,

The probability of an irrelevant cue $k$ being adapted at a particular trial is given by

(3.3.3) $$A(k, n + 1) = A(k, n)(1 - \theta) + \theta$$

for reinforced trials, and

(3.3.4) $$A(k, n + 1) = A(k, n)$$

for nonreinforced trials. The probability of a correct response on the $n$th trial is given by the proportion of functional (nonadapted) cues conditioned to the correct set. If $K$ is the total set of cues, the probability of a correct response on trial $n$, $P(n)$, is

(3.3.5) $$P(n) = \frac{\sum_{k \in K} \{F(k, n)[1 - A(k, n)]\}}{\sum_{k \in K} [1 - A(k, n)]}$$

Assuming that the subject has no response biases and that, initially, no cues are adapted, for a two choice problem we have

(3.3.6) $$P(n) = 1 - \frac{\frac{1}{2}(1 - \theta)^{n-1}}{r + (1 - r)(1 - \theta)^{n-1}}$$

where $r$ is the proportion of relevant cues in the universe of stimulus elements. The learning rate parameter $\theta$ is defined as the joint probability that a cue will be present and that a particular response will be reinforced. That is,

(3.3.7) $$\theta = a \cdot r$$

where $a$ is the probability of a particular response's being reinforced and $r$ the probability that cue $k$ will be present.

The expected number of errors on a given problem from trials 2 to $N$, is

(3.3.8) $$\bar{E} = \sum_{2}^{N} [1 - p(n)]$$

The only variable in the equation for $p(n)$ which is not under the control of the experimenter is $r$, the proportion of relevant cues in the universe of stimulus elements. This can be estimated by fitting a value of $r$ to the total number of errors. (There is a linear relation between the two.) By using the $r$ so obtained, a variety of interesting hypotheses can be made.

Cues are additive. Suppose that each dimension gives rise to an equivalent number of stimulus elements. Suppose further that when any dimension is relevant, a fixed proportion $k$ of its cues are relevant cues. In the two-choice problem, adding redundant relevant dimensions should increase the proportion of relevant cues. Let 1 represent the total contribution of cues from a single dimension (i.e., 1 is the size of an arbitrary subset of cues), $R$ the number of relevant dimensions, and $I$ the number of irrelevant dimensions. Then

$$(3.3.9) \qquad\qquad r = \frac{kR}{(R + I + c)}$$

where $c$ is the total of all uncorrelated cues arising from background stimuli.

The assumption of an equal number of cues per dimension is convenient in exposition but not necessary. To provide an intuitive demonstration of a test of the theory without this assumption, consider the case in which a color dimension provides 1.975 times as many cues, and when it is relevant, provides 47% more relevant cues.[5] The equation for $r$ would then reduce to

$$(3.3.10) \qquad\qquad r = \frac{K[(R - 1) + (1.47)(1.975)]}{(R + I - 1) + 1.975 + c}$$

when color is relevant, and when it is irrelevant,

$$(3.3.11) \qquad\qquad r = \frac{kR}{(R + I - 1) + 1.975 + c}$$

Parameter values could be determined by inspecting the obtained data. It is not trivial to fit the parameters and then say that the data fit the model. With parameters free, only one group of transformations will fit a model. Calibrating stimuli for values of $k$ and $c$ will be useful. These values can be used to predict $r$ for particular combinations of redundant relevant and irrelevant dimensions. This is what was done in the Bourne and Haygood (1959) experiments (but see footnote 5). In one of their studies, subjects solved a two-choice problem in which the stimuli exhibited binary variation in some of or all the following dimensions: size, color, form, horizontal and vertical position, and number of figures. The number of irrelevant and *redundant* relevant dimensions was varied systematically. By using parameters for $c$ and $k$ estimated from the data, and substituting equation 3.3.9 into equations 3.3.8 and 3.3.6, the model was used to predict difficulty of concept learning with various combinations of relevant and irrelevant dimensions. Their results are summarized in Figure 3-1.

Bourne and Restle were also able to fit the data from several other binary choice studies (Archer, Bourne, and Brown, 1955; Walker,

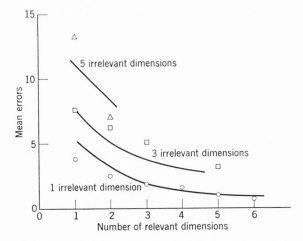

Figure 3-1. Mean number of errors as a joint function of redundant relevant dimensions and the number of redundant irrelevant dimensions. Solid lines are theoretical. (From Bourne and Restle, 1959, page 285. Reprinted with permission of the authors and the American Psychological Association.)

1958). In these experiments the number of irrelevant dimensions had been varied. A simple rearrangement of equation 3.3.9 produces

$$(3.3.12) \qquad \frac{1}{r} = \frac{1}{k}(R + B)\frac{1}{R} + \frac{1}{kR}I$$

where $B$ is the total background stimulation plus stimulation from irrelevant elements. If the number of relevant dimensions is held constant, $1/r$ should be a linear function of the number of irrelevant dimensions. When $1/r$ was estimated from total error scores, this prediction was generally confirmed for the experiments cited (Bourne and Restle, 1959, p. 288).

In another line of investigation, the implications of equation 3.3.7, defining $\theta$, were examined. Bourne and Pendleton (1958) introduced blank trials on which the subjects were not told what the correct answer was. In equation 3.3.7, this would reduce $a$, the probability that a response would be reinforced, and keep $r$, the probability that a relevant cue would be present, constant. Subjects made more errors than the model had predicted. To account for this, Bourne and Restle modified their model by introducing a "misinformative" stimulus trace from blank trials. This modification has not been tested.

Pishkin (1960) approached the same problem from a slightly different point of view. Instead of inserting blank trials in a two-choice problem, Pishkin inserted "misinformative feedback." On some trials the *wrong* response was reinforced with probability $a$. He also varied stimulus complexity by altering the number of irrelevant dimensions. As predicted by the model, mean errors were linear functions of both $a$ and the number of irrelevant dimensions. There was, however, an interaction between the two independent variables which was not predicted by the model. Restle (1957) had developed a "cue-validity index" to handle the problem of conditioning of cues that are partially correlated with the correct response. Pishkin's data indicated that this index did not provide a good estimate of errors in the misinformative feedback situation. Since both the 1957 and 1959 papers are specializations of Restle's original (1955) discrimination model, Pishkin's work casts indirect doubt on Bourne and Restle's model.

Bourne and Restle used a variation of the stimulus trace argument to account for the effects of delay in reinforcement. They adopted Estes' (1955) notion of stimulus trace fluctuation, which is an assumption that the number of elements in the sample of stimulus elements chosen decays exponentially with the time since the stimulus has been presented. Thus $\theta$, which can be interpreted as the probability that a particular cue is contained in a sample, declines to $\theta d^t (d < 1)$ if reinforcement is delayed by $t$ time units. By using this assumption to calculate $\theta$, Bourne and Restle were able to fit the data of an experiment by Bourne (1957) in which the response was followed, after an experimentally determined time period, by a signal indicating whether or not the subject made the correct choice. This was taken as presumptive evidence for the stimulus sampling description of learning. But later work has cast serious doubt on the conclusion. In Bourne's (1957) study (as in practically all studies used to test the Bourne and Restle model) the stimulus presentation was terminated by the response. The onset of the next stimulus occurred at a constant time period after the response. The "informative feedback" (reinforcement) signal occurred at an experimenter-determined point within the constant interstimulus interval. Increasing the time between response and signal decreased the time between the signal and the onset of the next stimulus. In the model the signal-next stimulus period is of no importance in determining behavior. But Bourne and Bunderson (in press) have shown that it is this period and not the response-signal period which does determine behavior. Bourne and Bunderson conducted a cue-conditioning study in which the response-signal and signal-next stimulus periods were orthogonally varied. They found that subjects made more errors when the signal-next stimulus period was shortened. Learning was not affected by increasing the response-signal period if the signal-next stimulus period was held constant. Since Bourne's earlier study had confounded these variables, Bourne and Bunderson re-interpreted his results as being the result of a short signal-next stimulus period. This interpretation, which appears to be correct, does not support Bourne and Restle's model. It also casts doubt upon the assumption of a fluctuating stimulus trace, a feature of Estes' (1955) theory as well as of Bourne's and Restle's model.

Perhaps the most interesting predictions made in using the Bourne and Restle model involve analysis of a four-choice task from the data obtained in the two-choice task. In the two-choice task, it will be remembered, there are $R$ *redundant* relevant dimensions. Each dimension transmits one bit of information, and this bit can be used to make the appropriate discrimination. In the four-choice task there are two independent relevant dimensions, transmitting a total of two bits, each of which is necessary for the appropriate discrimination. For example, in a two-choice task response $A$ might be assigned to all triangles, which were also always green; response $B$ would be assigned to all circles, which were always red. In the four-choice task, response $A$ would be assigned to all green triangles, response $B$ to all red triangles, response $C$ to all green circles, and response $D$ to all red triangles.

Considering relevant dimensions only, and representing stimuli by binary digits, we see that objects must be mapped into four response categories.

| | |
|---|---|
| 00 | $A$ |
| 01 | $B$ |
| 10 | $C$ |
| 11 | $D$ |

Let $X$ indicate an irrelevant dimension for a particular discrimination. The $0X - 1X$ discrimination is sufficient to distinguish between the two sets $(AB)$ and $(CD)$. Within each of these sets, a discrimination between elements can be based on $X0$ or $X1$. Alternately, the second bit may be used first, that is use $X0$ or $X1$ to distinguish $(AC)$ from $(BD)$ and then use the first bit for a discrimination within the subset. Although we do not know which path is followed in a particular situation, one of these paths to solution must be followed. Bourne and Restle consider each discrimination as a separate, independent, two-choice problem. The probability of a correct choice on the four-choice problem should be equal to the joint probability of correct choice on each of the two-choice problems which are involved. Let $(p_2)$ be the probability of correct choice on a two-choice problem.

The probability of a correct choice on a four-choice problem will be

(3.3.13) $$p_4 = (p_2)^2$$

The introduction of two two-choice problems also has an effect on relevant cues and on the conditioning rate. Assume that, on a given trial, the two two-choice problems split the stimulus sample between them. For each two-choice problem nested within a four-choice problem,

(3.3.14) $$\theta_4 = \tfrac{1}{2}\theta_2$$

where $\theta_2$ and $\theta_4$ are rate parameters in the two- and four-choice procedures.

The value of $r$ must be considered. In the learning of a discrimination based on one dimension, the other, independently relevant dimension is irrelevant. Thus if the two-choice problem based on one relevant dimension was described by

(3.3.15) $$r = k/(1 + B)$$

(with $B$ defined as in equation 3.3.12), the value of $r$ for a two-choice discrimination *within* a four-choice problem with two independent relevant and the same number of irrelevant dimensions, is given by

(3.3.16) $$r = k/(2 + B)$$

which reflects the addition of a dimension which is irrelevant at any *one* binary discrimination.

As part of the Bourne and Haygood (1959) study, some subjects solved a four-choice problem with a varying number of irrelevant dimensions. Calculations of $r$ from the number of errors, and the observed number of errors in the four-choice problem, agreed very closely with the $r$ and error scores predicted by using the data obtained from two-choice situations and making the appropriate substitutions. Prediction was rather poor for a similar experiment by Walker (1958), however. There were some methodological differences in the Walker study, particularly in the rate and method of presenting stimuli. On the other hand, Bourne and Restle (1959, p. 287) note that Walker's subjects produced some "irrelevant hypotheses" on the two-choice problem. Restle's (1955) discrimination model does not contain a provision for production and evaluation of subject's hypotheses. It seems crucial to the Bourne and Restle formulation to develop further the reason for the discrepancy between the Walker and Bourne and Haygood experiments.

Bourne and Restle's paper represents the most detailed attempt to analyze concept learning as a special case of stimulus discrimination.

In particular, it is the best development of the cue-conditioning theory of learning as applied to concept learning. It also represents the most detailed analysis of concept learning in terms of a direct attachment between the naming response and the physical cues provided by the stimulus. Since the data in support of this model are impressive, it is worth close analysis to determine its limitations.

The model is limited to analysis of conjunctive problems. It is assumed that if a set $S$ of cues is relevant to the use of a name, the cues which are elements of $S$ will always be present (perhaps in conjunction with a second set, $S'$) when the name is used. This would not be so if the concept were disjunctive, $S$ or $S'$. Of course it would be possible to develop a model for disjunctive concept learning by extending the notion that certain cues are less than universally valid. This was done, after a fashion, in Pishkin's study of misinformative feedback. In the misinformative feedback situation there is a random failure in the prediction of a name from the presence of certain cues. In disjunctive concept learning the failure is not random. The presence of a cue is a perfect predictor of the appropriateness of a given naming response, whereas its absence is not a perfect predictor of the inappropriateness of the same response. Humans can learn to use such information quite adeptly (Wells, 1962). A cue-conditioning model would evidently overpredict the number of errors that subjects make.

It is difficult to see how a subject is supposed to distinguish between an irrelevant cue which is to be adapted and a relevant cue which is to be conditioned. This would become a crucial problem in solving disjunctive concept-learning problems.

The model assumes that the probability of success at trial $n$ is independent of success on trial $n - 1$; that is, the model is path independent. The probability of an error on trial $n$ depends only on $P(n)$. So long as the total errors are in agreement with equation 3.3.8, any distribution of sequences of errors over learning trials is equally likely. This assumption applies to most stimulus sampling models and may be a general weakness. Recent experiments on probabilistic discrimination learning (in which the subject must guess which of two events will occur, the actual choice being determined at random with varying probabilities) have demonstrated that the path independence assumption is not tenable (Anderson, 1959; Anderson and Whalen, 1960, Suppes and Atkinson, 1960).

Perhaps related to this point is the question of whether or not subjects are "testing hypotheses." Goodnow and Pettigrew (1956) reported a probabilistic discrimination study in which subjects used their responses to test hypotheses such as "right after two lefts," etc. As a result, subjects frequently failed to gain information from the stimulus situation because they were concentrating on the stimuli of their own responses. Blatt (1961) and Blatt and Stein (1959) studied the use of responses more directly. Their subjects had to decode the PSI apparatus, a logical problem presented in a wiring diagram form (John, 1957). Subjects clearly displayed information-seeking behavior in their responses. Blatt (1961) even reported a change in physiological measures of arousal when the subjects' responses changed from information seeking to the testing of complex hypotheses. Since the PSI apparatus is an inductive reasoning problem amenable to description in terms of symbolic logic, it has a good deal of apparent commonality with concept learning. It is difficult to reconcile the results of these studies with the assumption that concept learning does not involve the testing of hypotheses.

Restle (1961) has developed a new model which does not involve cue conditioning. It assumes instead that the subject is testing hypotheses, and that this process can be described by a mathematical model. His new model will be discussed in Chapter 6. Suppes and Atkinson (1960), in describing their models for binary choice experiments, also provided a mathematical formulation for the testing of simple hypotheses. They argued that this could be reinterpreted as a cue-conditioning model. Even if Suppes and Atkinson were able to do this for binary choice situations, whether such a model could be extended to concept learning is an open question. In his new model, Restle introduces hypotheses as a primitive element, without reference to a stimulus sampling analogy.

## 4    An all-or-none model

In constructing stimulus sampling models, most theorists have adopted Estes' (1950) assumption that the stimulus is made up of a very large number of elements. The resulting models are models of the process by which a large number of elements become conditioned to the overt response before the response is made to the stimulus object itself. The original assumption was made to permit the stimulus sampling theory to handle the supposedly obvious fact that conditioning is a gradual process. It was assumed that the probability of emission of the conditioned response gradually increases as the stimulus is re-presented on successive learning trials. The fact of gradual conditioning was first seriously questioned by the findings from a series of experiments on paired associates learning (Rock,

1957). Although Rock's particular experimental results may have been due to artifacts (a controversy which does not concern us here), they generated an interest in the construction of "all-or-none" models of learning for paired associates experiments (Estes, 1960; Bower, 1961, 1962a). The models developed are nearly identical. Since Bower (1962b) has applied his model to the concept-learning situation, we concentrate on his argument. Bower states

> The basic notion of the model is the assumption that each stimulus item and its correct response become associated on an all-or-none basis. . . . If the item (stimulus response pair) is not conditioned . . . the probability that the subject will guess correctly is 1/N (N is the number of response alternatives). . . . The single parameter of the theory is the learning rate constant (c) which represents the probability that an unconditioned item becomes conditioned as the result of a single reinforced trial.
>
> Bower, 1962a, pp. 34–35 (italics mine).

The all-or-none model makes the counter-intuitive assumption that the probability that a stimulus response pair is learned on trial $n$ is independent of the number of previous reinforcements which the subject has received for giving the appropriate response to the stimulus in question. As learning trials are continued, an all-or-none learner does not gradually decrease his probability of making an error. This probability either remains constant at $1 - 1/N$, the chance level, or suddenly goes to zero. An explicit statement can be derived for the probability that a subject will make an error on the $n$th trial. This term $q(n)$ is the product of the probability that the subject does not get the item correct by chance on the $n$th trial and the probability that he has not learned the response on the $n - 1$ preceding trials,

$$(3.4.1.) \qquad q(n) = (1 - 1/N)(1 - c)^{n-1}$$

By using this basic equation, a great many detailed predictions can be made about the distribution of errors during learning. In particular, equation 3.4.1 can be used to predict the probability of an error following an error and the probability of an error on any trial before the subject has learned the concept. (This event is assumed to occur on the trial immediately preceding a long run of errorless trials, after which the experiment is terminated. It must be determined separately for every subject in the experiment.) The probability of an error prior to learning is assumed to be constant. The model has been shown to predict accurately the data obtained in paired associates learning studies (Bower, 1962a; Estes, 1960; Estes, Hopkins, and Crothers, 1960). Although several investigators have raised questions concerning possible artifacts that favor the confirmation of the predictions discussed, Bower confirmed several other predictions of the model. As a predictor of performance in the paired associates learning experiment, the all-or-none model is far more accurate than the psychological theories with which we normally deal. Only in psychophysics, and not always in that field, do investigators obtain such a close agreement between the data and the model.

Bower (1962b) and Ginsberg (1962) tested the ability of the all-or-none model to describe the data from concept learning experiments. They gave the same gross interpretation of the model in concept learning as in paired associates learning, although (as we shall see) the same precise definition cannot be used. They assumed that if the subject has not yet learned a concept, he will, with probability $c$, on a reinforced trial. Equation 3.4.1 is then appropriate as a predictor of the probability of an error. In the concept-learning situation, $N$, the number of response alternatives, is always less than the number of stimuli. In the experiments Bower and Ginzberg report, $N$ was always two.

In Bower's experiments college students learned two choice concepts based on stimuli with binary dimensions. The experiments were very similar to Bourne and Restle's (1959) two-choice problem. Logically, the problem was exactly the same. In the experimental procedure Bower permitted the subjects ample time to view each stimulus item, but they were not forced to do so. In a typical experiment the stimuli were five-letter clusters of consonants, constructed by choosing different combinations containing one of two letters from each of five pairs of letters. The model was confirmed in a striking manner. Bower's data were consistent with the hypothesis that each subject responded randomly until, on a stochastically determined trial, "something happened," the concept was learned, and from then on the subject made no errors. Of course, the model does not tell us what happened.

Ginsberg's (1962) experiments are by no means repetitions of Bower's. She used five-year-old children instead of college students as subjects. The concept her subjects learned was based on a property of sets of objects rather than on a property of objects. Finally, in her procedure the subjects practiced using the concept in a more specific way than do subjects in the normal cue-conditioning experiments. She showed the children three sets of objects in each display, and asked that they indicate which set "did not belong." Two of the sets contained the same number of objects, whereas the third, the "did not belong" set, contained a different number of objects. Ginsberg has also studied the performance of children learning other concepts based on the properties of objects and sets. She indicated, although without elaboration, that her results are very much the same. These results are simply that the all-or-none model provides a very good description of the data. The subjects responded randomly until they began a long series of errorless trials, thus indicating that they had learned the concept.

Since Ginzberg's and Bower's experiments are quite different, the fact that the same simple model describes both sets of results is very interesting. We have to be even more impressed when we remember that the all-or-none model is, if at all different, more accurate in describing the data from paired-associates learning experiments. Are there any aspects of the experimental situations which indicate either that the results are due to artifact or that the model is applicable only in certain special cases?

There are no obvious artifacts in the experimental procedure which favor spurious confirmation of the many predictions of the all-or-none model. The question about the model's generality is more difficult to answer. As it has been presented, the model makes no assumption concerning the process of concept learning. It is solely a mathematical device for summarizing certain statistics. It can be argued that this is all any model can be, and that the only sensible question to ask is whether the statistical summary is accurate. If this thesis is accepted, the construction of an hypothetical process of all-or-none learning is superfluous.

Restle (1959) has made the point that specification of a process underlying a mathematical model commits the model to a particular experimental situation. As the researcher changes this situation he may expect the model to be less and less accurate. If the process is clearly stated, the experimenter will also be able to predict what kinds of changes in the experimental setting will affect the accuracy of the model. The researcher who conceives of his model as only a data summarizer does not have this capability. Since we cannot possibly perform all the experiments that might be done, having the capability to generalize the model on logical as well as experimental grounds seems well worth the trouble of tying oneself to a particular process. In fact, Bower (1961) formalized the all-or-none model for paired-associates learning. He makes it a special case of the stimulus sampling model in which the stimulus is represented by only one stimulus element.

The same formalization of all-or-none process for concept learning is difficult to understand. Bower's stimuli, five-letter consonant clusters, are quite clearly made up of at least five elements, the letters, to which the subjects can respond differentially. There is, however,

a conceptually simple process which will lead to all-or-none learning
in Bower's experiments. Once Bower's subjects learned which letters
were relevant, the concept-learning problem was trivial. A given name
was always associated with the presence of a particular letter and
never with its absence. In other words, Bower's subjects had to notice
a sufficient and necessary property for assigning an object to a denotation before they could solve the problem. If we assume that subjects
noticed a few stimulus properties at random, each time an object was
presented (in the terms of Chapter 2, that they altered their descriptions), and that once a relevant stimulus item was noticed, the problem was solved, we have specified a process that leads to all-or-none
learning. This process emphasizes the perceptual aspect of concept
learning, the establishment of a relevant description, and de-empha-
sizes the problem of manipulating symbols to state a concept using the
terms of the relevant description. If this process model is correct, the
all-or-none learning equations should not provide a fit for the data
from subjects learning a problem that involves concepts based on
complex combinations of necessary and sufficient conditions.

This argument is quite appealing when applied to the experiments
by Bower and to the similar studies in support of Bourne and Restle's
(1959) model. It is less clear how it can be applied to Ginsberg's studies
of concept learning based upon properties of sets. In the terminology
of Chapter 2, Ginsberg's subjects had to derive a description in which
sets were described by the relative number of items in them. Once this
was done, the problem became trivial. The argument is not as com-
pelling as it was in Bower's experiments because we know very little
about the way in which children describe objects. A description based
on number is a relatively sophisticated one, even for college students
(see Chapter 4). Undoubtedly, five-year-old children do not initially
look at numbers, but they may have learned to do so after failing to
find any other way in which they could find a simple solution.
[Parenthetically, we should remember that Ginsberg's subjects had to
notice relative, not absolute numbers. This would certainly seem to be
within the capability of a bright five-year-old, although he might not
be able to recognize (i.e., have the concepts of) particular numbers.]

If we accept the foregoing explanation of the subjects' actions in
Bower's and Ginsberg's studies, we are accepting the idea that all-or-
none learning occurs in a situation in which "restructuring," finding
the appropriate way to look at the stimulus, is very important. The
Gestalt psychologists' view of thinking and problem solving stressed
the perceptual aspects in exactly this way. No Gestalt psychologists
(e.g., Wertheimer, 1959), however, ever developed such precise descrip-

tive models of the all-or-none hypothesis. It should also be remembered that a perceptual interpretation of the all-or-none model need not be made. There may be other process models which would give similar predictions for the reported situations and lead to quite different predictions if new experiments were to be performed. There is a particular experiment which provides a clear test of the perceptual explanation of all-or-none learning. If the explanation is correct, all-or-none learning ought not to be found in experiments in which the concept to be learned is based on complex disjunctions (e.g., the problems of Shepard, Hovland, and Jenkins (1961), to be discussed in section 8), especially if the experimental stimuli and procedure are such that the subject can do all the perceptual scanning he wishes.

The reinterpretations and suggestions for further experiments just presented are not meant as attacks on the all-or-none model. Establishment of the "truth" of a model is not a proper experimental goal. Any model can be shown to be inadequate if experimentation is precise enough or if the model is applied to enough different situations. The goal of experimentation is to establish the conditions under which different models generate accurate descriptions of the data. We wish to choose the simplest model that provides the required accuracy. To do this we must categorize concept-learning situations; we need concepts about concept-learning experiments! The aim of experimentation is to establish dimensions that are relevant to these concepts. The all-or-none model is clearly applicable to a set of experiments which we suggest may be defined by the relative importance of the perceptual and deductive phases of concept learning. Experiments testing an all-or-none model are being conducted. Their results may indicate whether or not this suggestion is correct. Even if it is, the all-or-none model is an important contribution to our understanding of the concept-learning process. The discovery of a relevant description is a necessary step in concept learning. A descriptive model of that discovery is required before the process itself can be understood.

## 5    Mediating responses

A behaviorist explanation of complex mental processes which admits only S-R bonds between physically present stimuli (as represented in the subject's sensory receptors) and the overt response is doomed to failure. We learn many concepts whose denotations are specified by symbols rather than by objects. For many people, "sin" is a concept which is learned in this manner. The concept that is learned is not a decision rule based on the characteristics of the symbols used to specify the denotation, it is based upon the characteristics of the objects for which the symbols stand. If a churchgoer wishes to know whether or not a particular act is sinful, he asks how the act is described, not whether it is described by words that have certain phonetic structure.

Concepts can be learned via symbols at progressively more and more abstract levels. This fact is not a complete refutation of the S-R model of learning. The way it can be explained was indicated by Hull (1930) when he introduced the "pure stimulus act." His position has been amplified by other learning theorists more concerned with complex mental behavior (Dollard and Miller, 1950; Goss, 1961; Kendler and Kendler, 1962; Maltzman, 1956; Miller and Dollard, 1941). The term "mediating response," or some variant of it, is normally used instead of Hull's original "pure stimulus act."

The mediating response explanation begins with the assumption that responses produce stimuli, which may serve as cues for further responses. When a stimulus is presented, its image in the organism is presumed to evoke certain previously learned responses. These provide stimuli which evoke another response, and so on. The chain of stimuli and responses, or some part of the chain, may consist of overt and covert responses. In concept learning the chain is ended with the occurrence of an overt naming response. It need not. In the use of concepts, the naming response would be an important cue to further action. (As in Ogden Nash's couplet "If you hear the call of a panther, don't anther.") The analysis of speech in terms of S-R learning theory stresses this role of the overt response.

Any stimulus will have a tendency to evoke several competing responses. The occurrence of one of these competing responses, to the exclusion of others, will affect the probability of obtaining a given response later in the chain. Concept learning can be seen as a problem in strengthening the links of covert S-R chains which lead to the appropriate naming response. For instance, training a subject to say "vegetable" to the stimuli "carrots, peas, and cabbage," and "mineral" to "gold, silver, lead," should aid in learning that the name "food" can be applied to the first set of words and not to the second. Learning could also proceed the other way, with "vegetable" becoming a response to be conditioned to the previously learned response-produced stimulus, "food." Notice that the logical characteristics of objects which distinguish food and not-food are not considered. Instead, the grouping is seen as being based on the evocation, for each object in the class "food," of a chain of responses that terminate in a common overt response. In any predictable world, the response chains learned in normal experience would correlate highly with the response chains implied by deductive reasoning. The model of learning need not consider this correlation explicitly. For this reason, Wertheimer (1959) described the S-R theory of learning as a process of blind learning which could not account for human thought. He felt that an accurate model of thought had to conceptualize a subject who actively regrouped and reinterpreted different aspects of the problems facing him.

In the foregoing analysis of S-R chains, the mediating responses were pictured as competing for evocation at different points in the chain. There is some difference of opinion as to the way in which a mediating response should be pictured. Certainly many learning theorists (e.g., Maltzman, 1955; Bousfield, 1961) do think of mediation as a chain of competing responses. The examples that are usually used suggest that we should think of a covert naming process, in which the object initiates some selection of names which could be applied to it. Osgood (1961) has taken issue with this. He suggested that mediation takes place by a process in which the stimulus-object is located in a continuous semantic space of meaningfulness. Osgood and his associates have shown that measurements may be made in this space (Osgood, Suci, and Tannenbaum, 1957).

Kendler and Kendler (1962) have developed a third position, which suggests that the mediating response should not be conceived of as "naming" at all; instead, it can be thought of as a response that orients the learner toward a particular aspect (dimension) of the stimulus.[6] The stimuli for the orienting response would be derived from the general experimental situation and not from the particular object to be categorized. This interpretation of a mediating response is particularly interesting, since it avoids a puzzling paradox. How is the initial selection of some aspect of attention to be made? If we think of the mediating response as being a response to the object to be categorized, we are forced to say that the learner scans all aspects of the object and then selects one as his focus of attention. If we hypothesize an orienting response, initiated by the experimental situation, the decision for selection takes place before the stimulus is presented. Thus we avoid the paradox of saying that, after observing $x$ and $y$ a "subconscious decision," whatever that is, is made to attend only to $y$. Since the orienting response hypothesis appears to be the hypothesis which represents the least amplification on the basic S-R position, we shall discuss it first.

6    *Orienting responses and reversal shift*

The most impressive evidence for the orienting response hypothesis is its ability to account for the behavior of subjects in a particular transfer situation known as *reversal shift*. The subject is required to solve two concept-learning problems in which stimuli have binary dimensions. The first problem is a simple two-choice discrimination— using binary dimensions—with one relevant dimension. The second problem requires either reversal or nonreversal shift. In the reversal shift condition the "correct" (or approach, or positive) instances all contain the binary value of the dimension which was relevant in the first problem *and* which was associated with *negative* instances. In the nonreversal condition the discrimination is based on a previously irrelevant dimension. For instance, if the first task required that the subject learn that triangles, regardless of size, were "positive" and circles were "negative," the reversal shift problem would have circles as "positive" and triangles as "negative." In the nonreversal condition, small objects might be "positive" and large ones "negative." If concept learning stems from the attachment of a naming response (i.e., the development of habit strength) to the element most consistently associated with the response, the reversal condition should be more difficult since it would require attaching a naming response to stimulus elements never before paired with the response. The naming response tendency attached to the (now negative) instances must be extinguished also. In the nonreversal condition, the learned habit strength would not bear a perfect inverse correlation to the correct answer, so learning should not be as difficult.

For human adults, the opposite is true. Kendler and D'Amato (1955) found that the reversal learning problem was considerably easier. This was true even during the early stages of the second problem, when the negative transfer effects on reversal learning should be at a maximum. Essentially the same finding was also reported by Buss (1953), who interpreted the results differently. Kendler and D'Amato concluded that the subject was learning two responses: a mediating (orienting) response to attend to a particular dimension, and an overt response to identify an instance as positive when a particular value appeared in that dimension. The first response should be learned to a greater habit strength since it was reinforced on presentation of both positive and negative instances. Although the nature of the mediating response was not clear (it could be either a physical orientation toward a stimulus dimension or a subvocalized designation of a particular dimension as important), the utility of a mediating response as an explanation seemed quite attractive.

Buss (1953) explained his experiments (and, tangentially, the Kendler and D'Amato results) without using a mediating response. He pointed out that in the nonreversal situation the originally correct discrimination is partially reinforced. Partial reinforcement is a situation known to lead to slow extinction of a response. Since the first response learned is incompatible with solution of the second problem, reversal shifts would be easier to make because they do not give partial reinforcement to the first response.

To clarify the issue, Buss (1956) performed the following experiment. Subjects first learned a simple, one-dimensional discrimination based, as in all these experiments, on geometric forms. Following this, the subjects were shown (without warning) a series of instances for which the experimenter's class identification was compatible with either a nonreversal or a reversal shift. Finally, subjects were asked to assign a third series of stimuli to different classes without being told whether or not they were correct. The class membership of instances in the third series varied, depending on whether or not they were assigned to classes on the basis of the reversal or nonreversal shift appropriate for the second series. Eighteen of Buss' twenty-five subjects classified the third series in a manner consistent with the "reversal" concept. Buss interpreted this study as unequivocal support for the mediation theory of concept learning. In a note to the experimental report, Kendler agreed.

Harrow and Friedman (1958) offered further support to the mediating response position. In Buss' second study, subject differences and possible differences in problem difficulty were not controlled. Using the Wisconsin Card Sorting Task, Harrow and Friedman compared the learning of reversal and nonreversal shifts to the learning of a concept based on the "shift" series without pretraining. In addition, their shift series used values of the irrelevant dimension which had never appeared in the first problem. A reversal shift problem was easier to learn than the same problem without prior training.

Learning to orient ourselves toward a particular dimension should be an important determinant of learning. Any condition which makes learning of the mediating response difficult should make concept learning more difficult. Once the mediating response is learned, however, it should exert no further effect on the solution of subsequent problems. This analysis has been supported in an experiment by Gormezano and Grant (1958). Their subjects learned to sort on the basis of one dimension while another, partially irrelevant, dimension contained a discrimination which was reinforced on 0, 25, 50, or 75% of the trials. After meeting a criterion on this task the subjects were shifted, without announcement, to a discrimination based on the previously irrelevant (or rather, partly relevant) dimension, with 25, 50, or 75% reinforcement of a third dimension which had been completely irrelevant during the first sorting. *Within* each stage, the difficulty of learning (measured by errors and trials to the criterion of ten correct sortings) was a function of the per cent reinforcement of an irrelevant dimension. Learning during the second stage was *not* a function, of the per cent reinforcement of the now correct dimension during the first stage. Since the Gormezano and Grant study involved 160 subjects in an efficient design, this negative finding can be received with some confidence. The failure of any habit strength to carry over to the second discrimination problem is powerful evidence for the need for a mediating (either verbal or orienting) response in S-R analysis of concept learning.[7]

To this point, an S-R theory, amplified by mediating responses, appears to explain satisfactorily the process of learning and transfer of concepts based on simple discrimination. A study by Gormezano and Abraham (1961a) suggests that there may be complications. Starting from Bourne and Restle's (1959) proposal that in concept-learning cues from dimensions are neutralized when more relevant dimensions (dimensions with a higher correlation to the correct response) are present, they investigated the process of "deneutralization," when formerly irrelevant cues become relevant. Subjects were presented with a series of Wisconsin Card Sorting Task problems; the discriminations were based on form, color, or number. Each subject was forced to make two discriminations of each type in the "shift" paradigm, no two discriminations of the same type following each other. Thus five non-reversal shifts were involved. During each color or number discrimination the irrelevant form dimension was reinforced 0, 25, 50, or 75% of the time. Since the Wisconsin Card Sorting Task has four values per dimension, low-reinforcement groups did not receive an approximate reversal shift task, even if the form dimension had been relevant in the previous stage. As expected, increasing the percentage of reinforcement of the irrelevant form discrimination decreased the sorting performance. This finding was consistent with the Gormezano and Grant results. The performance on the last three stages was significantly better than on the first three, however. The difference could be demonstrated in an analysis of perseverative errors, that is, the tendency to choose (incorrectly) a response that would have been correct on the previous discrimination. The improvement in performance was interpreted as showing that during the prolonged sorting task, subjects had learned how to drop a previously correct concept more rapidly. Without elaboration, Gormezano and Abraham point out that this is similar to the learning to learn phenomenon Harlow (1949) observed in primate discrimination learning. The subject, whether human or monkey, appears to learn *how* to solve discrimination problems. If this learning is discontinuous, the mediating response hypothesis is questionable because the response, itself, is not being learned in a continuous fashion. It may be, however, that mediation is still occurring. The subject might learn to respond to the stimulus of making an error by shifting his orientation (Goss, 1961).

Some interesting evidence on individual differences and comparative psychology supports the mediating response analysis, and, perhaps, offers a way of resolving a paradox present in Buss' (1956) study. It will be remembered that in Buss' study, although most of his subjects learned a reversal shift, seven subjects learned a nonreversal shift. Since S-R analyses refer to intraorganismic responses, the existence of a deviant case is quite interesting. Is it possible that subjects vary in their use of the mediating response? If so, is this variation consistent with the S-R analyses? The results of a series of studies on the relative ease of reversal and nonreversal learning in animals, children of varying ages, and adults (T. S. Kendler, 1960) suggest that the answer to both questions is "yes." Rats make nonreversal shifts much more easily than reversal shifts (Kelleher, 1956). The opposite holds true for college students. In children of kindergarten and preschool age neither finding holds. On the average, there is no preference for reversal or nonreversal learning in kindergarten children. Children who learn the first problem faster, however, perform best in the reversal condition, and children who learn the first problem slower perform best in the nonreversal condition (Kendler and Kendler, 1959). If younger children (nursery school age) are tested, they learn the nonreversal shift fastest (Kendler, Kendler, and Wells, 1960). Kendler and Kendler (1962) suggested that the mediating response is a verbal one. Older children (7 years versus 4 years) benefited more from verbalizing the correct, rather than an irrelevant, dimension during discrimination learning. It may be that although all those children who can speak verbalize an "orienting response" (or at least, some response which involves an orienting component), only the older children have learned to be proficient in attending to cues produced by their own spoken responses. A language-mediated theory of an orienting response seems more compatible with the data than a physical orientation theory. A rat or very young child would be capable of making the physical response. On the other hand, T. S. Kendler (1961) has also pointed out that the efficiency of reversal learning varies over the entire phylogenetic scale. That is, reversal learning becomes progressively harder as we change subjects from rhesus monkeys to newts and salamanders! None of these subjects speak, but they all have some capacity for physical orientation.


## 7    Verbal concept learning

The term "mediating response" is used with explicit reference to a verbal response in studies of verbal concept learning. As was pointed out in section 3, concept learning may be viewed as a particular case of the paired associates learning situation. In verbal concept-learning studies it is often suggested that the pairing is not between the stimulus and the overt response, but between the stimuli produced by a (previously learned) mediating response and the overt response. This is particularly true if the stimuli on which the concept is based can be considered to have had responses learned to them. In a sense, such previously learned responses could be considered the meaning of the object, and conditioning may refer to conditioning a response to a certain meaning.

Some authors (e.g., Bousfield, 1961; Skinner, 1957) prefer not to use terms such as "meaning" and "meaningful." They do make a distinction, however, between concept learning in which the naming response is conditioned to cues directly produced by each stimulus in the denotation, and concept learning in which the conditioning is to cues which the learner produces by performing an act previously conditioned to the cues presented with the stimulus object. The latter situation will often lead to more rapid learning. There is little doubt that the following stimulus-response pairings:

> beet-gax
> cabbage-gax
> corn-gax
> amethyst-roq
> onyx-roq
> granite-roq

present a list that is easier to learn than the following list:

> beet-gax
> amethyst-gax

cabbage-gax
corn-roq
onyx-roq
granite-roq

According to a theory of mediating responses, the first list is easy to learn because all stimuli to which "gax" is to be conditioned have previously had the response "food" conditioned to them. If "gax" is conditioned to "food" (or some other response produced stimulus, such as "vegetable") learning will be complete.

As we indicated in earlier discussion, learning theorists differ in the manner in which they picture the mediating response. Some, like Bousfield (1961), picture a chain of response and stimulus links in which each response competes with other responses for its place in the chain. Thus the response "cabbage" may elicit many responses. One which will occur with reasonably high probability is "food." If "food" has been a previous stimulus for "gax," the elicitation of the word "food" (as a covert response) increases the probability of the word "gax" as an overt response. An entire chain of S-R links may be reinforced so that at every stage there is an increased probability that its components will be elicited. Mowrer (1960a,b) has developed a theoretical model of how such chains are selected and reinforced, using only the principle of classical conditioning.

Osgood (1961) has argued that it is insufficient to represent meaning by the probability that a particular response or S-R chain will be elicited. Osgood represents the stimulus, internally, by a point in semantic space. The mediating response is the act of locating the stimulus in this space. The mediated stimulus is the location itself, and any response conditioned to this location (e.g., the overt naming response) will generalize to nearby locations. This explanation has been invoked by Osgood and his associates in their theory of language behavior (Osgood, Suci, and Tannenbaum, 1957). The discrimination and generalization hypotheses proposed by Gibson (1940) and Baum (1954) may be applied to locations in the semantic space as well as to objects represented by more physical dimensions.

The debate between different theorists as to the nature of the mediating response will often be irrelevant to the question of mediation in concept learning. Both Underwood (1952) and Osgood (1957) have presented mediating response analyses which say nothing about the form of the response. All mediating response hypotheses (except the orienting response hypothesis just discussed) assume that each object in a concept-learning experiment evokes cues which were conditioned to it before concept learning was begun. As Underwood (1952) saw the problem, the subject has to locate a set of cues which are elicited by the members of the denotation and which, if they are learned as cues for the naming response, will provide adequate discriminations. The problem is one of bringing the relevant cues and the required response in contiguity with one another. To Osgood or to Mowrer, this would be tantamount to selecting and reinforcing a particular chain consisting of an overt stimulus, a mediating response, a mediating stimulus, and an overt response. The role of the mediating response and mediated stimulus would be the same, however these entities might be conceived in the theory. It could be said that the mediated stimulus (or the mediating response, since the two are identical) is the "meaning of the concept." In the more precise language of Chapter 2, the stimuli produced by the mediating response become the decision criteria of the concept of the name. If they can be associated with an object, that object may be assigned the name.

Without attempting to test any formal theory of mediating responses, Reed (1946*a,b,c*) carried out a series of experiments which are quite relevant to the role of mediation in concept learning. In Reed's experimental situation, the subjects had to learn concepts based on sets of four words. Each set of words was placed on a card (so that the card was, in our terminology, the object to be categorized and the words on it its description). A nonsense syllable was designated as the correct response. Thus the appropriate responses might be

$$\{apple, \ stone, \ hat, \ emperor\}—guz$$
$$\{fox, \ rose, \ temple, \ eagle\}—jok$$
$$\{moose, \ town, \ rose, \ turnip\}—guz$$

Reed paired a given response with a set of words which contained, as one of its members, an example of a concept in colloquial English. This is illustrated in the foregoing example, where "guz" is paired with two sets of words, each containing the name of a food. The mediating response account of Reed's basic experiment is that the "key" words in each object set of words elicited a common mediating response and response-produced stimulus (e.g., "food"), and that this stimulus was then conditioned to the naming response.

In operation, the subject might learn the correct nonsense syllable response this way. He could also learn the appropriate pairings of word sets and responses by rote. Finally, he could do something in between, that is, responding to an inappropriate aspect of the stimulus, such as letter of the first word. By chance, such stimuli might be correlated with the correct response. Reed defined rote learning as "inconsistent," (a term he evidently also meant to be applied to the learning of inappropriate stimulus cues), whereas learning by discovering the English language concept was referred to as "consistent." Since Reed did not impose on his stimuli the strict ordering of dimensions and values that Hovland (1952) was later to recommend, he may have had partially consistent concepts in his problems.

The further details of Reed's procedure are similar to the experiments by Baum (1954) and Heidbreder (1946), which have already been discussed. In most of his experiments, forty-two cards were divided into the denotations of seven concepts, in the manner described. A single trial consisted of the presentation of all forty-two objects, one at a time, in the manner of a paired associates experiment. In addition to recording errors in naming, Reed encouraged his subjects to state their understanding of the concept. This information allowed him to divide subjects into two groups, depending on whether they learned a consistent or inconsistent concept.

Reed's first observation (1946a) was that concept learning took place far more rapidly than comparable learning of paired associates in which stimuli and responses were nonsense syllables. The improvement was most striking if the subjects were learning a consistent concept, less striking (but still large) if they were learning an inconsistent concept. The difference in speed of learning could be further increased, relative to paired associates learning, if subjects were given instructions that emphasized the possibility of using a common mediating response. When subjects learned consistent concepts, there was practically no decrement in performance after intervals up to 6 weeks. This is a marked contrast to the data on nonsense syllable learning, in which every attempt is made to prevent the occurrence of mediating responses. Not surprisingly, the performance decrement was greater for subjects who had learned inconsistent concepts, although their performance still exceeded the performance data available for nonsense syllable learning.

Two further experiments indicated the vital role of mediating responses. In the paired-associates task, increasing the length of a list increases the difficulty of the task. When Reed increased the length of his lists (but kept the number of concepts constant) (1946c) he did not find a comparable increase. For consistent concepts, increasing the length of the list from 42 to 60 items did no harm, although decreasing it from 42 to 21 did make the task easier. Increasing the list length did make the task more difficult for subjects who were learning inconsistent concepts. Most important, increasing the list length increased the frequency of occurrence of consistent concepts. It is as if the increase in the number of stimuli increased the chance for the correct mediating response to occur. Once it occurred, it would be available for attachment to all stimuli within a denotation. This is in accordance with Reed's interpretation of the data, a point to which we shall return.

If the mediating response is essential for consistent concept learning, inhibiting its occurrence should hinder concept learning. Reed (1946c) attempted to do this in two ways. In one condition he added irrelevant words to the set of words on the cards. In another condition, he added words that were partially relevant. For instance, suppose that all seven cards in one denotation contained somewhere an example of the English language concept "food." In Reed's final condition, four of the seven cards might also contain an example of "stones." As expected, Reed found that the presence of partially relevant information slowed learning, since subjects might fixate on a partially correct answer. There is an interesting similarity between his results and the later, better controlled, studies of partially relevant information which appeared after Bourne and Restle's (1959) analysis. The two experimental series are not duplicates, since Reed's manipulations clearly affect the occurrence of a mediating response.

These findings are consistent with a mediating response analysis of verbal concept learning. The mediating response in Reed's experiments would be a highly overlearned one. Once a naming response was attached to the stimuli produced by a mediating response, each presentation of an object represented an overlearning trial. This should have resulted in rapid and stable concept learning, in agreement with Reed's first two findings. Adding new instances within a single concept should not affect the established habit strength, since learning was nearly asymptotic. In a cue-conditioning theory, it would not affect the number of relevant elements conditioned since nearly all of them would already be conditioned.

The only finding not derivable from a mediating response analysis is the observation (Reed 1946a) that instructions to learn concepts facilitate concept learning. This indicates that a human subject can, in some manner, alter the production of mediating, stimulus producing responses, or alter his scanning of the stimuli so produced. It will be recalled that this problem of improvement in the handling of the mediating response appeared in the Gormezano and Abraham (1961a) study, in which extended practice seems to have produced "learning how to learn" in a situation where the mediating response analysis was necessary. Since the analysis assumes that a mediating response will, itself, follow S-R laws, any evidence of discontinuity in learning based on mediating responses casts doubt on the utility of an overt response model of hypothesized complex mental processes. Using the language of hypothesis testing, Reed confined himself to a phenomenological description of his results. He described his subjects as experiencing an initial period of disorientation, then searching for an appropriate mediating response, and finally evaluating its usefulness in a critical manner. He presented several protocols to support this position. Reed pointed out that hypotheses might be tried at several levels—common response based on letters in the first word, sounds of nonsense syllables, and, meaning of one or more of the words within each object-set. Practically concurrent with Reed's publication, Heidbreder (1945) made the process of successive abstraction central to her theory of concept learning. This will be discussed in Chapter 4.

Reed's work can be attacked on methodological grounds. Although the idea of a mediating response is central to his argument, Reed did not obtain careful measures of the extent to which different stimuli shared common mediating responses. Thus, one of his most crucial variables was left uncontrolled. There are two ways in which such control could have been achieved. The most effective method would be to control the learning of mediating responses by using nonsense syllables alone and training the subjects to use other nonsense syllables as responses (which might be used later as mediating responses) in a pre-experimental session. Alternately, we can obtain some measure of the probability of different responses to a given stimulus, either for words in the natural language (Underwood and Richardson, 1956a) or for nonsense syllables (Glaze, 1928; Archer, 1960). The experimental method provides a better control over the degree of learning. The use of natural language stimuli permits manipulation of a much wider range of associations in a setting that is more normal for the subject.

Any number of mediating responses could be made to a particular stimulus. For words, as an example, the noun "baseball" may produce the response of saying the words "hard," "white," or "round." Underwood (1952) reasoned that if concept learning is dependent on the placing of the relevant cue in temporal contiguity with the response, concept learning should be a function of the probability that the stimuli in the denotation will elicit the appropriate mediated response. Underwood and Richardson (1956a) gathered data on the probability of responses to a variety of nouns in a restricted association task. Subjects were presented with the stimulus word and asked to respond with the first sensory impression which they had (e.g., baseball —hard, jello—soft). The frequency with which a response was given for a particular stimulus word was defined as the response dominance of that stimulus-response pair. They then made use of this data in an experimental investigation of the role of response dominance in concept learning (Underwood and Richardson, 1956b). Subjects were presented with a set of common nouns, and told to give a response which the experimenter would designate as "correct" or "incorrect." The subject had to keep trying until he made all the correct responses. Actually, the arbitrarily selected response was a response which had varying degrees of dominance for the examples selected. For instance, in a high-dominance condition the response "round" was correct for barrel, doughnut, knob, and balloon. In the low-dominance condition it was correct for snail, cherry, grapefruit, and skull. If the appropriate response was a high-dominance one, the task was easier.

This study illustrates a basic difference between many verbal concept-learning tasks and tasks involving usual stimuli. Strictly speaking, concept learning, as defined in Chapter 2 or in the sense described by Hovland (1952), was not involved. Instead, the subject had to select one of his pre-established concepts (e.g., "round") as appropriate for this situation. Also, the name in the Underwood and Richardson study implies an established concept. In the logical analysis the name has no meaning except its concept.

In a study which does fit our definition of concept learning, Mednick and Freedman (1960) artificially varied response dominance. Their subjects first learned a paired associates list of twelve items. Four of the items in one of the two lists used were paired with responses for which the word "white" had high response dominance.[8] The other list, which contained the same stimulus items, did not pair these four items with responses with a common dominant response. However, it did pair a *different* set of four items with response words to which the word "soft" was response dominant. Finally, each list contained four items which were never paired with response words with a common dominant response. After the subjects had learned the paired associates list, they learned the same twelve stimuli as a verbal concept-learning list with a nonsense syllable as the name. The three four-item sets discussed were specified as denotations of each of three concepts. According to the mediating response analysis, the concept to whose instances a common dominant response had been "facilitated" should be easier to learn. The hypothesis was confirmed. Interestingly, at a subsequent interview the subjects did not indicate that they were consciously aware of the mediated response. This result suggests that Hull's (1920) finding that subjects can identify instances before they can explain their method of identification applies even with verbal stimuli. Here it seems that the finding would be least expected, especially in view of Reed's (1946c) description of verbal concept learning.

Freedman and Mednick (1958) also investigated the variance of the dominant response when measured over members of the set of stimuli to which a name is to be learned. Consider the case in which the appropriate mediating response has high dominance for some instances in the training set and very low dominance for others. The mediating response should occur to some instances of the training set, which would place the appropriate mediated stimuli in close temporal contiguity with both the naming response and the other instances of the training set. This contiguity should lead to an increase in both (a) the conditioning of the overt naming response to the stimuli produced by the mediating response and (b) the conditioning of the mediating response to the other members of the training set. A high-variance concept list would be easier to learn than a low-variance list, provided the mean level of each list was the same. This prediction was confirmed for verbal concept-learning lists equated for mean response dominance of the appropriate mediating response.

In their discussion, Freedman and Mednick allude to a problem we have encountered before in discussing Reed's findings relative to list length. How does the "correct" mediating response become dominant for the low-dominance items in the high-variance list? They suggest that

> The high response dominance instance quickly places the correct response in contiguity with the other relevant concept instances. This tends to polarize responses to the relevant instances and results in rapid attainment of the HV (high variance) concept.
>
> Freedman and Mednick, 1958, p. 465.

What is polarization? Loosely, the idea suggests that subjects have some method of manipulating the mediating response. A strict contiguity interpretation has been indicated, for which there is some additional evidence. If the mediating response is conditioned to the low-dominance items by temporal contiguity, learning should also be facilitated by placing all instances of a single concept together when the list of stimuli used in training contains examples of several different concepts. This prediction was tested and confirmed by Kurtz and Hovland (1956).

What is needed is an explanation of how some stimuli acquire a "feedback" capability to encourage their own production. Mowrer (1960a) has developed a variant of learning theory in which this phenomenon is central. Mowrer's conception of learning is based on stimulus selection, including selection of stimuli produced by mediating responses. If the results of reinforcement have stimulus properties, mediated stimuli are in the proper position to acquire reward or punishment properties by classical conditioning. The mediated stimuli should thus acquire secondary reinforcement properties and would increase the response dominance of the appropriate mediating response to the other instances in the set, since only this response would produce cues which had the capacity to encourage their own production.[9]

Whatever the nature of "polarization" in the Freedman and Mednick study, it must be a fairly effective mechanism. Their instances were presented at a four-second rate, so the subjects did not have a great deal of time to sort through possible mediating responses.

Gibson's (1940) analysis should apply within the space defined by mediated stimuli. Underwood (1957) tested this. He assumed that "overlap," the extent to which two words share the same high-dominance response, was a measure of mediated stimulus similarity. Underwood had his subjects learn several verbal concepts simultaneously. The particular training sets used for each concept differed in amount of overlap. As expected, rapidity of learning was negatively related to overlap. The difference was maintained only up to a point, perhaps because of the particular experimental techniques and/or the technique for measuring overlap.

The effect of mediating responses may sometimes be predicted even if dominance levels are unknown. Goss (1961) pointed out that whereas some relations between stimuli and mediating responses will facilitate concept learning, others may inhibit it. For simplicity, consider two subsets of objects $O_1$ and $O_2$, two possible mediating responses $M_1$ and $M_2$, and two final responses $R_1$ and $R_2$. Goss presented four prototypical patterns, for which he predicted differential effects in concept learning.

The mediating response would help most when, as in most of the situations we have considered, all stimuli share the same response. This is Goss's type $A$ pattern,

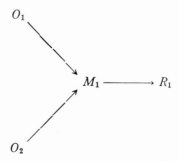

In a second pattern different mediating responses might help distinguish the denotations of different names. This is the type $B$ pattern,

$$O_1 \longrightarrow M_1 \longrightarrow R_1$$
$$O_2 \longrightarrow M_2 \longrightarrow R_2$$

An extreme-example of the type $A$ pattern is the high-dominance condition of the Underwood and Richardson (1956$b$) study. A type $B$ pattern is the epitome of the low-overlap condition of Underwood's (1957) study. In both situations concept learning is aided.

Mediating responses should hinder concept learning, however, in a type-$C$ pattern, in which the objects in two different denotations share common response-produced cues,

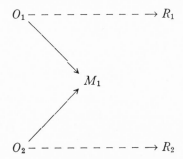

Here the conditioning of response $R_1$ to $O_1$ will also condition $R_1$ to some of the cues produced by $M_1$. Thus an incorrect generalization based on this conditioning may occur when $O_2$ is presented. The type-$C$ pattern corresponds to Underwood's high-overlap condition. Finally, two sets of objects to which a common response is to be learned might not share a common mediating response. This is the type $D$ pattern,

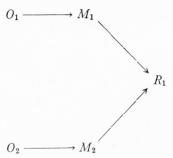

in which $O_2$ cannot benefit from mediated generalization as $R_1$ is being conditioned to $O_1$.

From the results of the previously cited research on naturally occuring mediated associations, we would expect that patterns $A$ and $B$ would be learned more rapidly than patterns $C$ and $D$. This expectation has been confirmed by Lacey (1961). He established the mediating response patterns by pretraining his subjects (children) to make nonsense syllable responses (the $M$'s) to appropriate objects (the $O$'s). Lacey's confirmatory study has the advantage that he established the mediating responses experimentally. In the response-dominance studies all patterns may have occurred simultaneously, with the experimenter measuring only the strongest ones.

In general, the need for a mediating response analysis of concept learning has been confirmed. If mediating responses are necessary, are we to conclude that they are sufficient? Can concept learning be understood by recourse to the S-R model, amplified by mediating responses? A strong case can be made for this model, but there are certain pertinent questions which have been left unanswered.

Introduction of mediating responses, unless they are rigorously specified, can destroy the predictive power of the S-R formulation. For the most part, mediation hypotheses have been limited to the prediction of inequalities; overlap makes concept learning more difficult, type-$C$ patterns are harder to learn than type-$A$, etc. Goss (1961) writes:

At present, there is no way of combining the separate presumed facilitative, inhibitory, or neutral effects into a net facilitative, inhibitory, or neutral effect.

Goss, 1961, p. 257.

If this is so, the resulting theory is bound to be weak. It will only be able to predict for simple situations, and even then predictions will have to be based on inequalities. What is required is a theory of mediated generalization rich enough to make detailed predictions. The concept-learning model presented by Bourne and Restle (1959) is an example of the form such a model could take. Rigorous specification should increase the predictive power of the mediation hypothesis without introducing new a priori assumption.

There is no reason that such a theory of generalization could not be developed. The only qualification is that it would have to be developed within the framework of a quantitative theory of direct S-R learning. If the basic learning theory were to be stated in terms of inequalities (as is Gibson's (1940) paper) quantification at the higher level of mediated generalization could not be achieved. Popper (1959) has attempted to develop and apply a mathematical model to situations which involved mediated generalization. Unfortunately, her own data do not always support her models. In spite of the present lack of success, it is clear that future mediating response models should stress quantification more than past ones have.

The mediating response analysis has yet to produce experiments which discriminate between the various theoretical interpretations of the nature of the mediating response. Some distinction between the idea of a chain of responses and the localization of an item in a semantic space ought to be attempted experimentally. This is a problem in the psychological study of all forms of verbal behavior and not just in the study of concept learning.

8    *Stimulus internalization and coding: a problem in S-R theories*

The nature of the stimulus trace has important implications both for psychological theories and for attempts to mechanize concept learning. For either a biological or a mechanical concept learner, categorizations must be based on an internal representation of an external object. Whether the transformation that creates the representation is a "parallel" one which produces elements to which response strengths are associated, or whether it is in itself subject to learning during a particular concept learning task, is a question which must be answered before an adequate model of human concept learning can be developed.

In both analyses of the role of mediational responses in generalization and concept learning, the idea has been accepted that a concept learning task can be broken down into a few, easily inferred, intervening S-R chains. (There is a temptation to say that experimenters have avoided situations where the chain could not be specified.) We have seen experimental results, however, which suggest discontinuities in the learning process.

Consider the type of internal definition of the stimulus required to produce Freedman and Mednick's (1958) results for their high-variance group. The correct mediating response had a quite high dominance for some of their instances and a very low dominance for others. The production of an appropriate mediated stimulus to one instance somehow resulted in the production of the appropriate (but normally very improbable) mediated stimulus to other instances, and it happened within a very short time (4-second presentation rate). In the framework of the serial mediating response analysis, it is hard to see how the correct mediating response could work its way to the top of the response hierarchy so rapidly. In the parallel response analysis, how could a very small part of the original stimulus trace become dominant so rapidly? Admittedly, parameters of learning curves could be found which would permit either occurrence. It is doubtful that such parameters could be reconciled to other available data, since they would require very rapid learning of simple concepts. This raises serious questions concerning definition of the effective stimulus. Perhaps instances are only defined *in context,* in the sense that either (*a*) a particular hypothesis is developed from a few instances and then checked on other instances, or (*b*) instances are initially defined by a parallel mediational process over part of the potential effective stimulus domain, followed by a contrast of internal representations. In the latter case, only the mediated stimuli that lead to discriminations between two or more instances which are in different classes *or* to similarities between two instances in the same class would be retained as part of the stimulus trace during later stages of the concept-learning process. It should be noted that either of these procedures would lead to rapid learning of a variety of partitions of the same set of objects, even though the objects might vary in their response dominance for particular orderings. For instance, by either a hypothesis checking or a contrast method, the following "concepts" would be learned rapidly: *bird*—(chicken, hawk) or *mammal*—(dog, fox). But so would the concepts *predator*—(fox, hawk), *domestic*—(chicken, dog).

Tangential evidence indicating a need to modify the S-R formulation of concept learning beyond mediation has been presented in some of the studies cited. Direct evidence of the inadequacy of the S-R formulation is now available in a series of studies by Shepard, Hovland, and Jenkins (1961). Since they are crucial to our argument, we shall discuss them in some detail.

In the basic experimental situation, subjects were required to learn an identical response to four of eight stimuli. The stimuli were constructed from all possible combinations of three-dimensional, two-valued objects. This universe of stimuli can be represented by a three digit-binary code, namely: 000, 001, 010, 011, 100, 101, 110, 111. In practice, Shepard et al. used a variety of stimuli: geometric shapes varying in size, form, and color; three geometric shapes of the same form and color, varying independently in size; three geometric shapes, one varying in size, the other in form, the other in color; and, finally, eight different combinations of familiar objects (nut or screw, candle or light bulb, horn or violin). There are seventy possible ways of splitting the eight-instance universe into two four-instance subsets. However, there are only six ways in which this can be done if we regard as equivalent all subsets which can be transformed into each **other** by redefinition of dimensions. The six possible methods of division are as follows:

Type I. All members of each subset have a common value on one of the dimensions, and no stimulus not a member of the subset has this common value on the relevant dimension. The partition (001, 000, 010, 011) versus (101, 100, 110, 111) is of this class.

Type II. All members of a set have either a particular combination of specified values on two relevant dimensions or, on the relevant dimensions, have neither of these values. An example is the partition (001, 000, 110, 111) versus (010, 011, 100, 101).

Correct identification of an instance in a Type I classification requires the reception of information from one dimension, but in a Type II classification correct identification requires reception of information from two dimensions. In the following four classes, all three dimensions may have to be used. The importance of each dimension (in terms of the information transmitted by it) varies.

Type III. As in Type II, each set of the partition contains two pairs of stimuli which share common values on two dimensions. If dimensions $A$ and $B$ are used to define the first pair of instances within a set, however, dimensions $B$ and $C$ will be used to define the second pair. For instance, using geometric forms, all the black circles (regardless of size) and big white objects would be found on the subset. Notice that the common value of dimension $B$ in the first pair and the second pair must change. An example is (001, 011, 000, 100) versus (010, 110, 111, 101).

Type IV. Each set contains three objects which have a common value on any one of the three dimensions. (That is, given any dimension, each subset will have three objects with a common value.) The fourth instance in each subset is arbitrary, but its complement (i.e., the object that has different values on all dimensions) will be the instance which is the "exception" in the other set. An example is (000, 110, 101, 100) versus (111, 001, 010, 011).

Type V. One subset contains three objects which have the value of a particular dimension in common. The fourth object is arbitrary. The "exception" instance in the other set differs from the exception in the first set by only one dimension instead of all dimensions, as in Type IV. This is the dimension that contains the common value of the other three objects in the subset. An example is (011, 000, 001, 110) versus (101, 100, 111, 010).

Type VI. There is only one partition of the eight objects that satisfies this definition. There is no abstract rule to assign objects to a subset so long as the rule requires a description in terms of dimensions and values. The partition is (010, 001, 111, 100) versus (011, 000, 101, 110).

In the experimental procedure of Shepard et al., two techniques were employed. In one study the stimuli were presented as in a paired associate task but with more stimuli than responses. In another study all instances were presented simultaneously. The subjects were given up to 1 minute either to develop a categorizing rule (in one condition) or to memorize the sorting that was presented (in the other condition). Error and time scores for memorizing and sorting were highly correlated across types of problems $(r > .90)$. In all experiments measurements of time to criterion and accuracy were also highly correlated.

Empirically, the results were quite clear. The order of difficulty of learning the classifications, either as a paired associates list, as a concept-learning task, or as a memorizing task, was I < II < (III = IV = V) < VI, *initially*. As a result of prolonged practice with different types (in the paired associates technique), subjects became quite adept at handling the Type VI problem so that it became easier relative to the others.

Generalization theories of concept learning cannot predict the obtained order of difficulty. In the experiments, stimuli could be similar in the sense that they had one, two, or zero values in common. (Notice that the nature of the stimuli makes it reasonable to assume that the same dimensions and values structure could be applied to the stimuli produced by a hypothetical mediated response.) A gradient of generalization notion requires that the difficulty of concept learning be *some* continuous function of the intraset similarity and the interlist distinctiveness of stimuli. (This definition even allows an inversion of the conventional generalization gradient.) Using coefficients of "confusion between stimuli" obtained from a conventional paired associates task with the same stimuli and eight responses, Shepard et al. computed a set of expected rank orderings—one for every possible continuous gradient of generalization. The obtained rank ordering was not in this set.

The authors concluded that the direct S-R generalization formula failed because it did not provide for sufficient abstraction in the internal representation of stimuli. This abstraction might be provided by an amplification of stimulus sampling models. Estes (1959) has suggested that unique patterns (e.g., "black triangle") have their own cues which cannot be derived from their components. Also, Restle's model of discrimination learning, which permits the adaptation of cues, would result in a learned distinctiveness of particular dimensions. These theories lead to more problems of interpretation, however. The admission of patterns as cues, without rules for the definition of patterns, opens a Pandora's box of theoretical loopholes that can be used to "explain" nearly any result. As for cue adaptation, it must meet the same objection. How does the subject determine that a cue is irrelevant and must be adapted?

Even if cues from pattern and cue adaptation are admitted, the results are still puzzling. Why does learning on the Type VI classification improve with practice? Again we seem to be encountering a "learning to learn" phenomenon, although this is of a much more complex type than is seen in simpler discrimination experiments.

There is a measure which is an excellent predictor of the original order of difficulty of the six classification types. This measure (derived by Shepard et al. in a mathematical appendix to the experimental report) is a detailed one; essentially, it reflects the extent to which *information* [in the mathematical sense, as defined by Shannon and Weaver (1949)] is spread across the three dimensions. The implication is that subjects are searching for some sort of maximally efficient decoding scheme. In doing so they are involved in two procedures, locating relevant channels of information and developing procedures to utilize these channels. (A channel may involve a number of dimensions in a particular combination.) This implies an active, hypothesis-forming subject rather than one who is passively building up response strength or adapting to and conditioning passively received cues. Shepard, Hovland, and Jenkins concluded that a concept-learning model which fails to take this aspect of human behavior into account cannot be considered valid. The present author agrees.

## 9  Evaluation of the learning theory approach

Learning theorists had originally hoped to devise a concept-learning model which treated complex categorization as a specialization of discrimination learning. This proved impossible. Some form of mediating response had to be introduced into the analysis of concept learning in the human adult. If this modification alone were adequate, it would represent a minor retreat from the original position. The learning of an overt S-R connection could still serve as a model to explain cognitive processes of the categorization type. Laws and theories based on pure measures of learning could be applied directly to the analysis of human thought processes.

Unfortunately, the mediation hypothesis is not adequate. Some form of mediation is certainly necessary in any analysis of concept learning. There appear to be two major flaws in a theory which introduces nothing else. Paradoxically, these two objections are somewhat inconsistent. (If either one of them is valid, however, the mediation hypothesis falls.) Unrestricted introduction of a mediating response into an S-R chain leaves the theorist in the uncomfortable position of being able to explain everything while predicting nothing. There is almost no behavior that could not be "analyzed" as being compatible with an S-R theory (or a theory of cue conditioning and adaptation) if the theorist is allowed to introduce new mediating links or to vary habit family hierarchies.

Fortunately, most learning theorists interested in complex mental processes have been aware of this difficulty and have specified in advance the form of mediation which is assumed to occur. For this, workers such as Kendler, Buss, Osgood, and Underwood deserve a great deal of credit. Their concern over control of the mediating responses, however, has led them to investigate relatively simple concept-learning situations. They have concentrated on situations in which there is either a one-one correlation between the naming response and the presence of either some element of the physical stimulus or some response-produced element elicited by the physical stimulus. In other words, they have dealt only with Shepard, Hovland, and Jenkins' Type I category. So long as S-R and cue conditioning studies are limited to such cases, the statement that more complex concept learning can be derived from them remains one of faith rather than belief. This belief receives little encouragement from the experimental results of Shepard, Hovland, and Jenkins (1961) or from tangential results of the studies of Reed (1946a), Freedman and Mednick (1958), and Gormezano and Abraham (1961a). At the primate level, Harlow's (1949) "learning to learn" phenomenon has remained something of an unexplained scandal to learning theory.

Several alternative theories are possible. One approach is to assume that human complex learning is different in kind from the "purer" (perhaps nonverbal) learning displayed by animals. We could then proceed to construct a human complex learning theory based on new principles or attempt to discover empirical relations (laws) which held only for the complex learning situation. The Gestalt approach to thinking as typified by Wertheimer (1959) is such an endeavor. Certain underived principles of behavior in problem solving are postulated after the phenomenon at hand is observed. These principles are then used to make an analysis of other complex mental behavior. Unfortunately, the Gestaltists have neither made their observations systematic enough nor their empirical laws explicit enough to offer hope of any solution in the immediate future. Although we shall review several "Gestalt-oriented" experiments in the next few chapters, it will be for their empirical findings rather than for their theoretical importance.

Perhaps a more fruitful approach would be a redefinition of the response. Is it unreasonable to assume that an adult human has learned several large "information processing units" which are specifically designed for the manipulation of an internally represented, symbolically coded environment? By using them the human could construct an internal model of the environment, one that could be used to predict external events. Such a conception of thought has been expressed by Campbell (1960) and, in particular, in the TOTE unit analogy discussed in a speculative monograph by Miller, Galanter, and Pribram (1960). In an extended learning theory model these routines would be considered as responses. As such they would be held accountable to the laws of learning. Presumably they could be broken down into smaller more unitary S-R connections. This should not be done, because the smaller responses would not occur in isolation in the adult. The stimulus of having completed one step in an information processing procedure should be a sufficient stimulus to elicit the occurrence of the next step. Only at a very few "choice points" would the stimuli arising from the results of information processing be examined before determining further responses.[10]

Building such a model requires vastly different techniques than those used in conventional S-R psychology. Responses can only be thought of as complex transformations on input data. Since the transformations provide varying stimuli, the rules for assembling strings of transformations must be stated. Here S-R or other conventional learning theories may help. We might find, however, that an S-R model could not provide enough flexibility in the application of these transformations. In fact, there may be learned transformations used to decide what transformations to use next. Learning itself may be a problem-solving situation.

Although the form of the transformations may be rather rigid, the variety of answers they produce in interaction with the stimulus environment may be quite rich. The relation of this point of view to artificial intelligence and, more particularly, to the proposals of Newell, Shaw, and Simon (1958) for information processing models of problem solving should be clear. A response is an information-processing routine. Computer-programmed routines can be used to

investigate the implications of different strings of complex transformations, different rearrangements, and different rules for choosing between transformations at particular branch points. No analogy to the
hardware aspects of the computer is implied.

In the artificial intelligence field response selecting problem solvers
are built for their own sake. Since *homo sapiens* is the most compact
and flexible problem-solving program known to us, a simulation of
his performance *may* have implications in the artificial intelligence
field. In return, the work in the artificial intelligence field *may* have
implications for psychology. The principles on which an artificial
categorizing machine should be built, or on which a biological categorizing machine is built, are far from clear. These are not necessarily
the same principles, but they may be.

What sort of research will this approach generate? First and foremost, responses must be identified. The responses, or transformations,
may exist in canonical form in four areas: the recognition and internalization of the stimuli to be categorized, the retention of information from previous experience, development and testing of hypotheses,
and the evaluation of possible alternative arrangements of responses
as a result of stimuli obtained from previous executions of the current
arrangement.

In the following chapters we shall review psychological evidence
relevant to these points. We shall then examine hypothetical cases
and obtained results from various artificial categorizing systems based
on different organizational principles. The design and exercise of
such systems is often a major undertaking. Building one can be quite
revealing without its being compared to, or generating new, experimental data.

REFERENCES

Anderson, N. H., 1960. Effect of first-order conditional probability in a learning
    situation. *J. exp. Psychol.*, **59**, 73–93.
Anderson, N. H. and R. E. Whalen, 1960. Likelihood judgments and sequential
    effects in a two-choice probability learning situation. *J. exp. Psychol.*, **60**, 111–120.
Archer, E. J., 1960. Re-evaluation of the meaningfulness of all possible CVC tri-
    grams. *Psychol. Monogr.* 74 (whole No. 497).
Archer, E. J., L. E. Bourne, and F. C. Brown, 1955. Concept identification as a
    function of irrelevant information and instructions. *J. exp. Psychol.*, **49**, 153–164.
Bartlett, F., 1958. *Thinking*. New York: Basic Books.
Baum, M., 1954. Simple concept learning as a function of intra-list generalization.
    *J. exp. Psychol.*, **47**, 89–94.

Blatt, S. J., 1961. Patterns of cardiac arousal during complex mental activity. *J. abnorm. soc. Psychol.*, **63**, 272–282.

Blatt, S. J. and Stein, 1959. Efficiency in problem solving. *J. Psychol.*, **48**, 193–213.

Bourne, L. E., 1957. Effects of delay of information feedback and task complexity in the identification of concepts. *J. exp. Psychol.*, **54**, 201–207.

Bourne, L. E. and C. U. Bunderson. Effects of delay of informative feedback and length of feedback interval on concept identification. *J. exp. Psychol.* In press.

Bourne, L. E. and R. C. Haygood, 1959. The role of stimulus redundancy in concept identification. *J. exp. Psychol.*, **58**, 232–238.

Bourne, L. E. and R. C. Haygood, 1961. Supplementary report: effect of redundant relevant information upon the identification of concepts. *J. exp. Psychol.*, **61**, 259–260.

Bourne, L. E. and R. B. Pendleton, 1958. Concept identification as a function of completeness and probability of information feedback. *J. exp. Psychol.*, **56**, 413–419.

Bourne, L. E. and F. Restle, 1959. Mathematical theory of concept identification. *Psychol. Rev.*, **66**, 278–296.

Bousfield, W. A., 1961. The problem of meaning in verbal learning. In C. N. Cofer (ed.) *Verbal learning and verbal behavior:* New York: McGraw-Hill.

Bower, G., 1961. Application of a model to Paired-Associate learning. *Psychometrika*, **26**, 255–280.

Bower, G., 1962a. An association model for response and training variables in paired-associate learning. *Psychol. Rev.* **69**, 34–53.

Bower, G., 1962b. Address given at Western Psychological Association meetings, 1962. Symposium on recent developments in mathematical psychology.

Bruner, J. S., J. J. Goodnow, and G. A. Austin, 1956. *A study of thinking.* New York: Wiley.

Bush, R. and F. Mosteller, 1955. *Stochastic models for learning.* New York: Wiley.

Buss, A. H., 1956. Reversal and nonreversal shifts in concept formation with partial reinforcement eliminated. *J. exp. Psychol.*, **52**, 162–166.

Buss, A. H., 1953. Rigidity as a function of reversal and nonreversal shifts in the learning of successive discriminations. *J. exp. Psychol.*, **45**, 75–81.

Buss, A. H., 1950. A study of concept formation as a function of reinforcement and stimulus generalization. *J. exp. Psychol.*, **40**, 494–503.

Buss, A. H., 1959. Supplementary report: maintenance of a previously learned concept as a function of partial reinforcement. *J. exp. Psychol.*, **58**, 414–415.

Campbell, D. T., 1960. Blind variation and selective retention in creative thought as in other knowledge processes. *Psychol. Rev.*, **67**, 380–400.

Dollard, J. and N. E. Miller, 1950. *Personality and psychotherapy.* New York: McGraw-Hill.

Estes, W. K., 1960. Learning theory and the new mental chemistry. *Psychol. Rev.*, **67**, 207–222.

Estes, W. K., 1960. Statistical models for recall and recognition of stimulus patterns by human observers. In Yovits and Cameron (eds.) *Self organizing systems.* New York: Pergamon Press.

Estes, W. K., 1950. Toward a statistical theory of learning. *Psychol. Rev.*, **57**, 94–107.

Estes, W. K., 1955. Statistical theory of distributional phenomena in learning. *Psychol. Rev.*, **62**, 369–377.

Estes, W. K. and C. J. Burke, 1953. A theory of stimulus variability in learning. *Psychol. Rev.*, **60**, 276–286.

Estes, W. K., B. L. Hopkins, and E. J. Crothers, 1960. All-or-none and conservation effects in the learning and retention of paired associates. *J. exp. Psychol.,* **60,** 329–339.

Freedman, J. L. and S. A. Mednick, 1958. Ease of attainment of concepts as a function of response dominance variance. *J. exp. Psychol.,* **55,** 463–466.

Gibson, E. J., 1940. A systematic application of the concepts of generalization and differentiation to verbal learning. *Psychol. Rev.,* **47,** 196–229.

Ginsberg, R., 1962. Address given at Western Psychological Association 1962 meeting, Symposium on concept learning.

Glaze, A., 1928. The association value of nonsense syllables, *J. Genetic. Psychol.* **35,** 255–269.

Goodnow, J. J. and T. Pettigrew, 1956. Some sources of difficulty in solving simple problems. *J. exp. Psychol.,* **51,** 385–392.

Gormezano, I. and F. Abraham, 1961*a*. Intermittent reinforcement, non-reversal shifts, and neutralizing in concept formation. *J. exp. Psychol.,* **61,** 1–6.

Gormezano, I. and F. Abraham, 1961*b*. Intermittent reinforcement of a formerly relevant dimension in concept formation. *Psychol. Rep.,* **8,** 111–116.

Gormezano, I. and D. A. Grant, 1958. Progressive ambiguity in the attainment of concepts on the Wisconsin Card Sorting Test. *J. exp. Psychol.,* **55,** 621–627.

Goss, A., 1961. Verbal mediating responses and concept formation. *Psychol. Rev.,* **68,** 248–274.

Guthrie, E. R., 1935. *The psychology of learning.* New York: Harper.

Harlow, H., 1949. The formation of learning sets. *Psychol. Rev.,* **56,** 51–65.

Harlow, H., 1959. Learning set and error factory theory. In S. Koch (ed.), *Psychology a study of a science.* Vol I. *General systematic formulation, learning and special processes.* New York: McGraw-Hill.

Harrow, M. and G. B. Friedman, 1958. Comparing reversal and non-reversal shifts in concept formation with partial reinforcement controlled. *J. exp. Psychol.,* **55,** 592–598.

Hebb, D. O., 1949. *The organization of behavior.* New York: Wiley.

Heidbreder, E., 1949. The attainment of concepts. VII. Conceptual achievements during card sorting. *J. Psychol.,* **27,** 3–39.

Heidbreder, E., 1945. Toward a dynamic theory of cognition. *Psychol. Rev.,* **52,** 1–22.

Heidbreder, E., 1946. The attainment of concepts. I. Terminology and Methods. *J. Gen. Psychol.,* **35,** 191–223.

Heidbreder, E., M. L. Bensley, and M. Ivy, 1948. IV. Regularities and levels. *J. Psychol.,* **25,** 299–329.

Hilgard, E. R., 1956. *Theories of learning.* New York: Appleton.

Hovland, C. I., 1952. A "communication analysis" of concept learning. *Psychol. Rev.,* **59,** 461–472.

Hull, C. L., 1952. *A behavior system.* New Haven: Yale University Press.

Hull, C. L., 1930. Knowledge and purpose as habit mechanisms. *Psychol. Rev.,* **57,** 511–525.

Hull, C. L., 1943. *Principles of behavior.* New York: Appleton.

Hull, C. L., 1920. Quantitative aspects of the evolution of concepts. *Psychol. Monogr.* (whole No. 123).

Hull, C. L., C. I. Hovland, R. T. Ross, M. Hall, P. T. Perkins, and F. B. Fitch, 1940. *Mathematico-deductive theory of rote-learning.* New Haven: Yale University Press.

Hunt, E. B. and C. I. Hovland, 1960. Order of consideration of logical types of concepts. *J. exp. Psychol.*, **59**, 220–225.

John, E. R., 1957. Contributions to the study of the problem solving process. *Psychol. Monogr.* **71**, 447 (whole No. 18).

Kelleher, R. T., 1956. Discrimination learning as a function of reversal and non-reversal shifts. *J. exp. Psychol.*, **51**, 379–384.

Kendler, H. H. and M. F. D'Amato, 1955. A comparison of reversal and non-reversal shifts in human concept formation behavior. *J. exp. Psychol.*, **49**, 165–174.

Kendler, H. H. and R. Vinberg, 1954. The acquisition of compound concepts as a function of previous training. *J. exp. Psychol.*, **48**, 252–259.

Kendler, H. H. and T. S. Kendler, 1962. Vertical and horizontal processes in problem solving. *Psychol. Rev.*, **69**, 1–16.

Kendler, T. S., 1960. Learning, development, and thinking. In Harms (ed.) Fundamentals of psychology: the psychology of thinking. *Ann. N.Y. Acad. Sci.*, **91**, 52–65.

Kendler, T. S., 1961. Concept formation. *Annu. Rev. Psychol.*, **12**, 447–472.

Kendler, T. S. and H. H. Kendler, 1959. Reversal and non-reversal shifts in Kindergarten children. *J. exp. Psychol.*, **58**, 56–60.

Kendler, T. S. and H. H. Kendler, and D. Wells, 1960. Reversal and nonreversal shifts in nursery school children. *J. comp. physiol. Psychol.* **53**, 83–88.

Krechevsky, I., 1932. "Hypotheses" in rats. *Psychol. Rev.*, **38**, 516–532.

Kurtz, K. and C. I. Hovland, 1956. Concept learning with different sequences of instances. *J. exp. Psychol.*, **51**, 239–243.

Lacey, H. M., 1961. Mediating verbal responses and stimulus similarity as factors in conceptual naming by school age children. *J. exp. Psychol.*, **62**, 113–121.

Logan, F. A., 1960. *Incentive.* New Haven: Yale University Press.

Luce, R. D., 1959. *Individual choice behavior.* New York: Wiley.

Maltzman, I., 1955. Thinking: from a behavioristic point of view. *Psychol. Rev.*, **62**, 275–286.

McGeoch, J. and A. Irion, 1952. *The psychology of human learning* (2d ed.). New York: Longmans, Green.

Mednick, S. A. and J. L. Freedman, 1960. Facilitation of concept formation through mediated generalization. *J. exp. Psychol.*, **60**, 278–283.

Miller, G., E. Galanter, and K. Pribram, 1960. *Plans and the structure of behavior.* New York: Holt.

Miller, N. E., and J. Dollard, 1941. *Social learning and imitation.* New Haven: Yale University Press.

Mowrer, O. H., 1960a. *Learning theory and behavior.* New York: Wiley.

Mowrer, O. H., 1960b. *Learning theory and the symbolic process.* New York: Wiley.

Newell, A., J. C. Shaw, and H. Simon, 1958. Elements of a theory of human problem solving. *Psychol. Rev.*, **65**, 151–166.

Osgood, C. E., 1953. *Method and theory in experimental psychology.* New York: Oxford University Press.

Osgood, C. E., 1957. A behavioristic analysis of perception and language as cognitive phenomenon. In *Contemporary approaches to cognition.* Cambridge: Harvard University Press.

Osgood, C. E., 1961. Comments on Professer Bousfield's paper. In C. N. Cofer (ed.), *Verbal learning and verbal behavior.* New York: McGraw-Hill.

Osgood, C. E., C. J. Suci, and P. H. Tannenbaum, 1957. *The measurement of meaning.* Urbana: University of Illinois Press.

Pishkin, V., 1960. Effects of probability of misinformation and number of irrelevant dimensions upon concept identification. *J. exp. Psychol.*, **59**, 371–378.

Popper, J., 1959. Mediated Generalization. In R. Bush, and W. Estes (ed.), *Studies in mathematical learning theory*. Stanford: Stanford University Press.

Reed, H. B., 1946a. Factors influencing learning and retention of concepts. I. Influence of set. *J. exp. Psychol., 36*, 71–87.

Reed, H. B., 1946b. II. The influence of length of series. III. The origin of concepts. *J. exp. Psychol., 36*, 166–181.

Reed, H. B., 1946c. IV. The influence of the complexity of the stimuli. *J. exp. Psychol., 36*, 252–261.

Restle, F., 1959. Survey and classification of learning models. In R. Bush, and M. Estes (ed.), *Studies in mathematical learning theory*. Stanford: Stanford University Press.

Restle, F., 1961. Statistical methods for a theory of cue learning. *Psychometrika, 26*, 291–306.

Restle, F., 1955. A theory of discrimination learning. *Psychol. Rev., 62*, 11–19.

Restle, F., 1957. Theory of selective learning with probable reinforcements. *Psychol. Rev., 64*, 182–191.

Restle, F., 1958. Toward a quantitative description of learning set data. *Psychol. Rev., 65*, 77–91.

Rock, I., 1957. The role of repetition in associative learning. *Amer. J. Psychol., 70*, 186–193.

Shannon, C. L. and W. Weaver, 1948. *The mathematical theory of communication*. Urbana: University of Illinois Press.

Shepard, R. N., C. I. Hovland, and H. M. Jenkins, 1961. Learning and memorization of classifications. *Psychol. Monogr., 75* (13, whole No. 517).

Skinner, B. F., 1957. *Verbal behavior*. New York: Appleton.

Spence, K., 1957. *Behavior theory and conditioning*. New Haven: Yale University Press.

Spence, K. W., 1936. The nature of discrimination learning in animals. *Psychol. Rev., 43*, 427–449.

Suppes, P. and R. Atkinson, 1960. *Markov learning models for multi-person interaction*. Stanford: Stanford University Press.

Suppes, P. and R. Ginsberg, 1962. Application of a stimulus sampling model to children's concept formation of binary numbers, with and without an overt correction response. *J. exp. Psychol., 63*, 330–336.

Underwood, B. J., 1952. An orientation for research on thinking. *Psychol. Rev., 59*, 209–220.

Underwood, B. J., 1961. An evaluation of the Gibson theory of verbal learning. In C. N. Cofer (ed.), *Verbal learning and verbal behavior*. New York: McGraw-Hill.

Underwood, B. J., 1957. Studies of distributed practice, XV, Verbal concept learning as a function of intra-list interference. *J. exp. Psychol., 54*, 33–40.

Underwood, B. J. and J. Richardson, 1956a. Some verbal materials for the study of concept formation. *Psychol. Rev., 53*, 84–95.

Underwood, B. J. and J. Richardson, 1956b. Verbal concept learning as a function of instruction and dominance level. *J. exp. Psychol., 51*, 229–238.

Walker, C. M., 1958. Concept identification as a function of amounts of relevant and irrelevant information. Unpublished doctoral dissertation, Salt Lake City: University of Utah.

Welch, R. L., 1947. A "behaviorist explanation" of concept formation. *J. genet. Psychol., 71*, 201–222.

Welch, R. L., 1940. A preliminary investigation of some aspects of the hierarchal development of concepts. *J. genet. Psychol., 56*, 359–378.

Wells, H. H., 1962. Transfer and stimulus effects in disjunctive concept learning. Unpublished doctoral dissertation, Yale University.

Wertheimer, M., 1959. *Productive thinking* (2nd ed.). New York: Harper.

FOOTNOTES

1. Hull's influence on modern psychology is probably exceeded only by that of Freud and perhaps Pavlov. Interestingly enough, however, his work is hardly known outside his own scientific group.

2. This term rather than "stimulus trace" was used to indicate that the neural representation of the instance contained elements which were isomorphic with various molecular elements of the stimulus. The nature of the transformation was never made clear. In particular, which relations between stimulus elements would be represented in the stimulus trace? If we knew this we could specify, or at least limit, the class of transformations which create the stimulus trace.

3. Hull (1943) attempted to derive patterning from an assumed interaction of simultaneous sensory events within the nervous system. Estes (1959) does this somewhat more directly, introducing cues for patterns as such.

4. Additional discussion of the experimental setting is given in Chapter 4, where the experiments relevant to the Bourne and Restle model are compared to experiments in stimulus recognition.

5. A situation in which more cues were added per dimension could arise if, as in Hull's (1920) experiments, a particular stimulus element were made more "striking" by underlining, increasing its size, etc. The percentage of relevant cues might be increased if the experimenter, in designing the stimuli, made the values of one dimension more discriminable from each other than the values on another dimension. This evidently happened in Bourne and Haygood's (1959) experiment. The data could only be fit by assuming that the dimensions of form, size, location, and orientation had half their cues relevant when the dimensions themselves were relevant, but that color, when relevant, contributed only relevant cues.

6. Goss (1961) has attempted to reconcile the two interpretations by introducing the response of naming a dimension. Without orientation, this would not produce discriminating cues.

7. A recent study by Buss (1959) might confuse the issue if it is not carefully evaluated. Using colored wooden patterns, Buss trained subjects to discriminate on the basis of shape. He then shifted his subjects to a form discrimination in which the previous shape discrimination was reinforced 0, 25, 50, or 75% of the time. Learning the second discrimination was impeded by reinforcement of the first concept. Similar results have been obtained by Gormezano and Abraham (1961*b*). The Gormezano and Grant results, especially the results on stage-1 learning, suggest that Buss could have obtained this result without using the first learning stage. Buss' high percentage of reinforcement procedure should increase the difficulty subjects would have in learning the correct orienting response as well as the correct naming response. This is particularly pronounced because the orienting response (not the naming response) on the first series will be correct with better than chance probability for all but the 50% group during the second series. (The 75% group receives partial reinforcement during the shift problem, the 0% group learns a reversal shift problem,

and the 25% group receives partial reinforcement for a reversal shift.) Thus Buss' results in no way conflict with a mediating response hypothesis, although he speaks of reinforcement of a unitary acquired concept in his discussion.

Incidentally, Buss makes what appears to be a misinterpretation of the Gormezano and Grant results. He states, "They (Gormezano and Grant, 1958) demonstrated that partial reinforcement of a concept during original learning impedes learning of a new response" (Buss, 1959, p. 415). This implies that partial reinforcement would attach a nondominant response to a stimulus element during original learning. This habit strength could then be transferred to a new learning situation. Such a finding would support a direct stimulus-response connection analysis rather than a mediating stimulus-response analysis. This is not what happened in the Gormezano and Grant experiment, however. They partially reinforced during original learning the concept that was *correct* in the second stage and *no* transfer effect was found (Gormezano and Grant, 1958, p. 626).

8. Mednick and Freedman used the Kent-Rosanoff word association list rather than Underwood and Richardson's (1956a) data.

9. Mowrer's analysis rests entirely on the acquisition by the response-produced cues of a reinforcement capability. Mowrer says this occurs by classical conditioning. The same acquisition could be derived from a theory of instrumental learning, in which a consummatory response or incentive function [from Spence (1957) and Logan (1960), but derived from Hull (1943, 1951)] was generalized to the response produced stimuli. Mowrer has made a more detailed analysis of the application of his theory to thought processes.

10. In a quite different terminology, Bartlett (1958) made a similar proposal. He considers thinking a skill, just as complex motor acts are skills. By analogy, he suggests that an adult can no more interrupt a thought process than a skilled player can interrupt a tennis serve after he has raised his racket toward his shoulder.

# 4

# Stimulus organization

## 1     *The problem of subjective definition*

Learning theorists are interested in how a stimulus becomes the signal for a response. In their models "stimulus" is a primitive term. Obviously, any learning must take place inside the organism. Pigeons, people, and rats do not learn to respond to a particular physical object, they learn to respond to their internal representation of that object. In learning theory we assume that this representation exists without asking how it is created. The role of the stimulus as an undefined variable can be seen most clearly by examining those learning models in which the stimulus, and changes in it, are represented solely by changes in the parameters determining the rate of conditioning (Bush and Mosteller, 1955; Bush and Estes, 1959). Restle (1959) has aptly described such theories as arrays of abstract linear equations, determining response probability, with different equations for each stimulus situation, reinforcement, and possible response. The only specific assumption that is made in such models is that learning is a single, continuous process of developing a bond between an unchanging stimulus and an unchanging response.

Not all theorists have used such a general definition of the stimulus. Although Hull (1943, 1952) also introduced an undefined term to represent the stimulus in his formal system (i.e., in the equations by which he stated his model), his accompanying expository remarks indicate that he was thinking of the stimulus as some form of momentary excitation in the organism, probably in the central nervous system. Even so, Hull made it quite clear that he did not wish theory to be dependent on physiological evidence.

"The stimulus trace . . . has a possible neurophysiological aspect—namely, the primary mechanism may lie in the neural response(s) of the receptor when stimulated . . . or, on the other hand, in the gradual weakening of some accessory muscle contraction. However, the physiological aspects are not our present primary concern."

Hull, 1952, p. 100.

The strategy of constructing a learning model independent of the data of physiological psychology and perception has been adopted by most investigators. Hebb (1949) is the only major exception. His learning model is based on a plausible organization of the brain. Since he was forced to work with a complex model, Hebb found it correspondingly difficult to develop quantitative theoretical predictions. This exemplifies the basic objection to physiological models of learning. Whatever their heuristic value, they cannot be used to make precise predictions since the mechanics of making predictions are, at best, involved. Although mathematical models are entirely divorced from physiology, they do provide a very clear method for developing testable theorems. Chapter 9 discusses an artificial intelligence system very similar to Hebb's brain model. The recent developments in computer technology make construction of physical simulations of the central nervous system feasible, and may lead to a resurgence of physiological theories of learning. This is, however, beyond the scope of the present text.

Abstract algebraic theories provide a precise treatment of an undefined stimulus term. The earlier learning theories discussed possible definitions of the stimulus, but did not use these definitions in a rigorous manner. The stimulus sampling models fall somewhere in between, since they do contain a commitment to represent the stimulus in a particular way. It will be recalled that the stimulus sampling models describe the stimulus as an aggregate of cues, each of which may or may not be conditioned to a particular response. Within the scheme of a cue-conditioning model, provision can be made for stimulus variation. For instance, Restle (1955) assumed that cues could become conditioned or adapted (psychologically neutral). He discussed the implications of these processes without describing their nature. Later he proposed (Restle, 1961a) viewing the stimulus as a collection of possible aspects, some of which were noticed by the subject at any one time. This change brings his position very close to ours, the verbal distinction between viewing alternate aspects and using different description processes (see Chapter 2) seems a small one. Again, without discussing how aspects are defined or how they are chosen by the subject, Restle is able, using mathematical deduction, to develop rigorous theorems predicting response probabilities in different situations. In discussions of undefined aspects, either of a stimulus sample or of a selected, undefined description process, the problem has been pushed to a lower level without being solved. The stimulus is now defined in terms of other primitives; cue, stimulus element, dimension, value, or aspect. These terms are not further explained.

Defining the stimulus as a composite of smaller, undefined elements is not trivial. It makes clear the analytic view of the stimulus which is implicit in both the cue conditioning and description process models. The stimulus is seen as the sum of its parts. This position can be contrasted to that taken by the Gestalt psychologists, who maintained that the perception of a unitary whole provided cues that could not be defined by an analysis of its parts.

There is no logical objection to a learning model that does not define the stimulus. Learning is the process of conditioning a response to a stimulus, and not the process of stimulus definition. But when a learning model is to be tested this neat separation cannot be maintained. There is evidence which indicates that stimulus definitions are at least partly learned (Solley and Murphy, 1960). If the act of defining the stimulus is itself subject to change during an experiment, an interpretation of the results which does not take this into account may lead to difficulty. Also, although the learning model may assume that the stimulus exists, its predictions cannot be tested unless an operational definition of the stimulus is made. In any experiment the making of operational definitions is a crucial step that ought not be taken without reconciling it to the logic of the theory behind the experiment.

The human capability to identify objects, apart from the learning of discriminations between classes of objects, has been studied in stimulus identification experiments. These experiments are relevant to concept learning, since the induction problem can hardly be understood without considering how the subject acquires his information. Even in the identification studies the problem of stimulus definition has often been avoided. Most studies of concept learning and of stimulus identification have assumed that stimuli are described by particular dimensions and values. It is certainly true that an experimenter can develop a relevant and complete description of his stimuli. It is usually assumed that the subject sees the stimuli in the same way, but this assumption is not always justifiable. How humans will structure any particular stimulus is an unsolved problem of perception. There can be little question that many times the dimensions the experimenter uses to describe the stimuli have psychological reality for the subject. We would cry "pedantry" to an objection that an experimenter had not proven that dots on a plane field are positioned, psychologically, by Cartesian coordinates. Such objections are not so readily dismissed when complex stimuli are used, as they often are in concept learning.

In Chapter 2, the dimensions of the description space (the set $\{\Omega\}$) were introduced as primitive elements. Here we are raising the question of how a description $\phi$ will be formed from the description space $\Omega$. We are not asking how $\Omega$ itself is to be defined. Intuitively, the description space can be thought of as the learner's total capacity for memory and sensory reception. But how will certain aspects of description space attract attention in a given experimental situation? How is the structure of the stimulus to be chosen?

After reviewing several current theories of perception, Allport (1957) concluded that one of the most important aspects of perception is the subject's choice of a structure. By "choosing a structure" Allport meant essentially what we have called "selecting a description process." There are many ways in which an object can be described. The choice of a particular description will depend largely on the compatibility of the information that can be obtained with it. Allport pointed out that one of the common problems, which has impressed all those who have studied perception, is the problem of accounting for a perceiver's search for balance in his environment. Description processes cannot be applied to one object in isolation. Several objects will be in the person's span of attention. Their descriptions must not conflict. An example in social perception illustrates this. During the late 1940s and early 1950s American newspapers discovered that stories about "Malenkov and Zhukov, the Communist leaders" were acceptable to their readers. Stories about "Eisenhower's friend, Zhukov, the hero of the war against the Nazis" were also acceptable. Zhukov's description was determined by the person with whom he was to be described as well as by his own accomplishments. Similar examples have been found in visual perception (Dember, 1960).

We do not have a rigorous theoretical formulation of how one description comes to dominate others. Several "pretheoretical models," useful more for their heuristic value than for the rigorous deductions which can be made from them, have been offered. Bruner (1957) has outlined a useful modification of the earlier Gestaltist ideas. Bruner's position is that perception is teleologically oriented toward the achievement of a perceptual field that is, in some sense, balanced. He envisages a subject who first receives a few tentative, prominent cues from his environment. The subject uses these cues to establish a tentative structure. This structure becomes more and more detailed as more important information is obtained. At all times future perception is under the partial control of present perception. The establishment of a tentative structure determines the action that the subject will take to get more information. This can lead to nonveridical perception if the tentative structures are inaccurate. As a particular structure is made more and more detailed, the perceiver is more and more likely to insist that new information be consistent with previously received information. For instance, if an animal has been tentatively identified as a "mouse," it is hard to credit it with green hair! The perceiver is more likely to question his own eyesight.

Bruner's description of perception is in no way a denial that many aspects of perception are learned. Indeed, most of his examples are clearly examples of situations in which the subjects have learned that cue *b* usually follows cue *a,* and therefore are set to interpret ambiguous information as cue *b* if they have already seen *a.* This could hinder concept learning. A subject might be led to an irrelevant description of the objects to be categorized because that description was consistent with his tentative structuring of the overall situation.[1]

Unfortunately, Bruner's and other models of perception have not been stated in nearly as great detail as have models of learning. As a general principle, the argument that the perception of objects will be influenced by the perceiver's history cannot be gainsaid. Neither can its opposite, that biological organisms have predispositions to accept certain descriptions and to attend to certain stimulus features, regardless of their learning experiences. Utilizing such broad principles in experiments or theoretical analysis is difficult. Supposedly "crucial" tests have been attacked or defended over minor points of experimental procedure. The overall evidence is that perception is somewhat labile, and may be influenced by previously received cues or expectations (Dember, 1960). But how much, and in what way in a particular situation, is extremely difficult to predict. This is particularly true when the relevant organization of stimuli requires a great deal of abstraction. The Gestalt school (especially Wertheimer, 1959) is correct in stressing the importance for the learner of finding a simple relevant description, but they have not presented a model of the process by which this is done.

The stimuli used in most concept-learning experiments have been intermediate between the simple stimuli (tones, lines, dots) of stimulus identification studies and the meaningful and/or complex stimuli (faces, reversible figures) of experiments on perception. This author's subjective impression is that *most of the time* an experimenter can predict the manner in which subjects will perceive these meaningless geometric patterns or nonsense syllables. Unfortunately, this introduces artistic judgment into what should be a scientific enterprise. The only way out of the dilemma is for experimenters to use extremely thorough pretest procedures to insure that they and the subjects agree on the definition of the formal description of the stimuli. Otherwise, their logical analysis of the task before the subject may bear little relation to the task as he sees it.

In this chapter the relations between stimulus identification, stimulus structure, and concept learning will be discussed. First we shall present a brief discussion of the techniques used to measure information transmission in stimulus identification and concept learning. Then we shall review the effect which varying stimulus complexity has on these tasks. In this review, it will be assumed that the experimenter and the subject have defined the stimulus in the same way. Finally, we shall present a partly empirical and partly conjectural description of how a description could be developed.


## 2    Intuitive information theory[2]

A slight mathematical detour is in order. Information theory measures, originally developed for use in communication engineering (Shannon and Weaver, 1949), are frequently used in stimulus identification studies. They also appear, although less frequently, in concept-learning experiments. Information theory is used to provide a measure of the efficiency of performance of subjects who can (imperfectly) discriminate between different sets of stimuli. Making thirty errors in the identification of one thousand objects seems to be better performance than making fifteen errors in the identification of one hundred objects. But how much better? Given the data for performance in $n$ identification situations, can we predict performance in the $n + 1st$? Information theory has been introduced into psychology to answer such questions. Several discussions of information theory and its use in psychology are available (Attneave, 1959; Luce, 1960). To keep this text self-contained, a brief review of some aspects of the theory will be made. The examples and explanations will be slanted toward the use of information theory in concept learning and stimulus identification studies. The mathematical techniques have much wider application.

We receive information only when we are surprised. A message bearing information ought to tell us something we did not know before. The newspaper headline "United States against Communism" carries little information to its readers. The headline "Giraffe attends classes in University" would. The symbols in the first headline are predictable, the symbols in the second are not.

Another example illustrates the more general definition of information and information transmission. Consider the problem faced by an avid reader of "Perry Mason" detective stories. At any point after the characters are identified the reader may guess who the murderer is. Suppose that every time the reader reads a story he makes a guess after reading the cast of characters, and again after reading the first $n$ pages of each book. After several books have been read, we will have two sets of guesses, $G^{(o)}$ and $G^{(n)}$. Any particular guess, chosen at random, is either right or wrong. It seems intuitively correct to say that the first $n$ pages of the typical story transmit information to this reader only if the probability of choosing a correct guess, at random, from $G^{(o)}$ is less than the probability of random choice of a correct guess from $G^{(n)}$. Information transmission must be defined both in terms of the stimuli (the pages) and the responder (the reader). Given the same pages, an increase in the probability of correct guessing will depend on the reader's ability to make use of the clues contained in the pages.

The foregoing ideas have been treated formally. Suppose that there are $n$ possible messages, the elements of the set $\{m_i\}$, which can be sent over a given channel. If each message occurs with probability $p_i$, the information contained in the $i$th message can be defined as the inverse of its probability, $1/p_i$. For several reasons (see Luce, 1960) it is convenient to transmit this to a logarithmic measure. The information $(H_i)$ contained in the $i$th message is thus redefined as

(4.2.1) $$H_i = -\log_2 p_i$$

Since each message is transmitted with probability $p_i$, the information $H$ in the entire set of messages can be defined,

(4.2.2) $$H = -\Sigma\, p_i \log_2 p_i$$

The set $\{m_i\}$ and the associated set of probabilities $\{p_i\}$ specify a sender. This can also be thought of as the set of inputs, or the set of stimuli shown to a subject. In general, let $x$, $y$, refer to populations of messages with associated probabilities. $H(x)$ is used to denote the information in population $x$, similarly for $y$, and $H(x,y)$ the information in the joint population. $H_x(y)$ is used to indicate the information in population $y$ if the message from population $x$ is known. Information measures are expressed in binary digits, or *bits*. One interpretation of $H(x)$ is that it is equal to the logarithm to the base two of the number of equiprobable stimulus alternatives necessary to transmit the same information. This is a heuristic interpretation and cannot be accepted literally since $H(x)$ need not be an integer.

Another interpretation of $H(x)$ that is of some use in concept learning can be developed by analogy to a guessing game situation. Sup-

pose the actual stimulus is $x_i$, chosen from one of the stimuli $x_i$ . . .
$x_n$. Each $x_i$ is chosen with probability $p_i$. Imagine an interrogator who
was not permitted to see the stimulus, but was allowed to question
an observer who could see the stimulus and answer "yes" or "no."
What would be the most efficient way for the interrogator to discover
the stimulus? He should partition the stimulus universe into two sets,
$S$ and $\bar{S}$, such that the probability that $i$th stimulus was in $S$ was as
close as possible to .5. He should then ask the observer, "is the stimulus
in $S$?" If the answer is "yes," the interrogator ought to partition $S$ in
the same manner and proceed. Otherwise he should subdivide $\bar{S}$. This
procedure would be continued until $x_i$ was identified. $H(x)$ is the
average number of questions the interrogator has to ask if he proceeds
in the fashion described. It can be shown that if he proceeds in any
other manner the average number of questions will be greater than
$H(x)$.

$H(x)$ is a measure of the information in a particular class of symbols.
(A message is, after all, only a symbol.) The symbols could refer to
stimuli or responses. We would like to have a measure of the information shared by two sets of symbols, $X$ and $Y$. For if $X$ is the set of inputs to a communication system and $Y$ the set of outputs from the
same system, we want a measure of the information transmitted from
input to output. This measure could have an important psychological
reference, since experimental stimuli can be equated with input, the
subject with a communication system, and the responses made with
output.

Any possible observable state of the stimulus-subject system can be
defined by a unique pair of inputs and outputs $\{x_i, y_j\}$. Each pair
occurs with probability $p_{ij}$, so the total information in the system is

$$(4.2.3) \qquad H(x, y) = -\sum_i \sum_j p_{ij} \log p_{ij}$$

If input and output were totally independent, then this would be the
sum of the information in each separate component, that is,

$$(4.2.4) \qquad H(x, y) = H(x) + H(y)$$

This result can be verified by considering the guessing game definition
of $H(x)$. It takes an average of $H(x, y)$ questions before the interrogator can establish the identity of an input-output pair. If the input
and output were independent, it would take him $H(x)$ question to
establish $x_i$. By assumption, $x_i$ would not be related to $y_j$, so he would
have to ask an average of $H(y)$ additional questions to identify $y_j$. On
the other hand, if there were a relation between $x_i$ and $y_j$, he could
use the information acquired by knowing $x_i$ to find $y_i$ in less than $H(y)$

questions. Transmitted information $T(x, y)$ is a measure of the size of this reduction;

$$(4.2.5) \qquad T(x, y) = H(x) + H(y) - H(x, y)$$

It is a measure of the extent to which the input is predictable from the output or vice versa. In psychology, it is convenient to think of this as a measure of the extent to which the response can be predicted if the stimulus is known. We shall also need a measure of the extent to which prediction of one member of the pair is *not* possible when the other is known. In our example, this is the number of questions the interrogator must ask about $x_i$ after he has determined $y_j$. The information theory term is the *equivocation* of $x$ with respect to $y$, $H_y(x)$;

$$4.2.6) \qquad H_y(x) = H(x) - T(x, y)$$

Equivocation is not symmetrical. For instance, after a concept has been learned, $H_x(y)$ is zero but $H_y(x)$ is not. If you show me any animal in Connecticut, I can tell you whether or not a man will say "dog" when he sees it, but if you tell me he said "dog," I do not know what animal he saw.

Equivocation is a measure of nonidentifiability. It ought to be related to performance errors. But how? This topic will be of considerable concern in the following sections.

Generalization of information theory measures to more than two variables is possible. Also, there are other information measures (notably channel capacity) which we have not discussed. The interested reader is referred to Luce (1960) or Attneave (1959).

## 3    *Variations in dimensions and values*

Few people would argue with the proposition that concept learning will be more difficult if the stimuli to be categorized are complex. This common sense statement received experimental support in studies by Hull (1920) and Reed (1946). Neither the common sense belief nor the early experimental studies progressed from the verification of the existence of a complexity effect to establishment of its form. This was at least partly because the early experimenters had no way to measure stimulus complexity. Such measurements can be made easily if the stimuli are defined by the values of a set of binary dimensions. Using such stimuli (e.g., big, red, triangles; small, blue circles) several experiments have been performed to study the relation between stimulus complexity and concept learning. We reviewed some of them in discussing Bourne and Restle's (1959) cue-conditioning model (Chapter 3).

We shall now discuss the empirical findings without reference to the model.

In the cue-conditioning experiments the subject must learn a concept by observing a series of geometric patterns. The first stimulus is presented, the subject is permitted to study it as long as he wishes, and then he presses a button to indicate the name he thinks can be applied to the stimulus. His response terminates the stimulus presentation. The next stimulus is presented after a 5-second intertrial interval. In the studies with which we are concerned the subject is informed of the correct choice as soon as he makes his response.

Stimulus complexity is varied by using different numbers of binary dimensions to create objects. The dimensions can be divided into $r$ relevant and $k$ irrelevant dimensions. In the usual cue-conditioning study every possible combination of values of relevant dimensions is used to define the concept of a different name. Thus there is a total of $2^r$ possible responses, and each response can be assigned to the $2^k$ objects which contain a particular combination of values of relevant dimensions. For instance, if figure and size were the relevant dimensions and color irrelevant, there would be a different response for big circles, little circles, big triangles, and little triangles. Responses would be assigned without regard to color.

In some experiments, in which relevant dimensions were also redundant, only special sets of values of relevant dimensions were allowed to appear. If value $x$ of dimension 1 always appeared when response $A$ was appropriate, dimension 1 would always have value $y$ if response $A$ was not appropriate. If dimension 2 was redundant and relevant, it had value $r$ if response $A$ was appropriate, and value $s$ otherwise. Such problems do not involve true conjunctive concepts. They are better described as variants of Shepard, Hovland, and Jenkins (1961) "Type I" concept, in which set membership of an object can be determined by observing the value of just one dimension. In the cue-conditioning studies any one of several dimensions could be chosen for observation.

In the cue-conditioning experiments, learning trials were continued until the subject gave a specified number of successive correct identifications of class membership. Usually either sixteen or thirty-two successive errorless trials were required.[3] The dependent variables recorded were trials to criterion and total errors. Of necessity, these measures are highly correlated. Since the same experimental procedure was used in almost every experiment, comparison of the studies is legitimate. On the other hand, any limitation in procedure will apply to all of the research.

One such limitation is the simplicity of the concepts used. All the subjects had to do was discover one or two cues (values of dimensions) whose presence or absence was an infallible predictor of the appropriate response. Contrast this sort of problem to the more complex ones used by Bruner, Goodnow, and Austin (1956), in which the concept was defined by the joint presence of several values of nonbinary dimensions. But if the cue-conditioning problems are simple, why do the subjects make so many errors? In fact, the cue-conditioning studies have produced quite reliable results, although it seems unreasonable that such simple problems should be difficult for the university undergraduates who served as subjects.

There is a very real possibility that the major difficulty that subjects have in these experiments is not in manipulating defined symbols, but in discovering them. As soon as the subject made his response, the stimulus was removed. The next stimulus was presented 5 seconds later, which may have placed the subjects under pressure. They could not re-examine a stimulus to determine why they made an error. Whenever a subject tried to respond rapidly, he well may have felt that he would have to set himself to notice only a few dimensions on each trial. If these happened to be relevant dimensions, he could easily solve the problem. But if the dimensions noticed were not relevant, the subject could not categorize with higher than chance accuracy. Not until the subject began to notice relevant dimensions could he possibly solve the problem.

This description of performance in the cue-conditioning experiments is not a criticism of the experimental procedure. The experiments are certainly legitimate tests of Bourne and Restle's (1959) model. It will be remembered that this model is a stimulus sampling one, and stimulus sampling is conceptually similar to noticing particular dimensions. The only real difference is that we think of random sampling in the stimulus sampling model, and of biased sampling in the dimension-noticing situation. If we cannot specify the form of the bias, we may have to approximate it by assuming that dimensions to notice are selected at random. In his later models of choice behavior, Restle (1961a, b) has adopted the language of the selective attention argument, although at places he is forced to approximate the behavior of groups of subjects by assuming random choice of dimensions to which the subject attends. Some of his new models lead to similar predictions of response frequencies in the cue-conditioning experiments as did the earlier sampling models (Restle, in press).

We can accept the cue-conditioning experiments as valid tests of certain models. Like the all-or-none models (Chapter 3) these models may be primarily models of how the subject learns to describe the stimuli. Different processes may be involved when subjects try to solve complex concept-learning problems based on easily described stimuli. With this reservation in mind, let us examine the empirical findings.

It has been clearly established that there is a linear increase in the total number of errors as the number of irrelevant dimensions is increased from one to five (Archer, Bourne and Brown, 1955; Battig and Bourne, 1961; Bourne, 1957; Bourne and Pendleton, 1958; Bourne and Haygood, 1959; Pishkin, 1960). No nonlinear relation between the number of errors and the number of irrelevant dimensions has consistently appeared. The studies cited are not repetitions of each other. The finding that the number of errors is linearly related to the number of dimensions often appeared as an incidental finding while other variables were being studied.

In the experiments just cited, the number of irrelevant *non-*redundant dimensions was varied. If two dimensions were not relevant to the discrimination to be learned, the value of one of them could not be predicted from knowledge of the value of the other. In most real world situations objects are not free to vary in such an independent manner. For instance, if we know a person's height and sex, we can usually make an accurate guess about his or her weight. A more formal way to say this, using the language of section 2, is that redundant dimensions do not transmit as much information as do the same number of nonredundant dimensions. The interesting psychological question is whether the complexity to which people react is determined by the amount of variation the objects to be categorized might exhibit (which would be determined by the number of dimensions) or the amount of variation actually exhibited (which is determined by the number of dimensions and the redundancy relations between them). This question can be broken down into two subqueries, concerning the relation between performance and relevant or irrelevant stimulus complexity. If a human subject can learn to capitalize on the redundancy relations between particular dimensions, he can reduce the number of dimensions he must scan. He may use the known value of one dimension to predict the value of dimensions redundant to it. This should make the process of locating the relevant dimensions easier.

Subjects can learn to make use of interdimensional redundancies. Bourne and Haygood (1959) found that less errors were made in cue-conditioning experiments in which the stimuli had a given number of redundant irrelevant dimensions than were made when the stimuli had the same number of independent irrelevant dimensions. In this and a later study (Bourne and Haygood, 1961) they also varied the number of redundant relevant dimensions. Increasing these dimensions made the concept-learning task easier. Furthermore, the relation between errors and the number of irrelevant dimensions depended on the number of redundant relevant dimensions. If there were a large number of irrelevant dimensions, increasing the number of relevant dimensions proved to be more effective in reducing errors. This may have been a "ceiling" effect; it is quite possible that a certain number of errors will be made while the subject adjusts to the overall situation, and that only the number of errors made beyond this minimum number (which will be made no matter how simple the task) are dependent on stimulus complexity. Anyhow, it is clear that humans can learn to react to the actually occurring stimulus variation, measured by the information content of the stimuli, and not to the theoretically possible range of variation.

An experiment by Battig and Bourne (1961) greatly extended the generality of the cue-conditioning findings. Battig and Bourne suggested that "learning a concept" implies that the subject has to form an intradimensional grouping. (This requirement is not implied by the way concepts are used in logic, but it does coincide with a view of concept learning as an extension of generalization.) Consistent with this point of view, they varied the number of values per dimension which could occur in instances within a particular denotation.

In Battig and Bourne's experimental situation the subject had to place each stimulus into one of four categories when it (the stimulus) was presented. After each trial the subject was told the correct answer. The correct concept in each problem involved the stimulus dimensions of form and width. The categories were based on all four combinations of wide versus narrow and triangular versus quadrangular figures. As the experimental condition demanded, irrelevant dimensions (color, position of the figure on the viewing area, and type of stripes on the pattern) were introduced. In some conditions new values which could be assigned to one of two *classes* of values on the particular dimension were also introduced. For instance, patterns could always be classified as "wide versus narrow." However, in the "many value" conditions four or six different widths—two or three in the "wide," and two or three in the "narrow" category—were used. Similarly, in the figure dimension values might be either equilateral triangles versus squares or equilateral, right, or obtuse triangles versus squares, rectangles, or diamonds. With the possible exception of form,[4] the dimensions all involved continua.

As in the binary dimension case, Battig and Bourne found a positive linear relation between the number of errors and the number of irrelevant dimensions. When additional values were added, errors also increased linearly. Their results support the Bourne and Restle analysis of cue conditioning in concept learning, although the exact effect of increasing the number of values had not been handled explicitly. In addition, Battig and Bourne found a linear × linear interaction term. The rate of increase of errors as a function of number of irrelevant dimensions increased as the number of values increased.

Bruner, Goodnow, and Austin (1956, Chapter 5) report an experiment in which subjects attempted to solve fourteen conjunctive concept-learning problems. All concepts used six-dimensional stimuli, but the number of relevant dimensions varied. Only one value ever appeared in a relevant dimension on positive instances, although the dimensions were not binary. The per cent of subjects solving a problem decreased linearly as the number of irrelevant dimensions increased. This would not necessarily mean a linear decrease in the average number of errors, but the results are not inconsistent with the Bourne and Restle formulation. Any agreement would be of interest, because this study had markedly different experimental conditions. Subjects saw each instance for 10 seconds and then wrote down their hypothesis about the concept. It is a classic finding (Hull, 1920) that the ability to state a concept requires greater abstracting ability than recognizing instances of the concept. To the extent that the findings of the cue-conditioning studies are replicated in the experiment by Bruner et al., their generality is indicated for experiments which use identification or statement criteria.

Battig and Bourne used a special type of dimension, in which the values form an ordered set; that is, the values could be related to one another by a transitive relation (but see footnote 4). This relation might have introduced a discrimination problem since subjects had to learn which values of each dimension might appear in positive and negative instances. Of course discrimination difficulties are no problem in an analysis based on Restle's (1955) model, since the whole argument is that concept learning is a form of discrimination. It is at least possible that subjects behave differently when they cannot discriminate values easily. The problem is again one which touches on the relation between stimulus identification and concept learning. The results of the Shepard, Hovland, and Jenkins' (1961) experiments suggest that concept learning involves the manipulation of coded symbols representing the objects to be categorized. The learning of values for dimensions would be part of the task of developing an encoding system. Different effects might be found if the difficulty of developing an encoding system and the difficulty of manipulating the coded symbols were varied independently.

A recent study by Shepard and Chang (personal communication) suggests that the processes of encoding and decoding are different. Shepard and Chang designed a situation in which encoding, the distinction of physical objects from each other, would be difficult. Specifically, Shepard and Chang used as objects eight reddish circles. These circles varied only in brightness and saturation. The set of eight circles was partitioned, several times, into two subsets of four circles each. Each partition was orthogonal to other partitions; given the four members of a subset in one partition, two of these would be in the same subset of another partition. As an example, the first eight positive integers can be partitioned in the following orthogonal ways, $[\{1,2,3,4\}, \{5,6,7,8\}]$ and $[\{1,2,5,6\}, \{3,4,7,8\}]$. The subjects were required to learn two responses, one to all members of the first subset of a partition and one to all members of the second subset. Thus each subset corresponds to the denotation of a name.

Shepard (1958) had previously obtained a measure of the probability that any two of the circles would be confused (i.e., one recognized as the other) in a stimulus identification study. Shepard and Chang used these measures as a measure of the underlying stimulus generalization gradient. They found that 80% of the variance associated with differences in the difficulty of learning the concepts based on different partitions was predictable from the generalization measure. This finding was markedly different from the Shepard, Hovland, and Jenkins' results, where only 41% of the variance between problems was predictable from a similar generalization measure. In the Shepard et. al. study the stimuli had been easily distinguishable from each other.

Shepard and Chang interpret this difference as being due to the greater difficulty of learning a symbolic code for their stimuli. They point out that in the Shepard et al. study learning the "code" was trivial. (Unlike the cue-learning studies, subjects had ample time in which to view the stimuli.) The question is whether the cue-learning studies are more like the Shepard and Chang or the Shepard, Hovland, and Jenkins' experiments. In cue learning there is a simple deduction problem and a trivial stimulus code. Using a rapid rate of stimulus presentation may make the learning of even this simple code difficult. If so, the effect of increasing stimulus complexity in concept learning should be paralleled by a similar effect in stimulus identification studies, where there is no symbol manipulation problem after an accurate stimulus description has been achieved. We shall now review these experiments.

## 4    *Stimulus identification*

Stimulus identification is certainly a part of concept learning. Errors in the identification and description of objects to be categorized are bound to influence the deductive processes, just as errors in the transmission of a message will effect the receiver's ability to use the information it contained. Any failure of the subject to perceive or remember correctly cannot be repaired by later deductions. Is it possible that the effects of stimulus complexity on concept learning are, at least in part, due to difficulties in creating veridical internal codes to represent the stimuli to be categorized? If so, effects parallel to those observed in concept learning should occur in studies of stimulus identification which do not require that subjects abstract a concept from the stimuli.

A convenient way to measure stimulus identification capability is to use the amount of information transmitted from stimulus to response. This measure $T$ was referred to in section 2. Using a measure of transmitted information, we can develop the concept of equivalent information. Suppose that for a total of $N_x$ stimuli and $N_y$ responses we measure $T(x, y)$ in bits. There will be some number $N'$ such that

(4.4.1)                                     $$T(x, y) \approx \text{Log}_2 N'$$

and

(4.4.2)                                     $$N' \leq N_x \text{ assuming } N_y \leq N_x$$

The $N_y$ responses can be interpreted as sharing as much information with the $N_x$ stimuli as would have been shared if the $N_y$ responses were perfectly correlated with $N'$ stimuli. Imperfect discrimination of many objects can be equated with perfect discrimination of a few. Imperfect discrimination implies that the subject is assigning certain nonidentical stimuli to equivalence categories. This is an approximation process which can be measured by comparing the size of the stimulus universe to the size of the hypothetical universe which could be perfectly discriminated.

Miller (1956) called the attention of psychologists to an interesting fact about stimulus identification experiments. He reviewed several studies in which humans responded to a varying number of stimuli, all of which could be described by a system of dimensions and values. Studies were included in which subjects identified stimuli varying in such different dimensions as tone, pitch, loudness, color, and position. Even though the sensory mode used was different, there was very little difference in the size $N'$ of the hypothetical, perfectly discriminable stimulus universe. In practically every case involving identification of points along a single dimension of stimulus variation, $N'$ was somewhere between five and nine. (Miller's title was—"The magic number seven, plus or minus two.") In addition, $N'$ did not vary within a single sensory dimension if the distance between the points of the scale were changed. (This finding does not rest on such a wide range of studies and should be replicated. Replication using visual stimuli is particularly important.) Subjects behaved as if they had only seven symbols with which to create internal codes for the stimuli, but they could assign them in any way. If more than seven stimuli were presented the symbol assignment would, of necessity, be approximate. Whether or not important information would be lost would depend on the distinction the experimenter made between the stimuli. In stimulus identification studies every symbol is considered as distinct, so the approximation would always be noticed. In concept-learning studies sets of stimuli are regarded as equivalent, insofar as the subject's identification of them is concerned, so the subject could eventually find an approximate coding scheme which an experimenter would accept.

Attneave (1959) amplified on Miller's observations. The stimulus identification results contrast with results obtained in psychophysical discrimination studies, where the subject's task is to make a contrast between simultaneously presented (or nearly simultaneously presented) stimuli. A large number of just noticeable differences (j.n.d.'s) are found in discrimination studies. In fact, psychophysical studies have been used to infer a continuous scale of psychophysical judgment (Stevens, 1960, 1961; Luce, 1959). Evidently other processes are involved in stimulus identification studies than are involved in psychophysical discrimination. If a subject is forced to assign a discrete response $b_i \in B_i$ to stimuli in a set $A_i$ which varies along a single physical dimension, he will make erroneous assignments if there are more than approximately seven stimuli in the set $A_i$. However, this does not mean that the subject could not distinguish between any two stimuli, $a_i, a_j \in A_i$, if they were presented to him simultaneously.

The "magic number seven" suggests a conceptual model for the process of stimulus identification. This model is interesting to us because it can be extended to some types of concept learning. Suppose that a subject is presented with a set of stimuli and a set of responses in a task which requires that he pair each stimulus with one of the responses. The pairing may or may not be unique. If the pairing is not unique, $A$ must be partitioned into subsets such that upon the presentation of any member of a given subset the subject makes a specific response. If we use the arrow to represent the subject's making a

response when a given stimulus occurs, perfect learning is reached
when $A$ is partitioned so that the following equations hold:

(4.4.3)         $A = \{a_i\} = A^1 \cup \ldots \cup A^j, \qquad A^i \cap A^j = \Lambda$

(4.4.4)                              $a_i \in A^j, \qquad a_i \to b_j$

Concept learning can be described this way. The stimulus identification process is assumed to take place in two stages. The subject first
transforms any $a_i \in A$ into a code response $c_i \in C$. Set $C$ represents the
set of internally available "code words." The code words provide the
actual stimulus to which the subject responds by choice of a response
$b_j$. The behavioral and internal chain of events can be represented by[5]

(4.4.5)                       $a_i \in A^j \to c_j \in C \to b_j \in B$

It follows that the size of the set $C$ will determine the limits of
identification ability, regardless of the subject's ability to make pair-
wise discriminations. The strong assumption is made that a subject
can make any desired partition of the sets $A$ and $B$ before creating a
particular group of connections.[6] Let $\eta(S)$ stand for the number of
items in a set $S$ (as in Chapter 2). From the "magic number seven,"
we assume that for unidimensional stimuli, $\eta(C)$ is approximately
seven. If $\eta(B)$ is greater than $\eta(C)$, each code word $c_i$ may be associated
with a particular probability distribution over the set $B$.

The following types of experiments have been performed by psychologists:

(1) Typical identification learning,

(4.4.6)                              $\eta(A) = \eta(B) = k$

Perfect discrimination is possible only if $k$ is less than $\eta(C)$. Otherwise
the maximum amount of information that can be transmitted is equal
to the amount of information that can be transmitted by $\eta(C)$ symbols.

(2) Classification learning, including concept learning,

(4.4.7)                              $\eta(A) > \eta(B)$

If $\eta(B)$ is equal to or less than $\eta(C)$ a partition of $A$ into $\eta(C)$ disjoint
sets, such that source sets (sets at the "foot" of the arrow) are always
disjoint, is possible. In addition, $C$ itself can be partitioned into $\eta(B)$
disjoint subsets so that at perfect classification learning,

(4.4.8)                        $a_i \in A^j \to c_j \in C^k \to b_k$

In this case, the classification problem would be solved. How such a
partition is created is the central topic of concept-learning research.

If $\eta(B)$ is greater than $\eta(C)$, only probabilistic classification is possible. This suggests a line of research in which subjects are required to learn a large number of classifications simultaneously. There should be a limit, imposed by transmission capabilities, on the number of classifications which could be learned.

The final logical possibility, $\eta(B)$ greater than $\eta(A)$, would of necessity involve probability learning. This possibility was explicitly excluded in our definition of the probem (Chapter 1).

In the model we have proposed the size of the set $C$ is crucial. Can this be manipulated? There is some experimental evidence to indicate that it can. Miller (1956) extended his review to stimulus identification studies in which the number of dimensions, as well as the number of values within a dimension, was varied. The transmission capability of humans increased as the number of dimensions increased. Eriksen (1954) showed that this increase was independent of the increase in stimulus information associated with an increase in dimensions. Eriksen's subjects had to identify stimuli which varied in size, brightness, and hue. These stimuli shared 4.1 bits of information with the subject's response, as compared with 2.7 shared bits for stimuli varying along only one dimension. However, Eriksen had used stimuli in which the variation in each dimension was perfectly correlated, so that the sizes of the stimulus universes (and the amount of information) in the single and multidimensional situations were the same.

Several other experiments have also shown an increase in the total information transmitted as the number of stimulus dimensions is increased. The relation is remarkably regular. Attneave (1959, pp. 73–75) has suggested that transmitted information is a logarithmic function of the number of dimensions. He obtained a very close fit to the equation

(4.4.9) $$T = k_1 \log_2 n + k_2$$

$k_1$ and $k_2$ positive constants, using data from an $n$ dimensional information transmission experiment by Pollack and Klemmer (1954). Pollack and Klemmer used up to seven dimensions, so this fit is impressive. In an informal discussion, Miller suggested to the current author that the same data could be fit by a square-root function,

(4.4.10) $$T = k_1 n^{(1/2)}$$

Empirically, it would be extremely difficult to distinguish between predictions from a logarithm or square-root function over the range of stimulus dimensions which has been investigated. Both predict much the same values in particular experiments. Figures 4-1 and 4-2 demonstrate this. The square-root function has the advantage of parsimony,

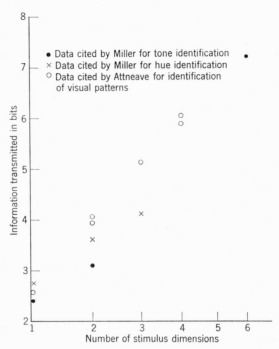

Figure 4-1. Information transmission plotted against logarithmic scale.

since it requires a single parameter $k_1$. The value of this parameter can be estimated from studies of one dimensional stimuli; $k_1$ should be the logarithm of the magic number seven. (A similar interpretation is possible for $k_2$ in equation 4.4.9, but not for $k_1$.)

What has this to do with concept learning? The code word model suggests that, at any one time, a concept learner can partition the stimulus universe into as many "equivalence classes" as he has code words. From the stimulus identification studies, we can assume that this is determined by the structure of the stimuli. Presumably the learner could try different partitions until he found one such that any subset of his partition was either a subset of the denotation of the name whose concept was to be learned or a subset of the complement of the denotation. In this case his partition could be related to a relevant description of the stimulus universe (see Chapter 2). It would also satisfy the criterion for concept learning expressed by equation 4.4.8. If the stimulus universe is large relative to the number of code words, as is the case if the number of dimensions or values are increased, there is a larger set of partitions for the learner to try, so concept learning ought to be more difficult. How much more difficult would depend on the way in which trial partitions are selected.

The code word model is largely conjectural. It has been offered as a bridge between stimulus identification and concept learning. Although it has not been tested directly, there is some tangential evidence which supports it.

There should be a limit on the number of names for which concept can be learned. If there are only $\eta(C)$ code words for a given stimulus universe, only $\eta(C)$ names can be learned as responses uniquely attached to a code word. Most concept-learning studies require that the learner find the concept of just one name. A few studies [notably those of Heidbreder (1946)] have required that the subject learn as many as nine concepts. In these studies complex stimuli were used, but nine does not seem to be an unreasonable size for the set of code words. In an interesting study by Shipstone (1960), subjects were asked to group

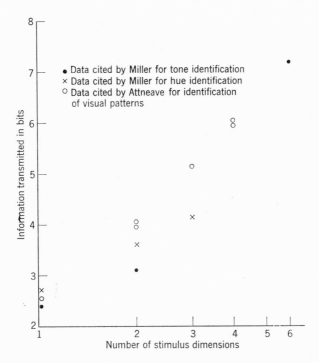

Figure 4-2. Information transmission plotted against a square-root scale.

strings of nonsense syllables (generated by one of Miller and Chomsky's (1958) finite state grammars) into as many classes as they wished, using any categorizing rule. Thus this study was more one of concept formation than one of concept learning. The subjects seldom used more than seven categories, they also avoided using a very small number of sets. At best this evidence is tangential. Still it is interesting to see that in categorizing as well as in identification, "seven is still a magic number" (Shipstone, 1960, p. 35).

The difficulty of learning a concept ought to be a monotonically increasing function of the difference between the number of stimuli and the number of code words. This is because equivocation can be defined this way in the code word model, and equivocation is a measure of the approximateness with which the subject describes his environment,

$$(4.4.11) \qquad\qquad H_c(A) = \eta(A) - \eta(C)$$

By substituting equation 4.4.10 into 4.4.11 to calculate the number of code words, the equivocation can be determined for the different conditions of Battig and Bourne's (1961) concept-learning experiment. This experiment is the cue-learning study which should have been most affected by stimulus identification factors. There was a highly significant positive linear relation between equivocation and errors. This contrast accounted for approximately three-fourths of the between experimental groups variance in number of errors. The residual contrast (i.e., variance orthogonal to the variance between groups), however, was significant at the .01 level.[7]

Again, this evidence is tangential but encouraging. The significant equivocation contrast indicates that a common ground between stimulus identification and concept-learning studies may be found. That the relation may be due to a common trial and error process of checking partitions is indicated by the fact that, in some cases, the equivocation value computed by 4.4.11 for the Battig and Bourne study was negative. This indicates a situation in which the full stimulus identification capabilities of the subject are not being strained. Under such conditions, subjects made few errors.[8]

Why the relation between errors and equivocation should be linear is an unanswered question. Equivocation is exponentially related to the number of partitions that could be tried, so the linear relation found indicates a highly efficient hypothesis-selecting mechanism. The significant "nonequivocation" variation in errors is also of interest. Evidently there are processes which are unique to concept learning, as well as processes shared with stimulus identification.

5    *Stimulus structure*

In the discussion so far it has been tacitly assumed that the subject knows and uses the experimenter's definition of the stimulus. Otherwise his description will not be relevant, and the concept learning problem cannot be solved.

Attneave (1954)[9] presented an analysis of visual perception which can be extended to the problem of stimulus structure in both visual and nonvisual presentations. Imagine a stimulus image represented by a matrix of (not necessarily binary) points. Each point has a value that corresponds to a sensation received along some psychophysical dimension. For convenience, think of only one sensory mode's being represented on the matrix. This is not necessary; different areas of the matrix could correspond to visual, olfactory, auditory, and tactile sensations. If there are $n$ points on the matrix, all of them the result of independent stimulation of the sense organs, and $v$ different values per point, there are $v^n$ possible states of the matrix. So long as the points are, in fact, completely independent, $n$ tests are required to determine the state of the matrix at any given time. However, if the $n$ points are not independent, it will be possible to predict the value of some points when the values of others are known.

Attneave suggested that perception is the process of making such a prediction. In the perceptual process, relations between points on the matrix are determined so that less than $n$ tests can be used to describe the matrix. The tests consist of examining the points whose value cannot be predicted from a knowledge of the value of other points. After these points have been tested, a prediction is made of the values of the remaining points. Perception then is seen as a two stage process. In the learning phase the perceiver locates points that transmit the most information (i.e., are least predictable) about the stimulus and determines how the values of these points are related to the values of predictable points. In the application state the perceiver will guess the state of the matrix after examining a few points.

The usefulness of a decision rule depends directly on the accuracy of the predictions it makes; inversely on the number of points which must be scanned, the complexity of the rule, and the accuracy required.

A particularly important class of perceptual decision rules can be loosely described as "template matching." The subject is assumed to have a large set of templates that can be fitted to any subarea of the projection matrix.[10] Each template requires certain information before it can be fitted. For example, the template for equilateral triangle requires that two vertices of the triangle be located. A maximally efficient rule would apply just one template to the entire projection matrix, using only a single sensory point to anchor the template, and do all this without any major loss in information.

The cost of applying a template can be separated into two components; the cost of testing the matrix to determine the input values for the template and the cost of testing to determine what template to apply. The latter cost can be considerably reduced if it is determined, before testing, that the correct template is a member of a relatively small set of possible templates. One way to determine this is to predict, from knowledge of the template applicable in one area of the matrix, templates that might apply in another. Suppose we know that we are looking either at a picture of a baseball player or a violinist. If we see that the man is wearing a ballplayer's cap, why test to discriminate between a bass violin or cello in his hand?

Dimensions and values play a role in a template-matching model. Each region of the projection matrix can be thought of as a dimension. The set of templates which could be applied to the region would represent the set of values for that dimension. The same template might appear in different dimensions and convey different information, since the information transmitted by a symbol is a function of the set of symbols from which it is drawn rather than a function of its own identity. Spiegelthal (1960) discussed an hypothetical machine for scanning mail which illustrates the principles involved. The machine would fit templates to addresses, scanning in a right-left, down-up pattern. It would scan the first complete word it encountered to see if the template for any state with a single word name fitted that word. This could be done on the basis of a relatively few tests. If all tests failed, the first two words would be checked against the pattern for all states with two word names. One of these two searches would have to succeed on all domestic mail. A search would then be made for a template from the set templates for city names within that state (a much smaller set than the set of templates for city names within the country) which could fit the remaining words on the bottom line. In some cases (e.g., New York) the same template might appear in different sets, each time conveying different semantic and mathematical information.

Such perceptual models are relevant to concept learning, since they suggest ways in which a description of the stimuli can be obtained. The Gestalt psychologists claimed that the act of establishing the description, the ability to "see things in the proper way," was central to cognitive behavior (Wertheimer, 1959). Their general position has been that descriptions are changed discontinuously, that the environment is "restructured" in discrete steps. The Gestaltists placed great emphasis on innate tendencies to describe situations in certain ways, although they did not deny that some structures (template fitting procedures?) may be learned. They particularly stressed an allegedly human tendency to see things as a structured whole, rather than as an analytically determined sum of parts of stimuli. What is the evidence for this position? Can it be reconciled with a mechanistic scheme of template matching?

Heidbreder and her associates (Heidbreder, 1945, 1946a,b, 1947, 1949; Heidbreder, Bensley, and Ivy, 1948, Wenzel and Flurry, 1948) performed a series of experiments designed to show that concept learning was influenced by a tendency to perceive stimuli as unified wholes. Most of these experiments used Heidbreder's "modified memory technique," a variant of paired associates learning. This technique was described earlier in evaluating Baum's (1954) experiment (see Chapter 3). Briefly, on each trial a subject would be shown nine stimuli, each to be paired with a given response. On the next trial, nine new stimuli would be shown; these were to be paired with the original responses. Each response was a name and had associated with it a concept indicating which new stimulus should be paired with it. The experiment was continued until the subject gave all nine responses correctly the first time a list of nine stimuli was shown.

The concepts were divided into three classes depending on whether they were decision rules based on the presence of an object of a certain type, an abstract pattern, or a particular number of objects within a stimulus picture. For instance, GELF might be paired with all pictures of animals, GYRT with all drawings containing the pattern x, and QORJ with any drawing containing two items, for example, two candles. Although it was not logically necessary, no one stimulus ever appeared as an example of two concepts. No attempt was made to analyze the stimuli in terms of dimensions and values.

The situation is thus somewhat similar to the verbal studies of dominance level. Subjects had to make a mediating response (e.g., "that's a pair of things") which was associated with a name. Heidbreder argued that the dominance of such responses was determined by the natural tendency to perceive concrete, familiar objects (good Gestalt) without abstracting smaller stimulus features. Therefore, the concepts based on objects should be the easiest to learn to use, then concepts based on physically present "part qualities," the patterns, and finally concepts based on the abstract number aspect. In general, her hypothesis was confirmed.

It has been claimed that the "object like" character was not what determined the order of attainment. Baum (1954, see Chapter 3) obtained data to indicate that Heidbreder's results could be explained by a stimulus discrimination and generalization model similar to that used by Gibson (1940) to analyze paired associates learning. A slightly different objection was made by Dattman and Israel (1952). They argued that it was not the "thing character" of the stimulus, but rather the "perceptual goodness" which determined the order of attainment of concepts. Dattman and Israel repeated some of Heidbreder's experiments with stimuli which were either clear or to which "noise" had been added by drawing additional obscuring lines. This noise was supposed to interfere with the perceptual goodness of the stimulus. In fact, obscuring stimuli in this manner did alter the order of attainment of concepts. But Dattman and Israel did not further define "perceptual goodness," so it does not seem that any theoretical clarification was obtained.

There is a suggestive relation between the number of dimensions needed to define the stimuli and the order difficulty of learning Heidbreder's concept types. We can think of "thinglike objects" as stimuli for which a single, overlearned template (e.g., schematic side view of a woman's face) is available. Complex geometric patterns would require the application of templates to several areas of the projection matrix; nonsense figures would require the application of templates to still smaller regions. The introduction of visual noise, as in the Dattman and Israel experiment, is equivalent to introducing more points on the matrix which cannot be fitted to a template. The same thing is true of the number of stimuli, which must be counted. If we equate the number of regions requiring separate templates to dimensions and the number of templates which may be applied within a given region to values, the order of difficulty of learning types of concepts varies with the number of dimensions and values needed to define stimulus objects.

Results supporting Heidbreder's order of attainment of concepts have been obtained by Grant and his associates, using analytically defined stimuli (Grant, Jones, Tallantis, 1949; Grant, 1951; Grant and Curran, 1953). The stimuli used were the cards of the Wisconsin Card Sorting Task. Each card has on it several identical colored geometric forms. The subject is required to sort cards by form, color, or number. Sorting by number is the most difficult task, sorting by form is the easiest. If the forms are regularly arranged on the card, number sorting is the easiest to learn. Grant and Curran (1953) proved that this is because the regular arrangement of forms creates a stimulus pattern that is perfectly correlated to number. Subjects respond to the overall pattern and not to the more abstract concept of number. If the forms are regularly arranged on the card only the leftmost (rightmost) boundary of the pattern need be established to determine the number of forms on the card. If the forms are irregularly arranged, the location of each figure must be established, as well as its separate identity. This means that the boundary, not of the pattern, but of the separate figures is important. Thus Grant and Curran's results are consistent with our analysis of dimensions and values based on stimulus scanning.

The intermediate difficulty of color sorting is not predicted by the template-fitting analysis. Only one point of the projection matrix is needed to determine the color of all figures on a card. Sorting for color is not the easiest sorting to learn. It may be that sensory perception of color is not as rapid as that of form, or that some order of searching for a particular cue is utilized.

The scanning analysis of perception can be interpreted within the neo-Gestalt position espoused by Bruner (1956, 1957). Perception is viewed as an act of inferring wholes from usually valid visual cues obtained from parts of the stimulus. Bruner (1957) hypothesized that the first step in perception is a primitive categorization of the stimulus by identifying a set of possible percepts. This set can be used as the basis of future "guesses" about object identity. After each guess, specific tests can be carried out to validate it. The information obtained from these tests will prescribe a smaller set of possible objects. Finally, when sufficient information is obtained to select a set consisting of only one object, a precept of the object is formed. At any stage a wrong guess could be accepted, since validation would not be complete. [It has been pointed out that perception requires some guessing, since the stimulus seldom contains enough information to specify it uniquely (Dember, 1960).]

In template matching a particular template may almost fit the projection matrix. If it is the best fit, or if the entire matrix is not checked to determine the fit, an erroneous template might be accepted. We have already seen (e.g., the example of scanning mail) that the information acquired from fitting a template in one region may be used to select trial templates for another region. This is nothing more than a process of guessing. Errors would be expected if the correct template for a particular region was not one that would normally be associated with the templates that fitted other regions of the same matrix, a prediction consistent with Bruner's guessing analysis. This sort of error can be demonstrated experimentally. Bruner (1956) reported that it took subjects longer to recognize a picture of a man dressed in a track uniform, hurling a violin, than a man similarly dressed, hurling a javelin.

What would happen if the stimuli from which a concept was to be learned could be fitted by a few highly overlearned templates? If these templates lead to erroneous perception of irrelevant dimensions there would be no effect. But if they lead to misperception of relevant dimensions, learning would be retarded. In particular, concept learning should be slower than the learning of informationally identical concepts based on less familiar stimuli. In the latter case subjects would be forced to apply templates to more localized regions of the projection matrix, thus abstracting more information about the stimulus. In the language of Chapter 2 this finer analysis, whereas it leads to a more complex description, is more likely to lead to a relevant one. On the other hand, if the internal correlations between the applicability of templates in different regions were related to the structure of the concept, a template-matching scheme which accentuated the correlation would aid in concept learning.

Within an experimental situation, subjects do react to the conditional probabilities that one stimulus element will be presented, given that another one has been observed (Solley and Murphy, 1960). Furthermore, they can use this information in stating their understanding of a concept. Two experiments support this assertion. Solley and Messick (1957) had subjects learn a concept based upon a hypothetical "tribe" of stickmen who could be happy, sad, short, tall, fat, or skinny, etc. Actually, the concept "stickmen" was based on a probabilistic discrimination; the joint occurrence of two values was a better (but not perfect) cue on which to assign the title "stickmen" than the presence of any single value of a given dimension. As has been typically found in studies of probabilistic discriminations, subjects "probability matched." When the subjects were asked to describe stickmen, or to guess the characteristics of a particular stickman, their responses reflected the statistical structure of the definition.

A related experiment was performed by R. Goodnow (1954, also reported by Bruner, Goodnow, and Austin, 1956). His subjects had to learn a categorizing task in which different cues had varying validities. One cue was associated with the correct response 100% of the time. In the experimental setting the subject might see a stimulus on which he could test only for the presence of one cue or for the presence of both. When cues were presented singly the validity of the 100% cue was slightly underestimated, that of the 67% cue was somewhat overestimated. When the cues were combined subjects first averaged the separate validities to determine joint validity. Later in the experiment they learned that if the information conflicted (in which case the response indicated by the 100% cue would always be correct), they should use only the 100% cue. However, this cue was responded to with the same (underestimated) frequence as when the 100% cue was presented alone. Goodnow noted that when conflicting cues were present subjects hesitated and appeared uncertain about their response. Perhaps this reflected their inability to make a rapid template matching to the projection matrix representing the stimuli?

Somewhat more direct evidence on the effect of matching appropriate and inappropriate templates is present in an experiment by Bruner, Goodnow, and Austin (1956). The performance of subjects on a concept-learning task using thematic material was compared to the performance of subjects learning a concept from informationally identical, nonthematic stimuli. The thematic stimuli were pictures of adults and children in various forms of dress and interpersonal interaction (e.g., a man in bathrobe giving a present to a smiling girl in street clothes). The nonthematic stimuli were geometric patterns. When the concept-learning task involved thematic material it was significantly more difficult. Some of the thematic stimuli were rather incongruous, such as a picture of a frowning child receiving a present. Also, unfortunately for our purpose in presenting the experiment, the stimuli were exposed throughout the experiment. This would minimize perceptual errors.

Although the Bruner et al. results are consistent with the template-matching analysis, the possibility exists (unfortunately, a strong possibility) that there is another explanation. Subjects may assume, erroneously, that certain dimensions are bound to be relevant. Bruner et al. report such biases. College students preferred to offer hypotheses relating the stimulus categorization used by the experimenters to the sex of the figures in the pictures. In a replication of one of his experiments, in which faces were used as stimuli, Goodnow found that subjects reacted to height of brow as a virtually certain cue regardless of its objective validity.

Because of these contaminating factors, the best we can say is that available evidence on categorizing from thematic material is not inconsistent with the analysis of perception as a scanning and template-matching procedure. More direct tests are needed before the relation between perception and concept learning can be understood.

## 6  Conclusion

We have examined evidence bearing on the relation between stimulus complexity and concept learning. The empirical relations between the complexity of the formal description of stimuli and the ease of concept learning are well established. There appears to be a parallel between these relations and the relation of stimulus complexity to difficulty of stimulus identification, which suggests that at least some common processes are used in the two experimental situations. Concept learning also has unique processes, however, that are not captured by extrapolating stimulus identification results to a cognitive task.

There is little evidence about how subjects structure objects presented to them. In part this may be because of the lack of a formally adequate theory of perception. A possible model, template-matching, which has not been developed formally, relies heavily on information reduction and categorization through utilization of conditional probabilities of joint occurrence of stimulus elements. On the basis of a much wider review of perceptual phenomenon, Allport (1957) has indicated that these factors may be very important in our ability to structure the perceptual world. It is also clear that reactions to such joint occurrences can be learned, giving a biological concept learner the ability to modify his perceptions depending on his previous experiences.

Until there is a more precise statement of perceptual theory, it will be impossible to carry out efficient experimentation on the role of perception in concept learning. It seems, therefore, that at least for the present experimenters should follow the procedure advocated by Hovland (1952): Have the experimenter and the subject agree on a definition of dimensions and values before the experiment begins. Even if this is done, the use of thematic material may prove confusing and should only be introduced for a specific purpose.

REFERENCES

Allport, F. H., 1957. *Theories of perception and the concept of structure.* New York: Wiley.

Amarel, S., 1960. An approach to automatic theory formation. Illinois Symposium on Self-organizing Systems.

Archer, E. J., L. E. Bourne, and F. C. Brown, 1955. Concept identification as a function of irrelevant information and instructions. *J. exp. Psychol.,* **49,** 153–164.

Attneave, F., 1959. *Applications of information theory to psychology.* New York: Holt.

Attneave, F., 1954. Some informational aspects of visual perception. *Psychol. Rev.,* **61,** 183–193.

Battig, W. E. and L. E. Bourne, 1961. Concept identification as a function of intra- and inter-dimensional variation. *J. exp. Psychol.,* **61,** 329–333.

Baum, M., 1954. Simple concept learning as a function of intra-list generalization. *J. exp. Psychol.,* **47,** 89–94.

Bourne, L. E., 1957. Effects of delay of information feedback and task complexity on the identification of concepts. *J. exp. Psychol.,* **54,** 201–207.

Bourne, L. E. and R. B. Haygood, 1959. The role of stimulus redundancy in concept identification. *J. exp. Psychol.,* **58,** 232–238.

Bourne, L. E. and R. B. Haygood, 1961. Supplementary report: effect of redundant relevant information upon the identification of concepts. *J. exp. Psychol.,* **61,** 259–260.

Bourne, L. E. and R. B. Pendleton, 1958. Concept identification as a function of completeness and probability of information feedback. *J. exp. Psychol.,* **56,** 413–419.

Bourne, L. E. and F. Restle, 1959. Mathematical theory of concept identification. *Psychol. Rev.,* **66,** 278–296.

Bruner, J. S., 1956. Going beyond the information given. In *Contemporary studies of cognition.* Cambridge: Harvard University Press.

Bruner, J. S., 1957. On perceptual readiness. *Psychol. Rev.,* **64,** 123–152.

Bruner, J. S., J. J. Goodnow, and G. A. Austin, 1956. *A study of thinking.* New York: Wiley.

Bush, R. and W. Estes, 1959. *Studies in Mathematical Learning Theory.* Stanford: Stanford University Press.

Bush, R. and F. Mosteller, 1955. *Stuchastic Models for Learning.* New York: Wiley.

Dattman, P. E. and H. E. Israel, 1951. The order of dominance among conceptual capacities: an experimental test of Heidbreder's hypothesis. *J. Psychol.,* **31,** 147–160.

Dember, W., 1960. *The psychology of perception.* New York: Holt.

Dollard, J. and N. E. Miller, 1950. *Personality and psychotherapy.* New York: McGraw-Hill.

Eriksen, C. W., 1954. Multidimensional stimulus differences and accuracy of discrimination. U. S. A. F. *WADC Tech. Rep.,* 54–165.

Frick, F., 1961. Pattern recognition. Unpublished address delivered at Western Joint Computer Conference.

Goodnow, R. E., 1954. Utilization of partially valid cues in perceptual identification. Unpublished doctoral dissertation, Harvard University.

Grant, D. A., 1951. Perceptual vs. analytic responses to the number concept of a weigl-type card sorting test. *J. exp. Psychol.,* **41,** 23–29.

Grant, D. A. and J. F. Curran, 1953. Relative difficulty of number, form, and color concepts of a weigl-type problem using unsystematic number cards. *J. exp. Psychol.,* **43,** 408–413.

Grant, D. A., O. R. Jones and B. Tallantis, 1949. The relative difficulty of number, form, and color concepts of a weigl-type problem. *J. exp. Psychol.,* **39,** 551–552.

Hebb, D. O., 1949. *The organization of behavior.* New York: Wiley.

Heidbreder, E., 1949. The attainment of concepts. VII. Conceptual achievements during card sorting. *J. Psychol.,* **27,** 3–39.

Heidbreder, E., 1946*a.* The attainment of concepts. I. Terminology and method. *J. gen. Psychol.,* **35,** 173–184.

Heidbreder, E., 1946*b.* The attainment of concepts. II. The problem. *J. gen. Psychol.,* **35,** 191–223.

Heidbreder, E., 1947. The attainment of concepts. III. The process. *J. Psychol., 24,* 93–118.

Heidbreder, E., 1945. Toward a dynamic theory of cognition. *Psychol. Rev., 52,* 1–22.

Heidbreder, E., M. L. Bensley and M. Ivy, 1948. The attainment of concepts. IV. Regularities and levels. *J. Psychol., 25,* 299–329.

Hochberg, J. E. and V. Brooks, 1960. The psychophysics of form: reversible-perspective drawings of spatial objects. *Amer. J. Psychol, 73,* 337–354.

Hull, C. L., 1920. Quantitative aspects of the evolution of concepts. *Psychol. Monogr., 28,* whole No. 23.

Hull, C. L., 1943. *Principles of Behavior.* New York: Appleton.

Hull, C. L., 1952. *A Behavior System.* New Haven: Yale U. Press.

Luce, R. D. (ed.), 1960. *Developments in mathematical psychology.* Glencoe, Ill.: Free Press.

Luce, R. D., 1959. *Individual choice behavior.* New York: Wiley.

Maltzman, I., 1955. Thinking: from a behavioristic point of view. *Psychol. Rev., 62,* 275–286.

Miller, G. A., 1956. The magical number seven, plus or minus two: some limits on our capacity to process information. *Psychol. Rev. 63,* 81–97.

Pishkin, V., 1960. Effects of probability of misinformation and number or irrelevant dimensions upon concept identification. *J. exp. Psychol., 59,* 371–378.

Pollack, I. and E. T. Klemmer, 1954. The assimilation of visual information from elementary dot patterns. USAF Cambridge Research Center Technical Report, 54–16.

Reed, H. B., 1946. The learning and retention of concepts. IV. The influence of the complexity of the stimuli. *J. exp. Psychol., 36,* 252–261.

Restle, F., 1955. A theory of discrimination learning. *Psychol. Rev., 62,* 11–19.

Restle, F., 1959. A survey and classification of learning models. In Bush, R. and W. Estes (eds.), *Studies in mathematical learning theory.* Stanford: Stanford U. Press.

Restle, F., 1961*a. Psychology of judgment and choice.* New York: Wiley.

Restle, F., 1961*b.* Statistical models for a theory of cue learning. *Psychometrika, 26,* 291–306.

Restle, F. (in press). The selection of strategies in cue learning. *Psychol. Bull.*

Shannon, C. and W. Weaver, 1949. *The mathematical theory of communication.* Urbana: University of Illinois Press.

Shepard, R. N., 1958. Stimulus and response generalization: tests of a model relating generalization to distance and psychological space. *J. exp. Psychol., 55,* 509–523.

Shepard, R. N., C. I. Hovland, and H. M. Jenkins, 1961. Learning and memorization of classifications. *Psychol. Monogr., 75,* (13, whole No. 517).

Solley, C. M. and S. J. Messick, 1957. Probability learning, the statistical structure of concepts, and the measurement of meaning. *Amer. J. Psychol., 70,* 161–173.

Solley, C. M. and G. Murphy, 1960. *Development of the perceptual world.* New York: Basic Books.

Spiegelthal, E. S., 1960. Computing educated guesses. *Proceeding of the Western Joint Computer Conference, 70–73.*

Stevens, S. S., 1960. The psychophysics of sensory functions. *Amer. Scientist, 48,* 226–253.

Wenzel, B. and C. Flurry, 1948. The sequential order of concept attainment. *J. exp. Psychol., 38,* 547–557.

Wertheimer, M., 1959. *Productive thinking.* (2nd ed.). New York: Harper.

FOOTNOTES

1. An example may illustrate the problem. The author once had a subject, an undergraduate enrolled in an introductory psychology course, who was unable to solve a very simple conjunctive concept-learning problem. When interrogated, it became obvious that she had structured the stimuli in terms of the presence or absence of what she thought were Freudian sex symbols. The stimuli were actually geometric patterns with colors, sizes, and shapes such as circle, triangle, etc., and this *had been* explained to the subject. But she knew that the experimenter was a psychologist, and she knew what psychologists were interested in. Her description of the stimuli followed from this assumed knowledge. Given this description, the sets of instances presented to the subject were only consistent with a very complex disjunctive concept.

   Shepard, Hovland, and Jenkins (1961) report a similar case in which the subject's coding of stimuli was completely irrelevant to the experimenter's. In this case, of course, the experimentally defined logical structure of the concept could not be recovered by the subject.

   Incidentally, the author hopes that this footnote will be taken as evidence for the prevalence of teaching about Freud in our culture, and not for the reality of Freudian sex symbols.

2. Readers familiar with information theory technique could skip to section 3 without loss of continuity.

3. A single exception occurs in an experiment by Pishkin (1960). He used misinformative feedback (i.e., subjects were sometimes informed that a correct response was wrong or vice versa) and continued training until errors over a block of trials reached a pre-set minimum.

4. Plane figures can be described along a continuum number of sides, from three to infinite (circles, ellipses). This is a fairly subtle ordering.

5. The reader may notice a similarity between equation 4.4.5 and the behaviorist models of covert responding during cognitive tasks (Maltzman, 1955; Dollard and Miller, 1950). The difference is mainly in our determination not to make any assumptions concerning the method by which a human creates the connective arrows.

6. Strictly speaking, $A$ should be conceptualized as the set of sensory events which occur when a particular set of stimuli are presented. Because sensory discrimination is not perfect, this may introduce error when $a_i$ is compared to the actually presented stimulus. Such errors can be avoided by separating stimuli by several j.n.d.'s. Attneave (1959) has pointed out that this does not affect the finding that human transformation capacity is constant for unidimensional stimuli.

7. The necessary data was provided by Professor Bourne.

8. That they make errors at all, and that the linear relation holds up for "negative equivocation," is not a violation of the code word model. In communication terms, negative equivocation means that some of the information-transmission system can be used to send error-checking signals or signals for independent, parallel computation. Such symbols (e.g., try out more than one partition at a time) should aid concept learning.

9. The present discussion is extended beyond the original article. Attneave's view of perception is closely related to a theory of the use of theories which can be represented in a machine (Amarel, 1960; see Chapter 9). Psychological evidence

consistent with Attneave's analysis has been obtained by Hochberg and Brooks (1960).

10. Template matching cannot possibly be the mode of recognition of patterns if we conceive of the template as being fitted to the entire matrix. The number of rotations and transformations of shapes, all of which are recognized as equivalent but which would require a separate template, is too large (Frick, 1961). The use of templates on small areas of the projection matrix, particularly if the matrix is normalized before the application of templates, meets some of the objections.

# 5

# Memory and concept learning

## 1   *Conceptualization of memory*

Just what is memory? To answer this question we must consider the role of data storage in problem solving. A problem solver receives information from the environment, makes calculations, and selects a response. The environment (the experimenter, if you will) evaluates the response and, as appropriate, rewards or punishes the problem solver. The problem solver wishes to improve his performance until he maximizes reward and minimizes punishment. To do this he must keep some sort of record of past experience. To be helpful, this record should contain necessary information; to be usable, the record must have information readily accessible.

The simplest information storage system is a direct-address filing system. This is the system used in most modern high-speed digital computers. In a direct-address system information is broken into units. Each unit is stored in a particular location (its address). To evaluate an information unit the problem solver must know the address of the unit. However simple this system is conceptually, few would propose it as a model of human memory.[1] Direct-address systems of any practical size could not, allegedly, retain data of the complexity retained by normal human beings (Von Neuman, 1958).

Instead, it has been proposed that human memory is of an associative type. The internal (neurological) correlates of a stimulus trace are assumed to be attached to each other, so that activation of part of the compound of nerve firing which occurred when the stimulus was originally presented will lead to the activation of the remainder of this compound. Thus the stimulus can be re-created, piece by piece. This explanation makes learning and retention the same physiological process. The process is neurologically defensible (Hebb, 1949). At the same time it introduces and is compatible with a mathematical model of stimulus elements which fade and interfere with each other. Most associative memory models view forgetting as the result of introjecting interfering stimulus traces, disrupting the sequence of firing necessary to recreate the original stimulus from its parts. Within this framework it is possible to develop a model that introduces ideas of fading and interchange of elements (confusions) during forgetting. The association principle of information storage has been used to design a machine that will recognize previously presented objects as old stimuli (Rosenblatt, 1958).

The principal objection to the association process is that memory is not a passive phenomenon. Bartlett (1932) argued that memory is an active reconstructive process. First a vague idea, or scheme, of the item to be recalled is developed. Then details are filled in, partly from memory and partly from reasoning what the event to be recalled must have been. Recollection must be sensible. Since what is sensible depends on what the subject feels to be true at the time of recall, memory should be greatly influenced by present knowledge and opinion. In a study that extended over several years (as contrasted to the usual interval of 2 weeks or less in most memory studies), Bartlett asked English students to recall a story in which the supernatural played an important part. The reality oriented Englishmen dropped this theme out of the story in successive recalls. It didn't make sense. Every day examples of memory modification can be found. Lawyers and policemen are familiar with the phenomenon of the witness who distorts his memory to avoid unreasonable implications of veridical recall. The literature of clinical psychology is full of such cases.

Association and reconstruction are not necessarily exclusive. Memory may operate in stages; at recall associations in memory may be searched to provide alternative reconstructions of the past event. These reconstructions could undergo a private screening before being made public.

There also may be a difference between short- and long-term memory processes. It has been suggested that the retention of information presented as recently as 15 minutes prior to recall actually involves different physiological processes than information retention over longer periods of time (Pauling, 1961). We shall discuss an experiment which is readily interpretable as showing that a different physiological process may be involved in information recall during the first few seconds after stimulus presentation (Sperling, 1960). In this discussion, we must remember that a model which could accurately predict the behavior of a subject trying to recall specific items per se might not predict the behavior of the same subject trying to use stored information to develop and evaluate hypotheses.

Unhappily for our purposes, concept-learning experiments have usually involved short-term memory *and* the potential use of stored data to evaluate hypotheses. Under the circumstances, it is perhaps not too surprising that there are no well-developed theories of the role of memory in concept learning. Only a few experimenters have studied this topic explicitly. Like perception, everyone agrees that memory is important in concept learning, but no one has a clear idea of how it is important. In an attempt to clarify the experimental data, and perhaps shed some light on the role of memory in concept learning, we shall first evaluate the logical role of stored data in any inductive reasoning task.

## 2    Stored information and inductive reasoning

A problem solver might store all the information he ever received. He could use this bank of knowledge to evaluate proposed answers as they occurred to him. Or he could store all conceivable hypotheses, and his current belief in each of them, and if he could do this, he could reason inductively without ever storing any specific information. Every time he encountered a new piece of data he could use it to readjust his belief in the plausibility of each of the hypothesis. This is the process of induction envisaged by Watanabe (1960). Chapter 2 showed that this process does result in an efficient evaluation of evidence without information retention. As a psychological model it is unrealistic, because there will be few cases in which a learner or problem solver will be able to state all his hypotheses before he begins work on a problem. A model which requires that the subject remember everything seems equally unlikely.

How much should a human concept learner rely on his memory for specific information presented at some prior time? This depends on his relative capacities for remembering evidence and evaluating hypotheses. If it is difficult to remember evidence it may be more economical to keep track of the likelihood of some set of hypotheses. No doubt hypotheses will be added to and dropped from this set as learning progresses. To avoid duplication of effort, some check ought to be made to see whether a new hypothesis can handle the evidence that the learner has already obtained before he evaluates it against new evidence. Thus the concept learner must have some capacity for remembering what he has learned about the stimulus universe.

## 3    *Techniques for remembering hypotheses*

Generally, it is more profitable to remember hypotheses than to remember specific instances. If the data retained is not controlled, however, memory for hypotheses alone will require more storage space than is available. An efficient scheme of selecting hypotheses would first be to select a set of hypotheses which must contain the answer, then retain information that particular hypotheses were or were not disconfirmed. If some orderly process of checking hypotheses were available, the human concept learner could reduce his memory load even more. All he would have to do would be to record the stage of the scanning process. Are there such techniques, and do humans use them?

In a particularly clever experiment, Seymour (1954, also cited by Bruner, Goodnow, and Austin, 1956) showed that the answer to both questions is "yes," at least for intelligent subjects. Seymour showed his subjects a board containing a universe of objects (geometric patterns) partitioned into a denotation and its complement. Initially the class memberships of the individual patterns were not indicated. The subject had to discover the concept by a test procedure which, as Bruner, Goodnow, and Austin point out, is very similar to scientific investigation. The subject would choose an instance, then the experimenter would indicate its class membership. After each trial the subject had to state his current hypothesis. He was only allowed to state one hypothesis, although an analysis of the inductive problem suggests that at any one time several hypotheses might be under consideration.

There are different hypothesis-selecting techniques, or *strategies,* which could have been used by Seymour's subjects. One is the aforementioned technique of using each identification of an object's name to evaluate every possible hypothesis. In the early stages of the problem this strategy (*simultaneous scanning*) forces the subject to keep track of an impossibly large number of hypotheses. One alternative is to evaluate only a few of the possible hypotheses at each trial. A second and more efficient alternative makes use of the fact that Seymour used only conjunctive concepts and that the subjects knew this. Therefore, they knew that the correct concept had to be the intersection of the sets of descriptive statements which applied to all objects in the denotation of the name (each *positive instance*). The required intersection could be found by taking, as a trial hypothesis, the intersection of the sets of descriptive statements applicable to successive pairs of positive instances.

We do not claim (nor did Seymour or Bruner, et al.) that subjects formulated their strategy in such an analytic manner. All that is claimed is that they either knew or discovered the very simple operational procedure which the foregoing analysis implies. For instance, suppose the subjects were asked to find a concept using stimuli that varied in form, size, and color. Furthermore, suppose the correct answer is *form-triangle*. If the first positive instance is a big red triangle, and the second positive instance a big blue triangle, the answer must be either big, triangle, or big and triangle.

In Seymour's experiment a subject could select the object that he wished the experimenter to identify. There is a strategy for selecting objects (*focusing*) which will lead the subject to the correct answer with a minimum information retention requirement. First the subject must locate one positive instance. The next object chosen should differ from this instance in the value of only one dimension. If this change produces a negative instance, the changed dimension must be relevant. Otherwise the dimension must be irrelevant. In the previous example, if big red triangles and big blue triangles were both positive instances, color could not be relevant. But if big red triangles were positive and big red circles negative, form would have to be relevant. The appropriate values within these dimensions can be established by reference to any previously located positive instance.

In a pilot study, Seymour found that seven of twelve Harvard students adopted some form of the focusing strategy.[2] The other five used the "scanning" technique of evaluating hypotheses. Since they were unable to evaluate all hypotheses at once, they had to introduce a new one from time to time. This imposed a greater memory requirement. Scanners had to remember which hypotheses they had evaluated and, when they introduced a new hypothesis, had to use a record of previous items to evaluate it. Seymour demonstrated the importance of this record by altering the experimental procedure. Instead of showing all instances all the time, he showed instances one at a time. The subject could still select the instance he wished to see, but after an instance had been identified it was removed. The new procedure made little difference to the focusers, who had never relied on specific records of previously presented instances. The scanners found the modified task exceedingly difficult.

As described, the focusing strategy requires that the subject be able to specify which instance will be identified next. Like the scientist seeking specific information, the concept learner can perform experiments. On the other hand, much concept learning is done by "bench bound lecture goers." They must observe only what nature or an experimenter provides. Bruner, Goodnow, and Austin (1956, Chapter 5) showed that a strategy very similar to focusing can be used to reduce memory requirements in this situation. The concept learner should concentrate his attention on positive instances. Assuming that the correct concept is a conjunctive one, he can "zero in" on it by taking the successive intersections of the descriptive statements (dimensions and values) applicable to the currently and all previously presented positive instances. Thus, his current hypothesis (or focus) always includes (but is not limited to) the correct hypothesis. No instance ever need be remembered as such. The only trouble with this strategy is that it

Table 5-1   Example of a conjunctive concept-learning problem in which the subject must either know, in advance, the number of relevant dimensions, or must observe negative instances

| Class | Description of instances | | | |
|-------|------|------|------|------|
| Positive | A-1 | B-1 | C-1 | D-1 |
| Negative | A-1 | B-2 | C-2 | D-2 |
| Positive | A-1 | B-1 | C-3 | D-3 |
| Negative | A-2 | B-1 | C-3 | D-3 |

will not work if the concept learner does not know the minimum number of dimensions involved. To see this, let us take a coded example in which letters represented dimensions and numbers values. Table 5-1 specifies four instances, two positive and two negative. By observing the positive instances alone, we can deduce that the concept is either $A$-1, $B$-1, or $A$-1 and $B$-1. The negative instances must be observed to discriminate between these three hypotheses.

Bruner, Goodnow, and Austin report a series of experiments in which Harvard and Wellesley undergraduates utilized the modified focusing procedure. Their subjects knew the number of relevant dimensions. After each instance was presented the subjects had to state their current hypothesis, so the experimenters were able to infer the strategy that was being used. Approximately 60% of the problems were begun with the focusing strategy. The correct rules for focusing were not always followed, but subjects did better when the rules were not violated.[3]

Tangential support for the Bruner, Goodnow, and Austin findings is provided by a study by Kurtz and Hovland (1956) which used as a dependent variable the subjects ability to make a correct statement of the hypothesis. If subjects are remembering their hypothesis about a concept, they should do better when all positive instances are presented together. Negative instances cannot help a pure focuser and might interfere with his ability to retain a picture of his current focus. Kurtz and Hovland's subjects learned four concepts (based on geometrical patterns) at the same time. Positive instances of three of the concepts would be negative instances of the fourth. Subjects found the task easier if all instances of a particular concept were presented successively, instead of having examples of the four concepts interspersed. The condition which favored focusing resulted in faster concept learning.[4]

The studies by Bruner and his associates, although among the most important in the field, cannot be taken as proof that humans normally use strategies which eliminate memory requirements in concept learning. It is certainly true that strategies exist which can eliminate most memory requirements. Some intelligent subjects utilize these strategies, not even all Harvard students do so. Less gifted learners might use them less frequently.

The use of strategies is difficult to evaluate since the experimenter must interpret a protocol. His biases must not affect the results. Ideally, the "blind" technique of evaluation, where two or more judges evaluate a protocol without knowledge of how it was obtained or rated by other judges, should be used.

The importance of information storage in concept learning varies, depending on the subject's strategies. For this reason, it is doubtful that a general statement about the role of memory in induction can ever be made for any unspecified human subject.

In fact, memory could be entirely eliminated and concept learning would still be possible. Restle (1961) has proposed a "no memory" model, which pictures a concept learner who samples a universe of possible hypotheses, selects one, and holds it until an instance is encountered which constitutes a counterexample. The current hypothesis is then dropped (or dropped with a certain probability), *returned to the universe of hypotheses,* and a new one selected. Since sampling is with replacement, there is no memory for hypotheses or previously presented instances. Eventually the correct hypothesis will be selected. Restle used a simple mathematical model embodying the idea of random hypothesis selection to obtain a reasonably good fit for data obtained from monkeys solving a discrimination task and from Michigan State students solving simple concept-learning problems (Restle, 1960, 1961). His model will be discussed further in the next chapter.

We seem to be in a quandary. Is there any place for memory in concept learning? Bruner et al. would have us believe that Harvard students behave so cleverly that they have no need for memory of past instances; Restle would have us believe that Rhesus monkeys and Michigan State students are unable to profit by remembering their own ideas. Somewhere in between, studies have shown that young adults do rely on memory both for past instances and hypotheses.


## 4    Memory for specific information

In the normal memory experiment a test stimulus is shown either before, after, or before and after, a series of interfering stimuli. To test his memory, the subject is asked either to recall the test stimulus or to recognize it when it is presented a second time. To show an effect of memory on concept learning, a rather different procedure is needed. The appropriate test is not whether the subject can recall or recognize a particular object, but rather whether or not he can make use of the information it transmitted about the concept.

This criterion presents problems. Just because a subject's hypothesis at time $v$ agrees (or does not agree) with the class membership of an object presented at time $v - j$, we cannot say that he has remembered it. The subject can make a guess which might be consistent with any particular previously presented piece of information. If the subject were choosing hypotheses at random, without regard to previously presented data, his choice would not be affected by the location of prior instances in the training series. If the location of a particular instance relative to the instances presented before it or intervening between it and the point at which the subject's hypothesis is offered influences the tendency of the subject to offer hypotheses consistent with this instance, we can infer some memory for the information it transmitted. Our belief in this inference would be strengthened if the same variables which affect specific memory, when tested as such, can be shown to affect concept learning in a parallel manner.

Whitfield (1948) showed that memory for specific instances is important in inductive reasoning. His task, although not concept learning as the term has been defined here, is pertinent because it involved the ability to develop and evaluate hypotheses based on previously present information. Subjects had to discover a particular experimenter-defined sorting of eight objects into $n$ slots. Three experimental conditions were used; eight objects into eight slots, eight objects, two in each of four slots, and eight objects, four in each of two slots. The subject would make a sorting, and then the experimenter would tell him how many, but not which, objects were correctly placed. This information was sufficient to tell the subject that certain other sortings could not be correct. For instance, if the subject is told that he has placed objects correctly in six of eight slots, he should not move more than two objects on the next trial. If there are two slots, and no objects correctly placed, the problem should be solved on the next trial. The only way that eight objects could be wrong in this condition would be for all the "slot *A*" objects to be in "slot *B*" and vice versa.

After correcting for guessing, Whitfield found that the eight-slot problem was easier than the others. This appears to have been partly due to memory requirements. In the eight-slot condition the subject can systematically alter sortings within each slot, using the experimenter's response to identify correctly placed elements on the basis of changes in successive sortings. In the two- and four-slot conditions, cases may occur in which correct placement of an object can be determined only by comparing its location on two, three, or more separated sortings. Whitfield felt that this was a major source of difficulty. In particular, he noticed that when subjects presented new but logically eliminated sortings, they were the least likely to be inconsistent with either the first sorting presented or the most recently presented sortings.

Whitfield's experiment has important implications for the study of concept learning. Using an inductive task rather different than concept learning, he observed strategies similar to the focusing technique Bruner, Goodnow, and Austin observed eight years later in conventional studies. His results increase the generality of the "strategies" finding. The report that subjects tended to retain information from either the first or most recently presented sorting suggests that the factors of primacy (tendency to remember instances presented early in a series) and recency (tendency to remember recently presented instances) will affect inductive reasoning. Although Whitfield did not present data (and probably did not have enough subjects for a satisfactory analysis), he suggested that individual subjects differ in their tendency to remember first-presented or recently presented information.

If verified, and Whitfield's report is only suggestive, his results concerning individual differences in the use of memory in inductive reasoning would be extremely important. Most studies of memory report group effects, treating interactions between individuals and experimental conditions as error (cf. reviews by McGeoch and Irion, 1952; Hovland, 1951). Perhaps this technique ignores an important individual difference.[5] On the other hand, the logical requirements placed on concept learners by different strategies may produce a difference in the way memory is used. Further investigation of the interaction between strategies and memory is clearly required.

Cahill and Hovland (1960) demonstrated an effect of memory for previously presented information in two different types of concept-learning problems. Yale students attempted to learn a concept based on either a simple conjunction of two values in different dimensions (gray circles) or a "two-level" disjunction, in which the correct concept was the union of four two-element conjunctions (white or gray circles or triangles) defined by the positive values of two relevant dimensions. In the experiment the concept was defined by negative instances; that is, subjects were never shown an example of the concept, but were shown enough examples of what the concept was *not* so that only one possible answer was left. The experimenter told the subjects the logical form of the concept. Because only negative instances were used, no focusing strategy was available.

Two methods of presentation were used. In the experimental condition instances were presented one at a time and then removed from the subject's view. In the control condition instances were presented one at a time and left in view. Thus in both conditions the subjects were presented with the same amount of information at any point. The only difference was that the experimental subjects had to rely on memory while the control subjects did not. Subjects had to write their current hypothesis after each instance was presented. The control group solved the problem sooner, duplicating a result previously obtained with series of negative instances by Hovland and Weiss (1952). Very few erroneous statements made by either group were inconsistent with the currently presented instance, which was always in view. In the control group very few erroneous hypotheses were offered that were inconsistent with previously presented (and still exposed) objects, and there was no tendency to concentrate such errors on a particular serial location. In the experimental group, however, the frequency of such errors was much higher. Error frequency increased as the number of instances intervening between the statement and the inconsistent instance was increased. As a further check, Cahill and Hovland divided the number of errors made in stating hypotheses by the number of hypotheses disconfirmed by all previously presented instances. This fraction also steadily increased as the number of intervening instances increased. The increase in error frequency was not as rapid early in the training series as later. Cahill and Hovland interpreted their results as showing both primacy and recency effects in the retention of information during concept learning.

Hunt (1961) extended the Cahill and Hovland findings. There were two major differences between his experiments and Cahill and Hovland's. The criterion of forgetting, instead of being an evaluation of a statement of an hypothesis, was the number of identifications of a series of test instances which were inconsistent with the information transmitted by a particular (key) training instance. The concept was based on geometric patterns. Both positive and negative instances were used in the training series. Probably less important, subjects were drawn from a population of generally lower intelligence (although still college students) than the populations used by Cahill and Hovland or by Bruner et al.

Subjects were told that the correct concept was a conjunctive one. In the first two experiments the correct answer was that the name "Alpha" had been assigned to all outlined figures enclosed in circular borders. However, only the key instance was an outline figure inside a square border. This was assigned the name "Bravo," as were all instances which did not have an outline figure *and* a circular border. Several black figures inside circular borders, all assigned the name "Bravo," were shown. In the test phase of the experiment subjects had to assign the names "Alpha" or "Bravo" to ten patterns which had outline figures in square borders. Assigning the name "Bravo" was consistent with the correct answer. Assigning the name "Alpha" was consistent with the answer "Alpha patterns have outline figures," which was refuted only by the key instance. On the basis of pretesting it was known that subjects preferred to use a simpler answer in the absence of specific information to the contrary. The number of training instances preceding the key instance and intervening between it and the test instance was systematically varied, using a factorial design. The average number of errors in identifying class membership of test instances increased linearly with the number of intervening instances, consistent with Cahill and Hovland's recency results. The number of errors was not consistently related to the number of preceding instances, so the primacy effect noted by Cahill and Hovland was not found.

These results could occur even if memory was not used at all. If subjects scanned the objects in some systematic order, a few dimensions at each instance, their ability to evaluate hypotheses about a given dimension would be a function of the location of instances transmitting information about that dimension in the training series. To insure that the results from the first two experiments were not subject to such an explanation, a third experiment was performed. Three key instances were used, each transmitting information which implied that a particular dimension, alone, did not define the correct concept.

The position of the three key instances was varied in a counter-balanced design. Both location and identity of the key instance were significant variables, indicating that although the earlier results on serial position effects are valid, subjects also have biases toward using particular dimensions in their answers. Such a finding is consistent with the result of the "order of dominance" experiments cited in Chapter 4.

Evidently memory for specific negative instances does play a part in concept learning. Just how large a part it plays will depend upon the current hypothesis the subject holds and how he attained it.


## 5   Strategies, hypotheses, and memory

In Hunt's experiments memory effects were reliable but small. Cahill and Hovland's experiment showed a large effect. Whitfield found an effect of intermediate size, but since his task was rather different from the usual concept learning-experiment, evaluating it is difficult. Finally, some of the reports of studies by Bruner, Goodnow, and Austin imply that practically no memory effects occurred. What is there in the different experiments that gives rise to such varied results?

Each experimental situation encouraged the use of different strategies of concept attainment. Conjunctive concepts, the most frequently encountered type in the literature on concept learning, are particularly affected by the choice of strategy which the concept learner makes. Conjunctive concept-learning problems can be solved by focusing on successive intersections of the descripton of positive instances. Since any positive instance will contain, within the elements of its description, all elements of the correct statement of the concept, there is little need to rely on memory for specific past instances. All the subject has to do is rely on memory to tell him (a) which dimensions have never changed over previously presented positive instances and (b) what the constant value of each of these dimensions was. The latter data must be available so that the concept learner can spot a change within the "focus" or set of previously constant dimensions, when one occurs. In focusing then (and in the successive presentation variety of focusing that Bruner et al. describe as the "Wholist" or "Partist" strategy), the subject must keep track of the state (constant value) of $n^{(v)}$ variables, where $n^{(v)}$ is the number of dimensions included in the focus at time $v$.

The task of keeping track of the current state of several variables has been investigated without reference to concept learning by Yntema

and Meuser (1960*a, b,* 1962). In their experiments *o* objects (designated
by letters) would have *a* attributes (designated by the class names
of nouns in English), each of which can change its state independently.
For instance, there might be two objects, *A* and *B,* with three attributes
—stone, animal, and direction—in each. The subject has to record a
series of messages (e.g., "animal of *A* is fox," "stone of *B* is ruby") and,
at aperiodic intervals, must respond to questions about the current
state of a variable (e.g., "What is the stone of *A*?"). The task becomes
one of keeping track of the current state of $o \times a$ variables which
have various degrees of interrelation. Applied to the learning of conjunctive concepts through the information presented on positive instances, we can think of the focus as being an object, and the $n^{(v)}$
dimensions within it as being attributes of the object. In most concept-
learning studies there will be seven or fewer dimensions within the
focus. The number drops rapidly as concept learning progresses.
Yntema and Meuser's (1960*a*) data indicates that keeping track of the
current state of the variables defined by seven or fewer attributes of a
single object is relatively easy.

A comparison of the concept-learning situation to the Yntema and
Meuser studies leads to other interesting analogies. Yntema and
Meuser (1960*b*) found that the probability of an error in identifying a
state of a variable increases with an increase in the number of messages
since the last message about that variable. If we regard each instance
as a message, but positive instances only as messages about the
variables of interest, we would expect that interspersing positive and
negative instances within a concept-learning task would make it
harder to keep track of the current focus, thus interfering with concept learning. This result was obtained by Kurtz and Hovland (1956).

One of Yntema and Meuser's less-expected findings was that keeping
track of six objects, each with the same attribute, is much more difficult than keeping track of six different attributes of the same object although the number of variables is the same in each case (Yntema
and Meuser, 1960*b*). They showed that this is so because, in the latter
case, we can identify the current state of each variable if we know
only which states are active. If we are trying to remember which of
six "animal" states are active in variable one, it is not too much help
to know that one active state is "dog," if the "dog" state can appear
in any variable. But if we know that the state "dog" is active, and
that there is only one variable which has as its states the names of
animals, the question is answered. This finding can be translated to
the concept-learning situation. Suppose that the objects to be categorized are described in such a way that each dimension can have the

same values. The memory requirements of the focusing strategy will be increased. The learner must remember what values appear in the focus and which values are assigned to which dimensions. This suggests a possible interaction between difficulty of learning, type of stimuli, and successive versus simultaneous presentation of objects in concept learning.

In disjunctive concepts the intersection of the descriptions of *all* positive instances may be the empty set. Does this suggest a different role for the use of memory in disjunctive concept learning? Such an idea is not attractive, since the role of memory should be a function of the subject's response to the problem and not a function of the correct answer. After all, the subject does not know the answer before beginning the problem. Fortunately, we do not have to assume that a subject behaves in a different way when he attempts to learn disjunctive concepts (although it can be argued that to be efficient, he should), since a modified form of focusing will solve disjunctive problems.

Any concept can be stated as the union of one or more sets of descriptive statements applicable to the objects to be categorized (Chapter 2). A concept is always expressible by a disjunction of conjunctions.[6] Each conjunction defines its own focus, or set of dimensions, $F_i$. The concept learner has then a set of foci $F_l \ldots F_k$ of which he must keep track. The task becomes one of making modifications within each of these foci. The number of variables will increase as the number of foci increases. This makes the memory task much more difficult since, not surprisingly, the more variables to which the subject must respond, the more errors he is likely to make (Yntema and Meuser, 1960a). The same dimensions may be contained in two or more foci, with either the same or different values. The concept learner is then faced with the problem of keeping track of variables with common states. An extrapolation of the Yntema-Meuser results suggests that the form of the correct answer will interact with memory requirements to determine problem difficulty. The amount of this effect should be controllable by altering the extent to which different foci contain the same dimensions, or dimensions which have the same values. There may also be nonmemory aspects of conjunctive and disjunctive problems which make them differentially difficult for subjects. It may be that the problems imposed by focusing are so great in disjunctive concept learning that the subjects adopt a new strategy.

At present, these hypothesized relations between memory experiments and concept learning are without experimental support. Whether an analysis of a focusing strategy in concept learning as a task involving keeping track of several variables is fruitful will depend on future research. In planning such research the differences between the concept learning and memory experiments should be considered. In concept learning, memory is only one of several stages of induction. How the other stages (e.g., hypothesis evaluation) will affect memory remains to be determined. If all that happens is that the absolute accuracy of memory is lowered, there will be no problem. But, as might be argued, a firmly held present hypothesis could interact with and distort memory for past experience. In concept-learning experiments the subject receives a message about several variables every time he is told an object's class membership. Each message in the Yntema and Meuser studies presented, in a discrete time period, information about only one variable. In the memory studies messages about variables which were extraneous to the present task were not included. In concept learning information about the state of dimensions not included in the focus is continuously available. The effect of introducing extraneous variables into a memory task is not known. Completely aside from concept learning, it appears to be an interesting problem with important referents.

## 6   Patterning, description, and memory

Objects may be described in several different ways. Will their description affect the way that they are remembered? On the basis of considerable evidence, Miller (1956) has suggested that recording stimuli into a few symbols is a method that humans use to increase their capacity to retain information. The limiting factor on human information capability is evidently not the amount of information per symbol, but rather the number of symbols to be stored. As an example, Miller showed how to remember a very large string of binary digits. Very few, if any, humans can remember a string of twenty-four randomly chosen zeroes or ones. On the other hand, remembering a string of eight symbols is not terribly difficult. Three binary digits can be used to define an octal digit; 000 becomes zero, 001 becomes one, and so on, until 111 is translated as seven. If you are highly practiced at translating from binary to octal notation and vice versa, you can remember a string of twenty-four binary digits by the simple trick of remembering the equivalent string of eight octal digits. The code and recode procedure does not result in the loss of information. But this method of recall does not always work. Suppose a person remembered red stars and red sickles as "Russian symbols" and yellow

stars and yellow crescents as "Turkish symbols." He could recall a
string of Russian or Turkish symbols perfectly and be unable to recall
the string of stars, sickles, and crescents.

Miller, Galanter, and Pribram (1960) have taken a stronger position,
claiming that coding is the normal method of information storage.
They specifically object to using of "meaningless" material in studies
of memory and cognition. In what is perhaps their most extreme mood,
Miller et al. suggest that the nonsense syllable string BOF-XAJ-MIB-ZYQ
might be remembered by a "recoding" mnemonic device, "BOF
XAJerates his MIBery because he is not ZYQ." (Miller, Galanter, and
Pribram, 1960, pp. 125–138.) They argue that a theory of remembering
which does not take into account mnemonic recoding devices throws
the baby, or at least one of the twins (since a two-factor theory is not
impossible) out with the bath.[7]

Presumably Miller, Galanter, and Pribram would argue that recoding in memory is even more important if the information to be
retained is to be used in later induction, as it is in concept learning.
The function of recoding is to reduce the number of symbols stored in
memory at any one time. However, if the symbols are to be of any
use at all, they must contain information relevant to the concept. At
the time of presentation the concept learner may not know what this
is. We may assume that he recodes so that he can store information
he believes may be relevant at the time an object is presented. If this
hypothesis is wrong, the information that he stores may be of no use
to him. At some later point when he changes to a relevant description,
it should be very hard for him to use earlier information. But experimental evidence to bolster this point of view is not now available.

If the concept learner has a relevant description and can utilize a
focusing strategy, the problem of recoding will not be crucial. Some
recoding may take place. Specifically, we would expect that only the
value of dimensions within the focus would be stored. So long as this
rule is followed, at least all relevant dimensions will be included
within the stored information. However, if the concept learner under-
intersects, storing only part of the focus, vital information may be
lost. Bruner, Goodnow, and Austin report that this is the most frequent
cause of failure in subjects' learning conjunctive concepts by the
"wholist" strategy.

We have already seen one case in which a focusing strategy is not
feasible. A disjunctive concept might make the memory requirements
of focusing too formidable. Focusing will not work well if there are
very few positive instances. In the extreme case, such as the experiments by Cahill and Hovland and Hovland and Weiss, the concept

could be defined entirely in terms of negative instances. Obviously, focusing would not be appropriate. In less extreme cases positive instances alone might not unequivocally define a single concept. This was the case in Hunt's experiments. Finally, the individual's style of cognitive behavior is important. Even when focusing is both appropriate and easy, not all individuals utilize it as a strategy.


## 7    Recovery of specific items of information

At the beginning of this chapter, the "scanning" alternative to a focusing strategy was proposed. Since there are a large number of hypotheses in the early stages of concept learning, a scanning procedure which involves complete evaluation of all of them is not feasible. If a repeated sample of a few hypotheses is chosen for evaluation against each object, the correct answer will be chosen eventually. If the concept learner can retain some information about previously presented instances as well, the chances of selecting an erroneous hypothesis during scanning will be reduced since selection will be made on the basis of more information.

What is the form in which such information must be stored? To evaluate a newly developed hypothesis, the concept learner must first decide what evidence he needs and then whether or not he has it. The first step is not a memory task; the second step does not require that the learner "remember" in toto a particular instance. Instead, he has to search his memory to see whether or not a particular subset of descriptive elements has or has not occurred jointly with a particular naming response. For instance, suppose that a subject in a concept-learning experiment develops the hypothesis that "all red stars are in the class 'Alpha.'" To evaluate his hypothesis he must search his memory, however conceived, to determine whether there is any representation of an object to which the descriptive statement "has a red star" and the name "not-Alpha" can both be applied.

Shepard (1961) has developed a "micromechanical" model of memory during recognition which can be extended to the use of stored information. In his model a stimulus is represented internally by a set of elements. When a stimulus is presented a set of activated trace elements is associated with its internal representation. After the stimulus is removed the activated trace elements gradually become deactivated or "migrate" to other internal representations. The probability that an element will transfer from one representation to another is specified, as is the probability of deactivation. In recognition, the unbiased probability that a given stimulus will be responded to as an "old" stimulus is proportional to the number of activated trace elements in its internal representation. The model has received experimental support (Shepard and Teghtsoonian, 1961).

To apply the model to concept learning we change the task slightly. The stimulus elements of Shepard's model are equated with the elements of the description of an object. Each value of each dimension becomes a stimulus element. The class name attached to each object is also assumed to be a stimulus element. During hypothesis evaluation a search will be conducted to see whether or not certain combinations of elements can be found. For example, a hypothesis could be evaluated by asking "Is there any case in which the name GLYMPH was (was not) associated with a red object?"

If memory takes this role in the execution of a simultaneous scanning strategy, the search of memory must be organized. Proper search techniques to retrieve information will be as important as proper coding to store it. This topic has not been investigated directly, but there are some tangentially relevant experiments which have shown that the probability of correct selection of an item to be recalled is as much or more influenced by biases operating at the time of recall as it is by biases operating when the item is stored. Lawrence and his associates (Lawrence and Coles, 1954; Lawrence and LaBerge, 1956) asked their subjects to report the values of particular dimensions of cards chosen from the Wisconsin Card Sorting Task. Accuracy of report on a particular dimension could be increased by giving the subjects a "set" (in the psychological, not logical, sense) to report a dimension. The set could be induced either before or after the stimuli had been presented. Either condition resulted in equally accurate reporting. This suggests that a constant amount of information is stored, more than the subject can recall. But at any one time there may be a limit to the amount of information that can be reported. Accuracy of report along a particular dimension (i.e., about stimulus elements thought to be important in evaluation of a particular hypothesis) could be obtained by biasing the subject's method of searching his memory.

A series of carefully controlled experiments by Sperling (1960) amplify the findings of Lawrence et al. Sperling exposed multiple attribute stimuli tachistoscopically and then asked subjects either to recall as many stimulus elements as they could (subjects exhibited little variation in their ability to do this), or to recall as many elements as they could of a particular attribute (e.g., the letters on the last line of a matrix of letters). Sperling argued that in the second case the stimuli within the attribute could be treated as a sample of the stimulus elements available to the subject. Since the subject did not know what attribute he would be asked to report, he could not bias his perception toward storage of relevant stimulus elements. Therefore, the accuracy of report of a particular attribute could be used as an estimate of the accuracy of memory for previously presented information. This estimate would be independent of a limit on the total amount that could be reported. Asking a subject to report as much as he could of the entire stimulus would not be independent of this limit, since the limit might be smaller than the total number of stimulus elements stored.

Sperling found that if the instruction to report occurred very soon (fractions of a second) after the stimulus presentation ended, the report of a single attribute was almost perfect. This result indicated that memory was nearly complete. When the instruction to report was delayed, however, memory accuracy, estimated from the sampled attributes, dropped until it was approximately equal to the number of stimulus elements that could be reported in the free recall situation. In addition, if the visual field was changed immediately *after* the stimulus had been presented, the estimated number of stimulus elements in memory decreased. Sperling interpreted his results as indicating that information storage consisted of a sensory image and a symbol storage phase. During the period immediately after stimulus presentation an image would normally be present. By concentrating his attention upon this image, the subject could select a limited number of stimulus elements to store; the information so selected would be available for later retrieval.

If Sperling's "image" theory accounts only for loss of information over a short time, it is probably of little interest in concept learning. During the time intervals used in concept-learning studies, hypotheses changes (which correspond to instructions to report particular stimulus attributes in Sperling's study) would be sufficiently removed from stimulus presentations so that they would operate entirely on symbol-storage memory. But there is no need to believe that all short-term forgetting occurs in the transition between stimulus and symbols. The Lawrence studies used considerably longer periods between stimulus presentation and "set" instructions for remembering. Here the intervals approached those that would be found in hypothesis evaluation during concept learning. The symbols stored might be periodically reviewed for their relevance, as defined at the time of review, and then reselected for retention; that is, Sperling's image process might be repeated on stored information. In the framework of Shepard's model, this process is equivalent to a change of parameters for dropping and exchanging stimulus elements each time a new hypothesis is developed. A model for information retention could be developed in which the probability of retaining particular information would be a function both of that information's relevance to the hypothesis in force at the time it was stored and of its relevance to later hypotheses.

At present, such a model is only an idea, and developing it will not be easy. Several problems stand out. Stimulus elements must be defined. Cue-conditioning models generally assume that the stimulus is to be represented by many elements. For an extension of Shepard's model to concept learning to make sense, stimulus traces must be limited to a relatively few elements. Stimulus sampling models which assume a small number of elements are becoming increasingly popular. (Bower, 1961; Estes, 1960; Suppes and Atkinson, 1960.)

Patterning will also present a difficult problem. Should separate stimulus elements within the trace be used to represent the joint occurrence of two more unitary elements? Intuitively it seems unreasonable to let the elements "blue inside" and "triangle" remain or drop independently from a stimulus trace if the stimulus itself was a blue triangle inside a white circle. In using a model like Shepard's, we can take an intermediate position between complete independence of basic elements and separate patterning cues. The element loss and element exchange parameters may be defined in terms of conditional probabilities, the probability of a particular element being lost or exchanged with another trace being defined under the condition that some other element was or was not lost or exchanged. Such definitions greatly complicate the mathematical model.[8]


## 8    Conclusion

There can be little doubt that concept learning is affected by memory. How and how much will be determined by the strategy of inductive reasoning used by the learner. This, in turn, will be a function of task requirements and individual differences. The focusing and scanning techniques of concept attainment make quite different use of retained information.

Recent advances in the empirical and theoretical study of memory have made the investigation of the role of memory in concept learning feasible. Future research should be considerably more precise than most of the studies reported in this chapter. These have been largely empirical studies. Theoretical models must be tested.

There is one speculation, however, which the author does not think will have to be abandoned. Any adequate model of the role of information retention in complex mental processes will have to take into account the phenomenon of recoding. Models which do not consider coding may be helpful, but they will never be able to account for enough of the data. In attempting to deal with such phenomena as recoding and mnemonic devices, psychologists may be forced to deal with much more complex models than the simple linear operators so often found in studies of learning. This is unfortunate, but is not an excuse for failing to do the research. It will be harder to develop rigorous models of higher mental processes than to develop models of animal learning; but then, the Taoist philosophers warned "Heaven and earth are not necessarily benevolent."

REFERENCES

Bartlett, F. C., 1932. *Remembering*. Cambridge: Cambridge University Press.

Bower, G., 1961. Application of a model to paired associate learning. *Psychometrika*, **26**, 255–280.

Bruner, J. S., J. J. Goodnow, and G. A. Austin, 1956. *A study of thinking*. New York: Wiley.

Cahill, H. and C. I. Hovland, 1960. The role of memory in the acquisition of concepts. *J. exp. Psychol.*, **59**, 137–144.

Estes, W. K., 1960. Learning theory and the new mental chemistry. *Psychol. Rev.*, **67**, 207–223.

Estes, W. K., and B. L. Hopkins, 1961. Acquisition and transfer in pattern vs. component discrimination learning. *J. exp. Psychol.*, **61**, 322–328.

Hebb, D. O., 1949. *The organization of behavior*. New York: Wiley.

Hovland, C. I., 1951. Human learning and retention. In Stevens, S. S. (ed.) *Handbook of experimental psychology*. New York: Wiley.

Hovland, C. I. and W. Weiss, 1953. Transmission of information concerning concepts through positive and negative instances. *J. exp. Psychol.*, **45**, 175–182.

Hunt, E. B., 1961. Memory effects in concept learning. *J. exp. Psychol.*, **62**, 598–604.

Hunt, E. B. and C. I. Hovland, 1961. Programming a model of human concept formation. *Proceedings of the Western Joint Computer Conference*, 145–155.

Kochen, M., 1961. An experimental program for the selection of disjunctive "hypotheses." *Proceedings of the Western Joint Computer Conference*, **19**, 571–578.

Kurtz, K. H. and C. I. Hovland, 1956. Concept learning with differing sequences of instances. *J. exp. Psychol.*, **51**, 239–243.

Lawrence, D. H. and C. Coles, 1954. Accuracy of recognition with alternatives before and after the stimulus. *J. exp. Psychol.*, **47**, 208–214.

Lawrence, D. H. and D. LaBerge, 1956. Relationship between recognition accuracy and order of reporting stimulus dimensions. *J. exp. Psychol.*, **51**, 12–18.

McGeoch, J. and K. Irion, 1952. *The psychology of human learning*. New York: Longmans, Green.

Miller, G. A., 1956. The magical number seven, plus or minus two: some limits on our capacity to process information. *Psychol. Rev.*, **63**, 81–97.

Miller, G. A., E. Galanter, and K. Pribram, 1960. *Plans and the structure of behavior.* New York: Holt.

Pauling, L., 1961. A molecular theory of general anesthesia. *Science*, **134**, 15–21.

Restle, F., 1960. Note on the "hypothesis" theory of discrimination learning. *Psychol. Rep.*, **7**, 194.

Restle, F., 1961. Statistical methods for a theory of cue learning. *Psychometrika*, **26**, 291–306.

Rosenblatt, F., 1958. The perceptron, a probabilistic model for information organization and storage in the brain. *Psychol. Rev.*, **65**, 368–408.

Seymour, R., 1954. Strategies in the utilization of information. Unpublished doctoral dissertation, Harvard University.

Shepard, R. N., 1961. Application of a trace model to the retention of information in a recognition task. *Psychometrika*, **26**, 185–203.

Shepard, R. and M. Teghtsoonian, 1961. Retention of information under conditions approaching a steady state. *J. exp. Psychol.*, **62**, 302–309.

Sperling, G., 1960. The information available in brief visual presentations. *Psychol. Monogr.*, **74**, (11, whole No. 498).

Suppes, P. C. and R. Atkinson, 1960. *Markov learning models, for multi-person interaction.* Palo Alto: Stanford University Press.

Von Neuman, J., 1958. *The computer and the brain.* New Haven: Yale University Press.

Watanabe, S., 1960. Information-theoretical aspects of inductive and deductive inference. *IBM J. Res. Developm.*, **5**, 208–231.

Whitfield, J. W., 1951. An experiment in problem solving, *Qtrly. J. exp. Psychol.*, 1951, **3**, 184–197.

Williams, J., 1961. A test of the all or none hypothesis for verbal learning. Unpublished doctoral dissertation, Yale University.

Yntema, D. B. and G. E. Meuser, 1960*a*. Remembering the present states of a number of variables. *J. exp. Psychol.*, **60**, 18–22.

Yntema, D. B. and G. E. Meuser, 1960*b*. Remembering the present states of a number of variables. III. Why it is difficult to keep track of several variables with the same set of states. M. I. T. Lincoln Laboratory Technical Report 58G-0013.

Yntema, D. B. and G. E. Meuser, 1962. Keeping track of variables that have few or many states. *J. exp. Psychol.*, **63**, 391–395.

FOOTNOTES

1. Certainly a perfect filing system model of retention is unrealistic. But what about an imperfect system as a model for human memory? In particular, what about a model in which discrete "chunks" of data (after Miller, 1956) are stored, together with a reference to a location in which an associated chunk was stored? The present author, in collaboration with Dr. Douwe Yntema of Lincoln Laboratories, M. I. T., has been interested in the development of such a model. This work will be reported separately.

2. The general topic of strategies will be discussed in the next chapter. Here they will be considered only insofar as they affect memory requirements.

3. The variations, which are interesting, are described in the next chapter.
4. The present author supports this analysis of the Kurtz and Hovland finding. The original authors did not discuss focusing in relation to their experimental results.
5. Yntema and Meuser (1960a,b 1962) have reported a series of experiments on human memory in which a very high degree of interindividual regularity was obtained although intercondition differences were large.
6. This principle is used explicitly in two "artificial intelligence" concept-learning systems (Hunt and Hovland, 1961; Kochen, 1961). Kochen's system uses a focusing technique (see Chapters 8 and 9 for details).
7. In a dissertation that was meant to defend associative learning against the one-trial position, Williams (1961) obtained evidence that mnemonic recoding may indeed account for the rapid learning of certain nonsense syllable pairs. The ease of learning paired associates within a given list was related to the availability of a mnemonic code for the pair. Williams' data also indicates that this does not account for all the learning in a paired associates task.
8. The problem is still more complex if the tendency to respond to the joint occurrence of two elements as a separate pattern varies during a particular experiment. Recent evidence (Estes and Hopkins, 1961) indicates that responses to pattern cues as such may be developed during discrimination learning.

# 6

# Strategies of
# concept learning

## 1  *Plans, totes, and functions*

Concept learning is a decision-making situation. During learning hypotheses must be chosen. The use of a concept involves decisions. The learner must decide what name applies to a particular object. In some cases the decision that ought to be made is that there is insufficient information on which to make a decision! This, in turn, implies decisions about the type of information needed.

All these decisions influence each other. The wrong choice of an hypothesis will lead to erroneous classification. Classifications of particular types will affect information gathering and, hence, the development of new hypotheses. If a physician classifies a patient as "healthy," he terminates the examination, gaining no more information. But if he classifies a patient as "possible lung cancer" and finds, by further examination, that the man has tuberculosis, he will have gained information that, among other things, may improve his future diagnostic technique.

Before the problem begins, the learner cannot state what his decisions are going to be. To do so would be equivalent to stating the answer to a question before the question was asked. What the learner can state are the rules that he will use to arrive at a decision. These are computing rules, analogous to functions in mathematics. They take as their argument the information the environment provides and produce as their value the new decision rule. The learner can even have rules for changing his rules.[1]

Is this a reasonable description of human behavior? Miller, Galanter, and Pribram (1960) have argued that it is. According to them, most, if not all, human behavior is organized by *plans*. A plan consists of four stages: a test to determine differences between the present and desired state of affairs, an operation to reduce these differences, a second test, and finally an exit when no differences exist. The entire cycle is a "TOTE unit" (an acronym for test, operate, test, exit).

The TOTE unit was offered as a more suitable unit for analyzing cognitive behavior than the S-R bond. Bruner, Goodnow, and Austin's (1956) analysis of strategies in concept learning is compatible with a theory of TOTE units. In concept learning the test phase corresponds to a check of the current hypothesis against known data. The operating phase is the strategy, an hypothesis-computing function. If the first test reveals that the current hypothesis is not compatible with known data, this function is activated. Its inputs are the current hypothesis and the information that this hypothesis led to a certain type of error. The value of the function is the new hypothesis, which will be tested in the second test phase. When a particular hypothesis-computing function is chosen, a strategy has been specified. Notice that we now have a "TOTE" unit. Given its test and operating functions, the results of applying the unit to any particular series of experiences (in concept learning, knowledge of the class membership of objects) are specified.

TOTE units may be compounded. Consider a TOTE unit whose test phase consisted of making observations of how well some subordinate TOTE units were working. The test phase of the higher-order TOTE unit would fail if a lower unit was, by some definition, not working. Failure could be defined by a weighted average of test failures *of different types* during the operation of subordinate TOTE units. For instance, in a TOTE for medical diagnosis, hypotheses which led to the error of not examining ill patients would usually be more serious than errors involving too much examination of healthy patients. When a failure was noted, the higher unit's operating phase would be applied to (*a*) the performance data compiled for the lower-order TOTE unit and (*b*) the lower-order TOTE unit. The result of the higher-order operation would be a new subordinate TOTE unit. Specification of the higher-level TOTE is equivalent to establishing a strategy for changing strategies.

Such pyramiding of TOTE units could be continued indefinitely. In most studies of concept learning only one or two TOTE units are needed for analysis. The procedure for developing an answer, the "strategy" being used to attain the concept, will always be present. A specification of this TOTE unit (represented in its general form in Figure 6-1) is equivalent to describing the actions of a concept learner performing a particular task at a specified time. At a higher level, we can analyze how he changes his actions as he gains experience in concept learning. The appropriate form of a TOTE unit is shown in Figure 6-2. To bring ourselves in line with the more traditional terminology of psychology, the operations of Figure 6-2 attempt to

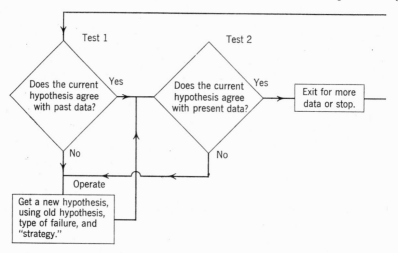

Figure 6-1. Schematic of a TOTE unit for developing hypotheses.

assemble maximally efficient discriminations and responses which serve as the test and operating phases of the unit depicted in Figure 6-1.

We could show a third TOTE unit that performed the same function of selection of components for the second unit as the second does for the first. This would correspond to "learning to learn" phenomena. A "concept-learning machine" developed from a three-level TOTE design could not only improve its performance, it could improve its methods of improving its performance.

Does a TOTE analysis help? Just talking about TOTE units is not equivalent to an analysis of behavior; the actual operations and tests must be specified. But even without specification, a TOTE analysis orients our thinking in a somewhat different way than does the more familiar S-R analysis. In a TOTE framework the function of the components is stressed. We are continually forced to ask: "What is this step for?"—"What characteristics must it have?" The argument is in no sense teleological; it is simply a statement of empirical necessity. To apply it to concept learning, all we are saying is that concepts can be learned by humans. The learning of concepts requires the execution of particular tasks, which in turn require mechanisms with particular performance characteristics. Therefore, humans must possess such mechanisms.

By stating the task requirements we may find that there exists only a small set of models which could possibly work. Without lifting an experimental finger, we can possibly eliminate all but one model. Hardly less important, we may show that certain models which seemed reasonable cannot be right.[2]

## 2    Requirements of a strategy

A strategy is a plan for arriving at a predefined goal at minimum cost. The goal in concept learning is the attainment of a definition of a concept which provides a satisfactory decision rule for assigning names to objects.

We say satisfactory rather than perfect because the value of a decision rule depends on the situation in which it is used. A perfect decision rule would cost nothing to obtain, cost nothing to apply, and never lead to an erroneous decision. But in how many situations can such an ideal rule be found? Certainly not in concept learning.

In fact, these three criteria for a good concept may be contradictory. One way of stating the cost of obtaining a concept is to state how many objects must be shown to the learner before he can develop the correct hypothesis. To minimize this number, the learner should

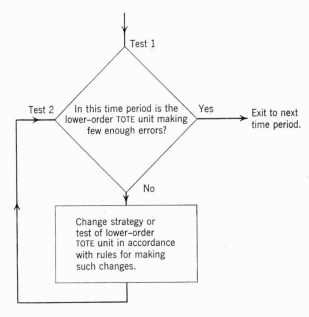

Figure 6-2. TOTE unit for evaluating strategies.

extract all available information from an object when it is presented. He should also extract all information from pairs of objects, triplets, etc. Minimizing the number of objects of known set membership which the learner must observe will maximize the amount of computing and data storage which the learner must expend on each object. Since cost factors for each of these can vary from situation to situation (and from learner to learner), no general statement of appropriate strategies is possible. There are contradictions in the definition of a desired terminal state of concept learning as well as the definition of a desired route to it. A categorizing rule can be described by the accuracy with which it assigns objects to the correct denotation. But error rate alone is not an adequate criterion, since different errors have different consequences. To return to the medical example, if there is any doubt, it is usually better to classify people as "ill, continue examination" than "healthy."

The example points out another problem in the use of concepts. Accuracy of classification is generally correlated with the completeness of the description of the object to be categorized. If the concept learner has to pay for new information (i.e., pay to find out the value of particular dimensions), he may at some point "go beyond the information given," assuming an object is in a particular denotation even though he has not made all relevant tests of the object's description. (As we saw in Chapter 4, this is characteristic of pattern recognition.) The advisability of guessing class membership from a partial description will depend on the cost of obtaining more information and on the cost and probability of the classification errors which may occur.

This discussion points out a fact that is sometimes forgotten in discussions of strategies of problem solving. The appropriate strategy can be determined only with reference to the cost functions involved. These, in turn, are defined by the requirements of the problem *and* the capabilities of the problem solver. Even given the same problem, a strategy that would be appropriate for a human being might not be appropriate for a concept-learning automaton. The solution should be chosen that will make the most efficient use of available facilities.

3    *Individual differences among adults*

Bartlett (1958) has suggested that mental skills in their organization are not different from motor skills. In tennis, for instance, a strategy exists when a player selects those conditions under which it is appropriate for him to make overhead shots, come to the net, etc. To execute the strategy he must be able to recognize the appropriate conditions *and* make the shot. A similar problem faces the concept learner. Solving a concept requires that he make abstract (descriptive) statements about objects. Then he must perform logical operations on the sets defined by the statements. The more powerful the basic operations that he can perform, the easier he will find a problem. We have no proof that all humans can perform all operations. To the extent that they cannot, their strategies must be different.

In discussing memory a semifacetious allusion was made to a "spectrum" of concept-learning ability conceived of as stretching from Rhesus monkeys to Harvard graduate students. There is a somewhat more formal body of evidence indicating systematic differences between adult humans. Guilford (1959, 1960), after examining several factor-analytic studies of human reasoning, conceptualized intellectual abilities in terms of three superclasses of factors: the contents of the problem material (e.g., figural material, symbolic material), the required product (a unit, a class, or a transformation), and the operations needed (memory, evaluation of evidence, convergent and divergent thinking, etc.) which are required to produce the different products from the problem material.

Guilford proposed that we use these three superclasses as dimensions in a space of possible cognitive tasks. Any problem would be locatable within this space. Guilford further maintained that corresponding to each point in the space defined by the intersection of a type of content, type of product, and type of operation, there exists a measurable human ability. By measurable, Guilford meant that this point could be defined in a factor analysis of human performance over a sample of all possible cognitive tasks. Such a grand factor analysis is not possible, and not all such abilities have been isolated. Guilford conceives of the idea of a three-dimensional problem space as a guide to tell us which abilities are locatable. We should use his problem space as a chemist uses the periodic tables, to indicate the conditions under which a new human ability could be located.

Concept learning evidently occupies that region of Guilford's problem space involving the production of classes and relations irrespective of the problem material and the operations required. Although for a particular problem the material is usually fixed,[3] the answer may often be reached through one of several operations. The concept learner can therefore exercise some freedom in assigning the problem to a particular point in the problem space. Since each point represents an ability, the learner will presumably choose his strongest ability.

This will define a particular operation to be applied, and different operations require different strategies. For instance, a person who was "good at" remembering symbols could use a strategy that relied on frequent evaluation of new hypotheses using previously presented data. Another person, handicapped by a bad memory, might prefer to use a slower, more methodical concept attainment procedure. If an informationally identical problem were presented using concrete objects instead of symbols, the roles of the two persons might be reversed.

Baggaley (1955) conducted an experiment which is relevant to the connection between Guilford's analysis and concept learning. He observed the correlation between performance on a conjunctive concept-learning task and performance on several tests of deductive reasoning. These tests had previously been used as markers of factors found to be common to many mental test situations (Thurstone, 1938). Baggaley concluded that two factors are important in concept learning; the ability to attend to only a few aspects of the stimulus at a time and the ability to perform well on deductive reasoning tasks. Although Baggaley's evidence is rather weak (he observed low, though significant, correlations) his findings are consistent with the model Guilford developed. To abstract, the learner must be able to suppress some aspects of the immediate situation. The abstracted stimulus must then be manipulated in a logical way.

Granted that there are individual differences that will affect our choice of a strategy, the reason why is far from clear. In the next section we shall review changes in mental capability as part of the developmental sequence. Certainly there are genetic differences between individuals. But these are not all that is important. There have been many studies of the effect of social and cultural pressures on individual functioning. There is tentative evidence of an interaction between the methods used to solve a problem and the sex of the problem solver. (Taylor and McNemar, 1955; Berry, 1959). Although physiological factors cannot be ruled out, this interaction seems to be due to cultural influences (Taylor, 1960). Sarason (1961) has pointed out that in an individual's life history certain types of approaches to problems may be encouraged. Bruner, Goodnow, and Austin (1956) have taken a stronger position. They claim that a preference for conjunctive concepts and strategies that discover them is largely the result of the intellectual heritage of Western culture.

These are fascinating but unproven ideas. It is a bit puzzling (at least to this author) why studies of individual differences in intellectual functioning have not made more use of concept-learning tasks in preference to vaguely defined "problem solving" tasks. However, they have not, and the field of individual differences in concept learning is largely unexplored.

## 4    Developmental stages and concept learning

The factor analytic approach stresses differences between mature individuals. In the process of growing up there is a sequence of developmental stages within a particular individual. Part of this sequence involves the ability to handle abstractions and to perform certain other manipulations upon symbols. Thus, as the child develops, he adds to the cognitive tools he has available to solve a concept-learning problem.

The "tool" whose acquisition has been studied the most is abstraction. As it has been operationally defined in psychological studies, abstraction is usually equivalent to the ability to apply the operation of inclusion to sets of objects defined by descriptive elements. For instance, the sets of objects "vegetable," "fruit," "meat," are all included within the set "food." "Food," then, is referred to as a higher-order abstraction. The ability to respond to such abstractions, instead of to all characteristics of a concrete object, is common in adults. Fiction writers can speak of "blondes" in the abstract without describing a particular individual. But the ability to notice and manipulate abstractly defined symbols decreases from college through kindergarten and nursery school (Kendler, 1960). This fact is probably because of neurological development rather than educational practice. Kendler (1961) has cited literature indicating that ability to use mediated responses (the S-R representation of abstraction) decreases not only within the human species but also across the phylogenetic scale. Goldstein and Scheerer (1941) reported that patients with brain injury may lose their ability to respond to abstract characteristics of stimuli.

The level of abstraction of which the concept learner is capable will determine the descriptions of stimulus objects which are available to him. Abstractions are essentially derived descriptions; if they are relevant to the concept to be learned (in the sense that relevancy was defined in Chapter 2), the description from which they were derived must also be relevant. However, if the description being used is not the most abstract relevant description, the form of the concept will change. Any more abstract element which appears in the concept must be replaced by the equivalent union of lower-level descriptive statements. A "Latin" becomes a Mexican or a Cuban or . . . etc. A conjunctive concept at one level of abstraction becomes a disjunctive concept at a lower level. The strategies suitable for solving conjunctive problems are not the same as strategies for solving disjunctive problems; indeed, the two may be incompatible (Bruner, Goodnow, and Austin, 1956; see also the remainder of this chapter).

Increased abstraction is not the only increase in ability that comes with age. Piaget, in his extended and unconventional research on intellectual development, has argued that cognitive maturation is divided into three stages. His thesis extends in scope far beyond concept learning per se, which he does not discuss directly.[4] Some of his points, however, are relevant to the study of concept learning as it has been defined here.[5]

According to Piaget, the child gradually develops an ability to manipulate sets. In the first stage (roughly, the first 2 years of life) the child must react only to concrete objects. In this stage Piaget would expect no true concept learning. In the second stage, which occurs roughly from age 2 to 6 or 7, the child can perform certain set-theoretic operations. He can now respond to the intersection of two classes as a class and can note that classes are included within classes. However, the idea of subtraction of sets has not yet occurred, which suggests that strategies which make use of information from negative instances cannot be developed. In the third stage, which is well established by age 8, subtraction of sets comes within the child's capability. Somewhat later, in a second substage, the idea of a union of sets as a set occurs. Only at this time is a "true" disjunctive concept-learning capability formed. Before this, however, the child should be able to form "pseudodisjunctive" concepts based on the separate learning of different conjunctive concepts with the same name. Piaget feels, apparently, that the contradictions apparent in such learning would not bother children in the first and second stages.

Seen this way, mental development is compatible with a description in the terms of symbolic logic. Piaget (1957) has developed a logic system for this purpose. Although it is not the logic system used in this text, there is a similarity in point of view. As the child grows older, Piaget describes his mental capabilities by a progressively more powerful logic system. The idea that more operations become available with increasing age fits in well with the point that the effective strategies of concept learning must be those which rely on operations and tests at which the concept learner is particularly skilled. Any TOTE analysis of behavior during concept learning will be particularly sensitive to this sort of individual difference. The analysis also stresses a limitation of most studies of strategies in concept learning. The studies are generally performed on young adults of above-average intelligence. There may be a qualitative difference between the performance of these subjects and other, younger or less gifted, humans.

## 5    Information and reward

We indicated earlier that the concept learner must solve two decision problems. Given his current state of knowledge (i.e., hypotheses), how should he classify a particular object? Given the information that his current hypothesis is incorrect, how should he modify it?

At first glance the classification problem seems trivial. Presumably the current hypothesis is the best the learner can do. Why should he not always follow it? In the very simplest of classification situations, he should. If the learner has only one hypothesis, and if the punishments for misclassification are symmetrical, regardless of the classification made and the one that was correct, he ought to always follow his favored hypothesis. The situation is seldom that simple. In most practical cases (e.g., the medical diagnosis problem given earlier) payoffs are not symmetrical. They depend on the compatibility of the action which will be taken on the basis of the classification with the action that is required by the true state of nature.

Nor is the learner required to have only one hypothesis. In Chapter 2 it was pointed out that usually he ought to have more than one. There are many cases in which we consider alternate theories. College admissions boards, for one, classify students as "acceptable" or "not acceptable" on the basis of a variety of sometimes conflicting cues.

The general problem can be pictured by the construction of a probability and payoff matrix. Each course of action is weighted by the faith we have in the hypotheses that recommend it and the strength with which they make their recommendation. (How this confidence index is to be obtained is a complex but not necessarily unsolvable question. For further treatment see Hunt, 1961.) The resulting weights can be used to establish estimates of the probability that different classifications are correct. These estimates must be combined with the effects of different combinations of naming response and correct classification before a decision can be reached.

Let us examine a somewhat whimsical example. Suppose a hunter is sent into the jungles with instructions to lasso and tie a zebra. We assume that this is a young hunter, and he is not sure what a zebra is. But he has three hypotheses: $H1$, all animals that are white are zebras (he believes this to be true with probability .40), $H2$, all animals without horns are zebras (believed with probability .10) and $H3$, all animals with stripes are zebras (with probability .50). At one point the hunter encounters an animal that is yellowish with black stripes, and has no horns. He can immediately construct the payoff matrix shown in Figure 6-3, in which $A$, $B$, $C$, and $D$ represent payoffs to him under

|                        | Animal is zebra | Animal is not zebra |
| ---------------------- | --------------- | ------------------- |
| Animal called zebra    | $A$             | $B$                 |
| Animal called not zebra | $C$            | $D$                 |

The hunter estimates that the probability of the animal
being a zebra is .60 (see text)

Figure 6-3. Payoff matrix for hunter chasing a zebra.

different combinations of action and true state of the world. There are certain things that can be said about $A$, $B$, $C$, and $D$ regardless of the actual identity of the animal. If the hunter ropes the animal although it is not a zebra, he will at least be able to reject two of his hypotheses. This should improve his future ability to capture a zebra. If he ropes the animal and it turns out to be a zebra, then he still will not know what the unique concept of "zebra" is, but he will have a zebra. But action is not always to be preferred to inaction. If there is an appreciable chance that "not zebra" can be interpreted "tiger," the negative value of $B$ is so large that no animal ought to be taken if this contingency has any appreciable chance of occurring.

The example illustrates the fact that, in the absence of a known concept, classification is a problem in decision making under risk. At least two alternatives exist, and the probability of either one being correct can be estimated (more or less accurately). Payoffs for various contingencies must be specified. Even so, the solution to such decision-making problems [a topic which has been treated extensively (Adams, 1960; Luce and Raiffa, 1957)] is not always clear. We raise the point to show that game theoretic considerations apply to concept learning.

Reward considerations are not limited to the decision of how to use the current hypothesis. They may also affect the choice of hypotheses and even hypotheses generating strategies.

Strategies can be chosen to bias errors toward inclusion in or exclusion from a particular class. As a simple example, suppose a child, new to the country life, notices that in the universe of insects yellow things that buzz are bees. On his first day in the country, he never encounters a yellow object that does not buzz or a buzzing object that is not yellow. He cannot distinguish between three possible concepts for the name "bee," yellow objects, buzzing objects, both at once, or either. If he can only remember a limited number of hypotheses at a time, he should, to be safe, retain the disjunctive hypotheses. Although he will call some butterflies bees, at least he will not be stung.

To make the matter still more complex, the payoff for classification should reflect the value of the information that can be obtained from each classification, even if it is wrong. This is particularly important in the so-called contingent case, in which the subject is simply told whether or not his classification was right or wrong. If there are more than two possible classifications, the only way to make a direct test of the membership of an object in a particular class is to assign it to that class. From the standpoint of gaining information this might be a reasonable thing to do even if the particular assignment was not felt to be correct.

There are other situational variables which may be as important as reward contingencies in determining the choice of an appropriate strategy. A particularly important variable is the logical form of the concept to be learned.

The concept learner does not usually know what the logical form of the answer is. This would be useful information, since some strategies which will solve conjunctive concept-learning problems will not solve disjunctive problems. Conjunctive concepts can be defined by the union of the descriptive statements that are common to every positive instance (member of the denotation). Negative instances are useful to prove that some subset of the descriptive statements in this set is not, by itself, a sufficient statement of the concept. (See the discussion of positive and negative instances in Chapter 5.) The positive focusing strategy, for instance, extracts information only from positive instances. This is not a foolish procedure. It can be shown that positive instances, on the average, eliminate more plausible hypotheses than do negative instances during the learning of a conjunctive concept (Hovland, 1952).

Positive focusing, and its wholist counterpart in reception strategies, are not suitable strategies for learning disjunctive concepts. There may be no descriptive element common to all positive instances. It is still possible to develop a disjunctive concept by a variant of focusing on positive instances. What the learner must do is develop a trial set of several conjunctive concepts, the union of which defines the disjunctive concept. This is the procedure suggested in Chapter 5, when disjunctive concept learning was considered as a problem of keeping track of the current state of several variables.

There are better strategies for learning disjunctive concepts. They rely on a comparison of positive and negative instances. If there are two instances, differing only in the value of one dimension, and one is and one is not an object to which a name is applicable, that dimension is relevant to the concept of the name. If there is a small number of relevant dimensions relative to the total number of dimensions, the concept may be defined by noting values which never appear on negative instances, a "double negation" as it were. (In an extreme case the complement of the denotation may have as its associated concept a conjunctive statement.) This strategy involves concentrating attention on negative instances.

Knowledge of the type of correct answer is useful in determining a strategy for concept learning. The efficient learner must be alert for cues indicating with which type of concept he is faced. Such cases may occur before he has sufficient information to define the concept itself. For example, the presence of two positive instances which have no descriptive elements in common is sufficient to indicate that the concept to be learned is disjunctive. But the learner still must discover the answer.

In discussing strategies for different types of concepts we have pointed out the desirability of comparing the class memberships of certain instances. But the availability of the objects to be studied may not be under the control of the learner. A comparison between a physicist and an astronomer comes to mind; the science of one is based on experimentation whereas the science of the other relies on correlational data. Choice of strategy may be limited by the control that a subject has over testing of instances. "Positive focusing," for instance, is the most efficient when all positive instances are presented in a single block. Indeed, it has been shown that learning conjunctive concepts is easier in this condition than if positive and negative instances are interspersed (Kurtz and Hovland, 1956). If the concept learner has control over object production, he can produce the desired sequence. Such control should be particularly useful in disjunctive concept learning, since the learner could make the desired contrasts between positive and negative instances without relying on memory of the features of instances presented at some time in the past.

Although the learner may not be able to control the choice of objects to be categorized, he can make use of knowledge about how the choice is made. The situation is similar to the inductive problem faced by the statistician. A hypothesis is a statement about distribution of objects in the universe. The correctness of the statement must be determined by observing a sample. A biased sample will do providing that the bias is known. In a concept-learning context, the example

(Chapter 2) of the learner trying to distinguish between the truth of the statements "Russian women are scientists and/or mother heroines" and "Russian women are either scientists or mother heroines" can be used to illustrate this point. If the sample of Russian women that he observed was drawn randomly from the entire population, we would expect that, assuming the truth of the inclusive disjunctive statement, eventually a woman who was both a scientist and a mother heroine would be encountered. If the sample was drawn from Russian women attending a moving picture, it might be argued that the absence of any such person was not evidence to discriminate between the two hypotheses. A person who was both a scientist and a mother heroine would be too busy to go to the movies.

6    *Preference for positively stated inferences*

Hypotheses may be verified by inference alone. In Stockton's famous story "The Lady or the Tiger," the hero is faced with the choice of opening one of two doors. Behind one of them is a beautiful and willing young lady, behind the other is a hungry tiger. Suppose the hero has an hypothesis that the tiger is behind the left door. Upon opening the right he finds the lady. Presumably he would feel no compulsion to check his hypothesis by verifying a prediction of a positive instance.

In experimental studies in which the payoffs are less extreme, people do seem to require positive confirmation. Bruner, Goodnow, and Austin (1956) report a study[6] of strategies employed when the concept learners could select the objects they had to categorize. The subjects had to learn a concept by observing the class membership of a set of geometric patterns. At the beginning of the experiment the subject was given a relevant description (in terms of dimensions and values) and told that the correct answer was a conjunctive concept. He was shown the set of all possible patterns and given an example of one positive instance. From that point on, the subject would choose a pattern and the experimenter would tell him whether or not it was a positive instance. The subject's task was to solve the problem with a minimum number of selections.

This situation favors a focusing strategy. Starting with the initial positive instance, the subject should select as the next object to be identified a pattern which differs from the first in *one* value of a dimension which might be relevant. If the new pattern is a negative instance, the subject knows that the dimension is relevant. If the new pattern is a positive instance, the subject knows that the dimension must be irrelevant. Its value then no longer needs to be controlled. So long as positive instances are encountered the subject can follow the simple strategy of changing the value of a different dimension on each choice. When a negative instance is encountered the subject should return to a previously identified positive instance as his focus and select the next pattern to be identified by changing the value of a possibly relevant dimension. Six of the twelve subjects adopted this strategy all the time, another used it sometimes.

As an example, suppose that the first positive instance was "two red squares inside one green border." A rational choice of the next pattern would be, according to the focusing strategy, "two green squares inside one green border." If the new pattern was a negative instance, the focusing subjects accepted the information that the color of the squares was relevant. But if the second pattern was a positive instance, proving that the color of the squares was *not* relevant, the information was harder to evaluate. Bruner et al. noted that the second choice of a pattern to be identified would often be designed as a check on the inference that a dimension was irrelevant (e.g., by asking the experimenter to identify the class membership of a pattern with two black squares inside one green border) instead of being de- signed to gain new information. Apparently (although the report is not completely clear on this point) such behavior increased when the subjects were not allowed to see previously identified instances.

The preference displayed here was not for reception of information from positive instances, but rather for reception of information from positively stated inferences. It can also be shown that there is also bet- ter utilization of information contained in positive instances. Smoke (1932, 1933) first suggested that subjects do not learn anything from examples of what a concept is *not*. He had subjects attempt to learn a concept defined either by a series of positive instances or a series of mixed positive and negative instances. There was no difference in time of solution in either condition. Hovland (1952) criticized Smoke's procedure on the grounds that it did not control for the information content of the two series. One, both, or neither of Smoke's conditions may have unequivocally defined a concept. Hovland and Weiss (1953) then replicated Smoke's results, using visual stimuli which were equated for information content and, in one study, for number of instances. Concept learning was the most difficult when all positive instances were used and least difficult when the concept was defined by negative instances. This difference appeared when instances were presented either simultaneously or successively.

If the subjects were proceeding to learn a concept by the "focusing" method, this result would be expected. Bruner et al., in another series of experiments, pointed out that when the choice of objects to be identified is *not* under the control of the concept learner, the optimally efficient procedure is to use a "positive focus" on the successive positive instances, ignoring negative instances. (This is the wholist strategy described in Chapter 5.) Thus extracting information from successively presented negative instances would be even more difficult for a focuser than extracting information from simultaneously presented negative instances. Hovland and Weiss obtained this result.

But their results cannot be explained entirely by the biasing effect of focusing strategies. In the first place, some of the problems Hovland and Weiss employed did not have a conjunctive solution. Instead, they were similar to the Battig and Bourne (1961) intradimensional variation condition; a relevant dimension might have several values over positive instances. Subjects knew this before the experiment began, and they knew how many values could appear in a relevant dimension. Positive focusing would not work, even with positive instances. In one of the Hovland and Weiss problems the complement of the denotation actually had a conjunctive concept associated with it. Here the "all negative" condition should have made it easy for the subjects to learn what the concept was *not,* an equivalent answer. This was, instead, a very hard problem to learn, especially if only negative instances were shown to the subject. (This finding has been verified in an unpublished study by Bregman and Hovland.)

Wason (1959), using a setting other than concept learning, also demonstrated that humans cannot easily evaluate negatively stated inferences. Wason showed his subjects diagrams containing a colored star placed in one of four quadrants (upper left, lower right, etc.). A statement about the star accompanied each diagram. The statement was either a proposition that a certain fact was consistent with the diagram (e.g., "There is a star in the upper-right quadrant.") or a statement that a particular fact was contradicted by the diagram (e.g., "There is no star in the upper-right quadrant."). Thus the statements could be regarded as affirmative or negative. Wason asked his subjects to rephrase some of the statements so that they were true, he asked that others be rephrased so that they were false. Wason measured the time that the subjects took to do this and the errors they made. He found that the order of difficulty of the task depended on both the type of statement and the instruction given. The order of difficulty, from least to most difficult, was: affirmative-true, negative-true, affirmative-false, negative-false. Wason's results readily generalize to concept learning. A positive example of a concept is essentially a statement that an object with a certain description is found in the denotation of a name. By definition, presenting a positive instance is similar to making an affirmative statement about the concept. Wason pointed out that it is not at all surprising that subjects are better at evaluating affirmative statements. Verification of an affirmative statement generally conveys more information than verification of a negative one.

Do negative instances play any role in human concept learning? Wallach (1958) suggested that they serve as a "contrast class" by which attributes may be defined. Objects may be described in a great many ways; we have seen that establishing the proper relevant description may be one of the major tasks in concept learning. One criterion for a relevant description is that positive and negative instances are always assigned different descriptions. Wallach argued (if we understand him correctly, since he did not use these terms) that in the early stages of concept learning a variety of descriptions may be tried. Whenever a particular description process results in an identical description of positive and negative instances, the learner knows that the process cannot be relevant. Although the test is crude, it is easy to apply. Perhaps negative instances should be utilized early in training to establish an appropriate contrast class. Further testing and theoretical development of this idea appears worthwhile. It will probably be found that whereas humans can learn from negative instances, they normally do not. An ancillary role of negative instances, either to establish a contrast class or to check hypotheses derived from positive instances, may be a vital part of the strategy of efficient concept learners.

7     *Strategy preferences designed to discover certain types of answers*

If strategies are appropriate descriptions of human concept learning, we would expect them to be revealed by the differential difficulty of experimental situations designed to support or hinder them. The results of studies involving transmission of information by positive or negative instances can be viewed in this way. Data more directly addressed to the point would be desirable. Seymour (1954) performed a series of relevant experiments. Harvard graduate students learned a conjunctive concept under the simultaneous presentation-subject controlled selection technique used in the Bruner et al. experiment just cited (in which Seymour had participated as an experimenter). In one condition—ordered presentation—instances were arranged so that each pattern differed from the one next to it in just one value of one dimension. In the second condition—random presentation—patterns were placed in front of the subject without regard to the nature of the neighboring patterns. Seymour argued that the ordered condition would favor the adoption of an efficient focusing strategy, since the next instance required by a focuser would be available without extensive searching. An analysis of instances chosen for identification did show more focusing in the ordered condition. In this condition subjects learned the concept in fewer choices.

Seymour's study indicates that human concept learners can, within limits, adopt a strategy which is suited to a particular task. It also affirms the belief that the extent to which the experimental situation supports focusing is related to the difficulty subjects will have with a problem. But this cannot be the only factor determining difficulty, since not all subjects use a focusing strategy correctly or at all.

Bruner et al. report that in conjunctive concept learning the largest deviation from focusing occurs as a sort of "focus gambling." In a maximally efficient focusing strategy the subject should select as a new object one that differs from the last positive instance along only one dimension. But suppose that the subject changes the value of more than one dimension. If the object so produced is positive, he gains information, since both dimensions must be irrelevant. If the resulting object is negative, one or more of the dimensions changed must have been relevant, but the subject does not know which one. Thus there is a gambling aspect to the problem; the concept learner might discover the answer rapidly.

In fact, Bruner et al. report that people can use this strategy when required. They repeated the selection experiment, but required that the concept be attained in one, four, or an unlimited number of choices. Focus gambling increased when choices were limited, again indicating that humans can adapt their strategies to the experimental situation.

Bruner et al. report that a similar variation of focusing occurred when subjects could not control the order in which objects were presented. In the reception strategy, it will be recalled, the appropriate variety of focusing is to take as the hypothesis the intersection of the description of all previous positive instances. The set of descriptive statements which defines the correct concept must be identical to or a subset of the set defined by this intersection. It was found that subjects would take as their current hypothesis a subset of the intersection. If at some later time they found that their focus did not contain the correct answer (a condition indicated by encountering a negative instance which contained the focus), subjects had to correct themselves by expanding the current focus. Memory for past instances would be useful in doing this. Again we see that memory, problem type, and strategy interact.

Focusing strategies are oriented toward the discovery of conjunctions. What will happen if the problem has a disjunctive answer? In such problems there will be no unique focus, common to all positive instances. The studies presented suggest that disjunctive problems will prove to be unusually difficult and will most decidedly not be a preferred solution. But will they ever be learned, and if so, how?

Two experiments have tested the "preference" prediction; in both cases subjects preferred conjunctive answers. Hunt and Hovland (1960) showed subjects a series of geometric patterns classified in a particular manner. They then asked subjects to sort some additional patterns "according to the same rules." Actually, three different rules could be used to reproduce the first sorting: a conjunctive concept involving two dimensions, a disjunctive concept involving two dimensions, and a rule based on the relation of the values in two dimensions. In a sense, the relational statement was conjunctive. It involved a "one-element conjunction" (i.e., Shepard, Hovland, and Jenkins' (1961) Type I problem) with relationally defined dimensions. The subjects' sortings of the second set of patterns were approximately equally distributed between the sortings that would be required by the conjunctive or the relational concept. Only a very few subjects sorted by the disjunctive rule; an equal number of subjects produced inconsistent sortings. As an interesting sidelight, most subjects appeared amazed to find that there was more than one answer.

The presence of a relational answer complicates the interpretation of this experiment. Wells (1962) presented subjects with a similar choice problem in which there was a disjunctive and a conjunctive answer. Only seven of one hundred and two subjects gave a nonconjunctive answer, seventy-nine subjects solved the problem as a conjunctive problem, and sixteen failed completely.

Wells then divided seventy-two of his "conjunctive solvers" into three groups. A control group solved eight additional choice problems. Experimental groups solved either two or four problems which had disjunctive answers only and then attempted a test problem which had conjunctive or disjunctive answers. The control group gave conjunctive answers to all choice problems; in the two experimental groups approximately half the subject gave disjunctive answers to the second choice problem.

Wells' results show two points rather clearly. Whether it is called a response or a strategy, some behavior of human concept learners biases them toward conjunctive solutions. This behavior can be overcome, since subjects who exhibit it will learn to solve disjunctive concept-learning problems. But what will they learn while doing so? In particular, why have *some* subjects shifted their preference to disjunctive concepts on the second test trial?

In an earlier study of disjunctive concept learning, Bruner et al. analyzed "strategies," using the selection technique. Their subjects were told what a disjunctive concept was (as Wells' subjects were) and that the correct answer was a disjunctive concept (as Wells' subjects were not). Even so, disjunctive concepts proved extremely difficult to learn. Bruner et al. suggested that the most efficient strategy would be to start from a *negative* instance and alter the values of its dimensions, one at a time, until a positive instance was obtained. The change that obtained this positive instance would define a relevant dimension *and* a value which could appear on that dimension in positive instances. (There might be more than one such value for each dimension, as in the Hovland and Weiss experiments.)

Bruner et al. found that this strategy, which is practically the reverse of the positive focusing strategy so useful in conjunctive concept learning, was seldom used by their subjects. Furthermore, they did not learn to use the strategy over a series of three fairly difficult problems.[7] What subjects did do was to adopt strategies "appropriate" for conjunctive problems. They would either offer hypotheses based on elements found in positive instances or, if there were no completely common elements, the elements that appeared in most of the positive instances. Such a hypothesis will define a set of objects included in, but not identical to, the set of positive instances. Another strategy observed was an attempt by subjects to find a positive instance and then contrast it to a negative instance, taking as their hypothesis the values of the positive instance which were changed. This strategy, adequate for conjunctive concepts, will define the answer only if the positive instance used in the contrast contains within its description the *union* of all descriptive statements used in the definition of the concept. In some concept-learning problems (for example, exclusive disjunctions) this cannot happen.

Two other possible strategies should be mentioned. One is a form of scanning using negative instances. The complement of the denotation of a disjunctive concept is identical to the set of objects defined by the conjunction of the *complements* of all descriptive elements relevant to the disjunctive concept. In other words, the concept could be defined by what nonexamples are not. This definition involves a double negation, suspiciously close to Wason's (1959) false negation, which subjects had great difficulty in evaluating. When concept-learning tasks are based on such statements, they are extremely difficult to learn. Still, Wason's subjects did learn to evaluate double negations; subjects in concept learning might also. This strategy would be particularly appropriate if only a few descriptive elements were used to define the stimuli. In the limiting case, if there were only two values per dimension, the complement of the denotation becomes a simple conjunction. For instance, if we are classifying strings of letters, each letter a capital or small letter, then "*A* or *B*" is equivalent to "not *a* and *b*." [8]

Finally, there is a strategy, *conditional focusing*, which utilizes positive instances to define a disjunctive concept. Given a set of positive instances, count the descriptive statement which is most frequently applicable to them. Check against a set of negative instances to see if this statement can ever be applied. If not, this statement is one of the elements of the disjunctive answer. If the statement can be applied to any negative instances, consider only the subset of instances (both positive and negative) to which it can be applied. Repeat this procedure within the subset, recursively, until a conjunction of descriptive statements is obtained which never can be applied to negative instances. This conjunction becomes an element of the disjunctive answer. Then continue the procedure on all unclassified instances. An answer is obtained when all positive instances are included within the hypothesis. This procedure has been used in an artificial intelligence system designed to learn concepts (Chapter 8).

As a summary of the conditional focusing technique, consider how a concept learner would state his definition of a "strike," in baseball. The term would be defined by a string of conditional statements—"If the batter swings and misses" *or* "If the ball is hit foul and there are no previous strikes" *or* "If the ball is hit foul and there is one previous strike" *or* "If the pitch is in the strike zone and the batter does not swing" *or* "If the ball is bunted foul." Notice that the statement is logically correct but is not the most economical phrasing. In particular, if the phrase "except on the third strike," a negation, were introduced, the answer would be much simpler.

Negative scanning will work only if the learner knows the number of values of the attributes to be considered. In other words, a suitable description must be obtained. This could be equated to Wallach's (1958) idea of a contrast class; negative instances would be used to show that certain identities in description did not exist across classes. Conditional focusing, on the other hand, begins with positive instances. Negative instances are used only to check undeveloped hypotheses. Consider also the performance of negative scanners (or, in the terms of Bruner et al., negative focusers) against people using either a (fallacious) common element or a conditional focusing routine. Both can solve disjunctive problems, albeit that the subjects using a "positive" scheme *may* be somewhat slower. But when the subject is given a test problem solvable by conjunctive or disjunctive answers, differences should appear. Subjects using the focusing technique will first discover the conjunctive concept, which appears as the common element in either an anchoring or common-element strategy (Bruner et al.) or as the first and only conditional statement. Subjects using a negative scanning strategy will discover the disjunctive concept first, since they will note the *absence* of particular descriptive elements in negative instances.

Perhaps this is the explanation of Wells' results. At the beginning of his experiment his subjects were probably using some variety of scanning or positive focusing. When these techniques failed a new procedure would have to be tried. Either negative or conditional focusing techniques could be adopted. Which choice was made should be reflected on later test trials. Twenty-five of Wells' forty-eight subjects gave disjunctive answers to the test problems; the others gave conjunctive answers.

## 8 *A mathematical theory of hypothesis testing*

We have concentrated our discussion on possible strategies of concept learning. In doing so, we have noted that strategies may vary within an individual and among individuals within a given situation. At our present state of knowledge it is quite difficult to predict who will use which strategy when, or how strategies will be modified. Until predictions of this sort can be made, an analysis of concept learning in terms of cognitive hypotheses will remain in the category of *post hoc* description of obtained data. This is no mean accomplishment, an adequate reduction of obtained data is certainly as scientifically respectable as a poor prediction of new data. We agree with Miller, Galanter, and Pribram (1960) that models that do not reflect human capabilities to offer and test complex hypotheses cannot account for the data of many interesting psychological experiments. But this is a negative statement, and is more of an attack on oversimplified theories than a justification for a particular cognitive model.

Restle (1961, and in press)[9] has proposed an interesting mathematical model which can be considered an approximation to a rigorous theory of hypothesis testing. Where the strategies analysis at times forsakes rigor in the interest of detail, Restle has forsaken a detailed description of particular hypotheses while maintaining a rigorous approach. What Restle has done is to show that many aspects of concept-learning behavior can be predicted by assuming that hypotheses are being tested, rejected, and offered, without saying what these hypotheses are.

Assume that the subject has a set $H$ of hypotheses. (This can be conceived of as naming responses to be given when certain descriptive elements appear in the stimulus. Restle uses the term "strategy" for this response tendency. Most authors use "hypothesis" for the response tendency and "strategy" for the method by which hypotheses are changed. The latter terminology is used here.) The hypotheses are not further specified. It is assumed that the set $H$ may be partitioned into a set $C$ of hypotheses which will always lead to the correct answer, a set $W$ of hypotheses which will always lead to a wrong answer, and a set $I$ of hypotheses which are right or wrong at random. The lower case letters $c$, $w$, and $i$ will be used to refer to the proportion of hypotheses in $H$ which are in $C$, $W$, or $I$ respectively.

In Restle's first model it is assumed that on the first trial the subject chooses at random one hypothesis from $H$. This is maintained until it leads to an error, then it is returned to $H$ and a new hypothesis is chosen. This process is continued until a hypothesis in $C$ is chosen. This hypothesis will be maintained without further error.

In Restle's second model, the subject begins by considering all hypotheses in $H$ simultaneously. The probability of a particular response is proportional to the percentage of hypotheses in $H$ which recommend that response. After making the response, the subject sets aside all those hypotheses which did *not* recommend it. Thus, he might set aside all correct hypotheses. But notice that at the first correct response he will set aside all wrong hypotheses. The process is continued recursively until the subject has either selected a single, correct response or until he is left without any hypotheses. In the latter case he begins again, reconsidering the entire set $H$.

The third model is a compromise between the first two. It assumes that the subject selects a sample of hypotheses from $H$ and repeats the process for the second model on this sample.

Each of these models is, in effect, a strategy for changing unspecified hypotheses. Surprisingly, the three models are equivalent in an important way. They each lead to the same expression for the probability, $p_j$, of an error on the $j$th trial following an error.

(6.8.1) $$p_j = w + (\tfrac{1}{2})i \quad \text{if} \quad j = 1$$

(6.8.2) $$p_j = i(\tfrac{1}{2})^j \qquad \text{if} \quad j > 1$$

Restle has shown that his models can be used to predict many detailed features of the course of learning. All these features are statistical (e.g., the distribution of runs of errors, the probability of error on a particular trial, etc.). There is little difference between these predictions and the predictions based upon "additivity of cues" in Bourne and Restle's (1959) cue-conditioning model of concept learning.

We have presented models that assume that a subject will always recognize when his current hypothesis is incorrect. This is too strong an assumption, especially when the models are applied to animal discrimination learning data. Restle has shown that the model can be generalized to the situation in which after an error the current hypothesis is rejected with a given probability. He has also shown that the model can be generalized to situations (e.g., disjunctive concept learning) in which two or more different descriptive elements may be cues for a naming response.

On the other hand, it can be objected that the models do not give human subjects enough credit. When an hypothesis is dropped the new one is selected from *H, with replacement,* so the immediately disconfirmed hypothesis is as likely as any other to be either adopted (in the first model) or included in the set of hypotheses under consideration (in the second and third model). This feature of Restle's theory is not consistent with the position taken in discussing cognitive theories, that a strategy is a procedure for modifying the current hypothesis in some efficient manner. This is not in itself, however, a reason for dropping Restle's models from further consideration. So long as random selection models are adequate to account for the obtained data, they ought to be preferred to more complex models on the basis of simplicity alone.

What Restle's models cannot do is go beyond a statistical account of the data. They make no provision for predicting which hypothesis a subject will have on the $j$th trial, nor do they relate probability of error to the description of the object to be categorized. In principle, then, the cognitive models which can make such predictions have a development potential that the mathematical models do not. In practice, as we noted earlier, very few predictions have been made using cognitive hypothesis-testing models. Until such predictions are made and verified, the rigor and simplicity of Restle's models make them quite attractive to psychologists interested in concept learning. At the very least, they are useful interim steps between abstract conditioning models and detailed TOTE analyses.


## 9    What is learned in concept learning?

The studies of concept learning with disjunctive problems raise an old issue: what is learned when a problem is solved? A specific concept is certainly only one of the items learned. In the long run it may be the least valuable.

Wertheimer (1959) saw this problem as the crux of psychology. He explicitly denied that psychologists can reduce learning phenomenon to a pyramid of "habits" based on association between stimulus and response, because this leads to "bad" problem solving (sic) and solution by rote. Instead, Wertheimer argued, the problem solver must "understand the requirements of the problem." This just rephrases the question. How does a problem solver learn to discover the requirements of the problem?

Newell, Shaw, and Simon (1958), Taylor (1960), and Miller, Galanter, and Pribram (1960) have suggested that information-processing techniques are learned. They maintain that problem solving consists of the application of (in the last named author's terminology) TOTE units; test to determine the difference between current knowledge and the desired state, operate to reduce these differences, and then test again. This new brand of cognitive psychology, particularly the work of Newell, Shaw, and Simon, makes a strong appeal to the computer program as a model. A computer may be programmed to test data, to operate to reduce differences, and then to retest. The answer produced will be a joint function of the input data and the operators made available to the program.

Hovland and Hunt (1960a,b) have analyzed the process of concept learning during the solution of a single problem in this manner. Within a single problem, a strategy, in the sense used by Bruner, Goodnow, and Austin, can be programmed. (Bruner (1960) has agreed with this point.) Hovland and Hunt (1960a) reported a computer program that solves concept-learning problems by positive focusing. But this is not the whole story. The model must contain some provision for changing and improving its performance. The opening section of this chapter proposed that this change, too, could be handled by a TOTE unit that observed the performance of a subsidiary unit. The subsidiary unit would itself be the strategy. When the master unit tested it and found it wanting, it would be replaced. As experience was gained, stronger and stronger failure tests could be made, so that faulty strategies would be detected earlier.

Once a failure was detected, the faulty strategy could be replaced with any of several other TOTE units. On the particular problem under consideration it might not matter which unit was used. But on a second problem there might be a very great difference. One of the things that the subject might learn is what to do when the current strategy fails. Learning to select TOTES is similar to "learning to learn" (Harlow, 1949, 1959). In the TOTE analysis *any* transfer study is a study of inductive problem solving or, perhaps, concept learning. The objects are problems which can be described by their physical structure and by the feedback (e.g., success or failure of a particular operation) received when a strategy is applied to them. By observing this feedback, the concept learner could develop concepts to define the types of problems on which particular strategies will work. Often his experience will not be sufficient to permit him to learn an unequivocal concept about problems. Therefore he will have to guess about the "best" strategy to try; at some time this guess may lead him into an incorrect classification. This would be revealed by an incorrect choice of a strategy.

In Chapter 3 we examined the proposition that inductive problem solving was reducible to learning. We are now suggesting that learning can be viewed as a case of inductive problem solving. Which point of view is more fruitful scientifically is a question that can only be answered by the production of research. To date, learning theory has produced more. But, at least in the concept-learning field, a learning theorist has complained that little real progress is being made (Kendler, 1961). Will the second point of view be more fruitful? It seems more logical. After all, any inductive problem must begin by the statement of a priori probabilities. What can they be but the result of previous inductions?

REFERENCES

Adams, E., 1960. Survey of Bernoullian utility theory. In H. Solomon (ed.), *Mathematical thinking in the measurement of behavior*. Glencoe, Ill.: Free Press.
Baggaley, E., 1955. Concept formation and its relation to cognitive variables. *J. Gen. Psychol.*, 52, 297–306.
Bartlett, F., 1958. *Thinking*. New York: Basic Books.
Battig, W. F. and L. E. Bourne, 1961. Concept identification as a function of intra- and inter-dimensional variability. *J. exp. Psychol.*, 61, 329–333.
Berry, P. C., 1958. An exploration of the interrelations among some nonintellectual predictors of achievement in problem solving. Technical Report No. 4. Depart-

ment of Industrial Administration and of Psychology, Yale University Contract Nonr 609(2) (NR 150–166).

Bruner, J. S., 1960. Individual and collective problems in the study of thinking. *Ann. N. Y. Acad. Sci.*, 91, 22–37.

Bruner, J. S., J. J. Goodnow, and G. A. Austin, 1956. *A study of thinking.* New York: Wiley.

Goldstein, K. and M. Scheerer, 1941. Abstract and concrete behavior. *Psychol. Monogr.*, 53, No. 2.

Guilford, J. P., 1960. Basic conceptual problems in the psychology of thinking. *Ann. N. Y. Acad. Sci.*, 91, 6–21.

Guilford, J. P., 1959. Three faces of intellect. *Amer. Psychologist*, 14, 469–479.

Harlow, F., 1949. The formation of learning sets. *Psychol. Rev.*, 56, 51–65.

Harlow, H. F., 1959. Learning set and error factor theory. In S. Koch (ed.), *Psychology, a study of a science.* Vol. III. *General systematic formulation, learning and special processes.* New York: McGraw-Hill.

Hovland, C. I., 1952. A "communication analysis" of concept learning. *Psychol. Rev.*, 59, 461–472.

Hovland, C. I. and E. B. Hunt, 1960a. Computer simulation of concept attainment. Address given at American Association for Advancement of Sciences, New York.

Hovland, C. I. and E. B. Hunt, 1960b. Computer simulation of concept attainment. *Behavioral Sci.*, 5, 265–267.

Hovland, C. I. and W. I. Weiss, 1953. Transmission of information concerning concepts through positive and negative instances. *J. exp. Psychol.*, 45, 175–182.

Hunt, E. B., 1961. The evaluation of somewhat parallel models. *Proc. 1961 Western Management Science Institute, Conf. on Math. Models in the Behavioral Sciences.* Also published as Western Management Science Institute Working Paper No. 1, University of California at Los Angeles.

Hunt, E. B. and C. I. Hovland, 1960. Order of consideration of different types of concepts. *J. exp. Psychol.*, 59, 220–225.

Kendler, T. S., 1961. Concept formation. *Annu. Rev. Psychol.*, 12, 447–472.

Kendler, T. S., 1960. Learning, development and thinking. *Ann. N. Y. Acad. Sci.*, 91, 52–65.

Kurtz, K. and C. I. Hovland, 1956. Concept learning with different sequences of instances. *J. exp. Psychol.*, 51, 239–243.

Luce, R. D., 1959. On the possible psychophysical laws. *Psychol. Rev.*, 66, 81–95.

Luce, R. D. and H. Raiffa, 1957. *Games and decisions.* New York: Wiley.

Miller, G. A., E. Galanter, and K. Pribram, 1960. *Plans and the structure of behavior.* New York: Holt.

Newell, A., J. C. Shaw, and H. Simon, 1958. Elements of a theory of human problem solving. *Psychol. Rev.*, 65, 151–166.

Piaget, J., 1957. *Logic and Psychology.* New York: Basic Books.

Piaget, J., 1950. *The psychology of intelligence.* London: Routledge and Kegan Paul.

Polya, C., 1954. *Induction and analogy in mathematics.* Princeton: Princeton University Press.

Restle, F. The selection of strategies for cue learning. *Psychol. Rev.*, in press.

Restle, F., 1961. Statistical methods for a theory of cue learning. *Psychometrika*, 26, 291–306.

Sarason, S., 1961. The contents of human problem solving. *Nebraska Symposium on Motivation.*

Seymour, R., 1954. Strategies in the utilization of information. Unpublished doctoral dissertation, Harvard University.

Shepard, R. N., C. I. Hovland, and H. Jenkins, 1961. Learning and memorization of classifications. *Psychol. Monogr.*, **75** (13, whole No. 517).

Smoke, K. L., 1933. Negative instances in concept formation. *J. exp. Psychol.*, **16**, 583–588.

Smoke, K. L., 1932. An objective study of concept formation. *Psychol. Monogr.*, No. 191.

Taylor, D. W., 1960. Thinking and creativity. *Ann. N. Y. Acad. Sci.*, **91**, 108–127.

Taylor, D. W. and O. McNemar, 1955. Problem solving and thinking. *Annu. Rev. Psychol.*, **6**, 455–482.

Thurstone, L. L., 1938. *The primary mental abilities.* Chicago: University of Chicago Press.

Wallach, M., 1958. On psychological similarity. *Psychol. Rev.*, **65**, 103–116.

Wason, P. C., 1960. On the failure to eliminate hypotheses in a conceptual task. *Qtrly. J. exp. Psychol.*, **12**, 129–240.

Wells, H. H., 1962. Transfer and stimulus effects in disjunctive concept learning. Unpublished doctoral dissertation, Yale University.

Wertheimer, M., 1959. *Productive thinking* (rev. ed.). New York: Harper.

FOOTNOTES

1. A somewhat facetious example is offered. At the start of a trip a motorist does not decide where he will stop his car. Instead, he decides upon a set of decision rules. Some of these may be "red light—stop, green light—go, yellow light—go very fast." He may also have a rule to change the last rule to "yellow light—stop," after the $n$th traffic ticket.

2. As an example of functional analysis in another field, Luce (1959) has argued for a "revocation" of Fechner's law by considering what psychophysical judgments must do. Luce used a rigorous mathematical approach that is far preferable to a TOTE analysis. A less rigorous functional approach, one that deals with problems more complex and ill defined than concept learning, is Wertheimer's (1959) Gestalt analysis of problem solving. The present exposition, dealing with a problem of intermediate complexity, will be of intermediate rigor. The distinction between rigor of analyses is similar to Polya's (1957) distinction between heuristics and algorithms. Of particular importance is the fact that an algorithm may be needed to show that a problem cannot be solved by a particular approach.

3. The problem content is not always fixed. Arithmetical problem solving involves a change from the manipulation of objects (oranges, bananas, cannibals, missionaries, etc.) to the manipulation of symbols. Often there may be some freedom of choice in making this translation. Most problems have a geometric and a symbolic interpretation; the author's impression is that there are strong individual differences as to the preferred alternative. For a further discussion of this, see Polya (1954).

4. Piaget does use the terms "concept" and "acquisition and utilization of concepts." (See, especially, Piaget's (1950) discussion of causality.) He uses the term "concept," however, to mean an explanatory principle, such as the concept of mass or force in physics.

5. My discussion of Piaget's theories in relation to concept learning is based, in part, on a brief paper prepared by Dr. H. H. Wells. I acknowledge this aid but must accept responsibility for the conclusions. At this time, Dr. Wells has not published his note.

6. This study was described briefly in Chapter 5. The small number of highly selected subjects (twelve Harvard graduate students) raises some doubt about the generality of this study.

7. This is an apparent contradiction to Wells' data. His subjects did learn, although the problems and presentation conditions were somewhat different. Wells presented all training instances simultaneously and already classified. Interestingly, in this phase of his investigation Wells used students from a small college much less selective than Harvard, the prime source of subjects for Bruner et al.

8. How strong the positive focusing tendency is has been illustrated in an unpublished study by Bregman and Hovland. Subjects (from the same source as Wells' subjects in his first experiment) had to learn a categorization of patterns in which one side (denotation) could be defined by a disjunctive concept, the other side a conjunctive concept. The experimenters arbitrarily labeled one side as "positive" and the other as "negative." The problem was significantly easier if the positive side was conjunctive. Huttenlocker, working with Bruner, has obtained similar results (personal communication).

9. Dr. Restle has kindly made available some of his work prior to publication.

# 7

# Artificial intelligence

1    *What is artificial intelligence?*

Through the media of the press, radio, television, and cartoons in the *New Yorker,* the term "electronic brain" has become common. Is "artificial intelligence" a more sophisticated name for the same thing? After all, machines have been demonstrated which do fascinating things; select questions for contestants on a television quiz program, predict election results, and play music. To be sure, the first two acts involve sheer gadgetry, and the third has been criticized as "no more music than a rock and roll singer." [1] Still, machines do impressive things. But are they intelligent?

This is an unanswerable question. There is no adequate definition of intelligence. Psychologists and the general public both use the term in an "intelligence is as intelligence does" way. Intelligence is what the intelligence test measures. If an entity can solve problems which require intelligence, it is intelligent. The English mathematician A. M. Turing (1950) pointed out that since this is the way the term is used, the test for an intelligent machine is established. According to Turing, the question "Can a machine think?" has meaning only if it is rephrased as "Over a particular set of problems, is there a way in which an observer can distinguish between the performance of a human being and a machine?" If the answer to the second question is "no," either the machine is thinking or the human is not. This criterion, and the whimsical setting in which it was placed, have come to be known as "Turing's test."

At one time machine intelligence was practically equated with an ability to pass Turing's test. Recently, there has been more stress on a deficiency in it. Must intelligence be equated with human performance? For the purpose of explaining human behavior, this is an appropriate criterion. But suppose a machine outperforms a human on an intellectually demanding task. Such a machine might be highly desirable. In concept learning, for instance, there are inductive problems which humans are, regretfully, unable to solve. The perfect medical diagnostician has not yet been born. One of the goals of research in artificial intelligence is to design machines that can extend, as well as replace, human intellectual performance.

If a man says he has an intelligent machine, what does he mean? To the mythical man in the street, the phrase probably suggests a very large device well armed with flashing lights. Actually, very few of the workers in the field of artificial intelligence have been concerned with creating an unusual piece of hardware. The goal of most of their research is a design for a machine that might be built without a major *scientific* advance beyond current knowledge. (A major technological advance, such as an improvement in circuitry, might be necessary.) It is historically true that many artificial intelligence designs have been realized as programs for a digital computer (Minsky, 1961*a*), but this fact must not be allowed to confuse the issue. The digital computer has proven to be a useful device for building experimental models of a particular design, just as the wind tunnel is a useful device for building experimental models of aircraft wings. In both cases ideas are to be tested. The hardware used to test them is incidental. It should be remembered, however, that if *some* appropriate hardware is not available, it may be impossible to test a design. The flexibility of a digital computer is useful in artificial intelligence research because it permits the testing of a wider range of designs for intelligent machines. All the computer does is add and compare numbers, in itself it is in no way intelligent.

At a very abstract level, there are three parts to an artificial intelligence system. One part is the set of inputs, or stimuli, or the set of problems. Each member of this set is a possible state of the external world. Each state may be assigned a number, say an integer from 1 to $n$. The final product of the system is some member of a set of possible solutions, outputs, or responses. The third, and in some ways the most interesting, part of the system is the information processor. The information processor is a rule for specifying which response to select, given a particular problem as input. In other words, the information processor is equivalent to a mapping from the input to the output set. At any given moment the output will be determined solely from the input.

This mapping may be explicit and unchanging. If so, it could be represented by a table, and would hardly be what we mean by artificial intelligence. The act of using a table of logarithms is not considered problem solving, although the act of deciding to use the table may be. To add intelligence to the information processor, the machine must be given the capability of controlling its environment. An information processor can do this if it can partition its environment into three subsets of stimuli. The first of these subsets is the set of inputs that can be presented to it, the set of problems it may be asked to solve. The second subset is the set of possible states of the information processor's own internal configuration. This configuration may depend on both the computations that the processor can make and its "history" of problems it has encountered. The final subset of facts about the environment includes records of rewards and punishments that the processor has received from some external trainer. To benefit from this record, the processor should be able to make the response of changing its own internal configuration.

Within this expanded environment, the processor itself becomes a set of rules for proceeding from a problem to a solution. These rules can be phrased as successive questions: "If the external problem is $A$, and *if* the internal configuration is $B$, select response $C$. Otherwise, if the external problem is $D$, and the internal configuration $B$, select $E$."

A processor that can control its environment in the manner specified may, if the decision rules are suitable, exhibit both "education" and "learning." "Education" is possible if the processor's rules include a rule to examine the current problem to see if it is similar to any problem on the record of previous problems, and if it is, to take appropriate action. "Learning" is more subtle. As part of its input at time $t$, the processor may have a record of its response at $t-1$ and a record of the response of a trainer (which could be the environment) to that response. With this information as input, the information processor can apply a prespecified rule to change its own internal state to one that specifies a problem-solution mapping that receives more rewards than the present one. Even with imperfect feedback records, such a system may be able to move toward a reward maximizing internal configuration.[2] Several experimental machines which do this have been built (Sluckin, 1960). Ashby (1960) has maintained that machines which can adjust themselves by feedback control can perform any of the allegedly intelligent functions involved in adaptation to an environment. In particular, they have the overt characteristics of an organism seeking a goal, but do not require a teleological explanation. Because of the adjustment capability, Weiner (1948) coined the term *cybernetics* (from the Greek word for "steersman") to describe feedback control.

## 2    *The organization of artificial intelligence systems*

This section will discuss some of the types of rules which have been proposed for the abstract information processor discussed in the previous section. Although it is too early to offer any definitive treatment of the topic, certain trends in the design of artificial intelligence systems are developing.[3] One of the most clear-cut distinctions is between the so-called "self-organizing systems" and the systems that are preorganized for specific information-processing tasks.

Self-organizing systems change their internal states in some random manner until they reach an internal stable state. By definition, a stable state is one that corresponds to a stimulus-response (or problem-solution) mapping that, over the range of inputs tested, does not cause the system to receive signals (e.g., punishments) that would cause it to make a further change in its internal state. The idea of a self-organizing system as a model for learning is by no means unique to artificial intelligence. Stimulus-sampling models (Estes, 1950) and stochastic-learning models (Bush and Mosteller, 1955), which were discussed briefly in Chapter 3, can be considered random self-organizing systems. Both artificial intelligence and psychological models of random self-organization are cybernetic devices. They emit a response that causes a trainer to input (or fail to input) a reward signal, thus completing a feedback loop.

Imagine a system that can receive three inputs, (0, 1, 2), and emit three possible responses, (0, 1, 2). For simplicity, let us require that the system, when it is responding perfectly, use the mapping (0-0, 1-1, 2-2). We shall also introduce a feedback loop, a signal when the appropriate response has or has not been made. This system can be self-organizing if it functions in the following, very primitive way. Initially it selects at random one of the nine possible mappings. If the correct one has been selected the system will never receive a failure signal. Whenever the system does receive a failure signal it selects a new mapping, also at random. Eventually this system is bound to reach the mapping we desire.

All this illustrates is that if error can be recognized, trial and error will work for a random mechanism. A few simple constraints on the random changes may result in rapid improvement of the system's performance. Consider how much more rapidly the correct mapping would be realized if whenever an error signal was received only the response to the problem at hand was reselected. Thre are still more sophisticated rules for constraining the random change, and, of course, the network of (randomly chosen) decisions to be made before a response is selected may be made much more complex than the simple input-output mapping of our example.

Complex networks, randomly organized and reorganized on the basis of feedback signals, have attracted attention for different reasons. In themselves, they are interesting because they show that the seemingly goal-directed behavior of biological organisms can be simulated by a constrained process of random selection. Such systems can learn in the sense that they give progressively closer approximations to the desired mapping between problem and solution. The simple example of the previous paragraph, under the condition in which it selected *one* new problem-solution pairing after each error, would do this. The exhibition of something overtly similar to purposive behavior has raised the question of whether biological organisms exhibit any behavior a random that self-organizing system cannot display. Several British researchers have answered "no." Sluckin (1960) has reviewed their work.

These same researchers have concentrated on the analysis of prototypical situations in which feedback control and random reorganization can occur. Occasionally these analyses have been supplemented by experimentation with primitive cybernetic systems, but these are more demonstrations of previous analyses than true experiments. Their results can be thought of as analogous to existence proofs in mathematics. They have shown that there is no a priori reason why random machines cannot be designed to do tasks which require learning or adaptation, even to a changing environment. The British cyberneticists, particularly Ashby (1960), maintain that a mechanical model of the brain could be built. But they do not claim to have built one.

Random reorganization might be used as a basic principle in the design of a model of the mammalian brain. In the United States several such models have been constructed. These research programs have used digital computer simulation, since they were more concerned with the accuracy of a complex model and less concerned with a demonstration of pure feedback control. Since the demands that such models have placed on the digital computer are interesting in themselves, and since these studies are simulations of biological systems rather than artificial intelligence studies, a discussion of them will be postponed until simulation itself is discussed.

Random nets, with or without random reorganization, appear to be less useful as practical problem solvers. One of the characteristics of a random, self-organizing system is that it begins a problem without being biased toward a particular solution. Within the constraints of the randomization process, it will eventually reach a solution determined solely by its own problem-solving experience. This has suggested to some experimenters that the random reorganization principle is suitable for an artificial intelligence system that is to operate in an environment where humans do not know how to arrive at a solution. An interesting example of this is the "bubble chamber problem," which *may* be an example of concept learning.

The bubble chamber is a device which produces photographs of the tracks of subatomic particles. Most of the photographs it produces are quite routine, but an occasional one portrays an interesting event, such as the creation of an antiproton. Such pictures, which are quite easy for a human physicist to recognize, should be set aside for further processing. The problem is that the bubble chamber produces pictures faster than people can scan them. Some sort of automatic scanner should be built. Unfortunately, the physicist cannot tell an engineer how to build it, because the physicist cannot state the process by which he recognizes an interesting event. A possible solution to this problem is to let the scanner be controlled by a random reorganization decision device. Initially the device would be "shown" a series of interesting and routine pictures and be reinforced for the correct binary decision. The hope is that as a result of this training period the feedback-controlled reorganizing device would adjust its own internal state so that it could recognize new pictures of interesting events. It could then replace the human scanner, even though we still did not know how the human scanner did his job.

This approach has not been particularly successful, either in the bubble chamber or in other applied problems. There are two reasons for the failure of random devices as practical problem solvers. One is technological and may be solved in the near future. For a random net to have sufficient flexibility of reorganization it must be able to produce a very large number of combinations of external environment and internal state of the processor. This implies a large number of random choices—each of which must be brought to its proper value— and this in turn forces an increase in size and/or operating time of the system. Even with transistorized circuitry, the hardware problem is formidable. The development of solid-state computers and superconducting elements (Ittner and Kraus, 1961) may possibly overcome it, but this is not certain.

Even if the technological problems are overcome there is a logical objection to problem solving by random selection. Finding the solution to a problem is analogically similar to finding a needle in a haystack. The needle (the correct mapping) is hidden among a large population of similar elements (all incorrect mappings in the set of possible mappings). Some search procedure is needed. Using a randomly organized device is like starting the search in a randomly chosen location in the haystack. Before starting most problems, a consideration of what we are doing will usually provide a better than random starting point, one reasonably close to the final solution. If our goal is a device that will solve problems, there is no reason why we should not use all available knowledge in designing the system.

Minsky (1961a) feels that this reasoning applies to random reorganization. If several decision processes are changed, and the whole change results in a better, but not optimal, solution, some thought should be given to discovering which changes helped. This problem is critical when large information processing systems are involved.

Suppose that one million decisions are involved in a complex task (such as winning a chess game). Could we assign to each decision element one millionth of the credit for the completed task?

Minsky, 1961a, p. 20.

The argument is not against reorganization or trial and error in problem solving, it is against random reorganization and trial. We could design a system which had specific rules for selecting its next action on the basis of its analysis of the present situation. This is one of the functions of teaching. A mathematics teacher cannot anticipate all the problems his students will ever have to solve, so he should not attempt to teach rote methods that work well on particular problems. According to Polya (1957), the *good* mathematics teacher teaches his students how to proceed under different contingencies. For instance, in statistics a student should be taught that (*a*) it is usually useful to transform data to normal distributions and (*b*) there are several transformations which remedy certain distortions. He should *not* be taught "Take the logarithm of the data." If the appropriate rules can be stated for students, they should be statable as the design for an intelligent machine.

The validity of this argument has been demonstrated by the construction of several such machines. The pioneer effort in the field was the construction of the Logic Theorist by Newell, Shaw, and Simon (1956). In its design form, the Logic Theorist is a set of good (although not infallible) rules for solving problems in symbolic logic. The fact that these rules have been stated as a program for a digital computer (Newell and Shaw, 1957) is irrelevant here. In a later paper, Newell et al. (1958) pointed out that the Logic Theorist, or any similar system, is a theory of how an organism might solve problems of a particular type.

Artificial intelligence systems designed in the spirit of the Logic

Theorist are instructions for solving particular types of problems, not problems in general. The instructions can be made very specific. At one extreme is the normal computer program, a complete specification of the steps needed to solve exactly one mathematical problem. This hardly qualifies as intelligence. Of more interest are systems that deal with interesting problem areas. Some examples are the Logic Theorist itself, Wang's (1960) algorithmic method for proving problems in symbolic logic, Slagle's (1961) system for solving calculus problems, and Gelernter's (1959) artificial geometer. These systems differ among themselves, particularly as to whether or not they insure that a solution will be found, or as to the generality of their techniques outside the original problem area, but they all have certain key features in common. Instead of beginning with random transformations of input to output data, they apply transformations which, in the experience of their designers, are known to be helpful in handling certain problems within the problem area. To return to the needle in the haystack analogy, the transformation from search at location $A$ to search at location $B$ is based on some knowledge about the mechanics of needles and haystacks.

Unless the system designers are quite unfamiliar with the field, artificial intelligence devices of this type are almost bound to be more efficient than random nets. As our examples illustrate, they are also usually problem specific. Newell, Shaw, and Simon (1959a) have designed a General Problem Solver which is not as specific as the others. It contains procedures useful in solving a wide range of problems. The particular rules will be discussed in a later section on the selection of a solution. The General Problem Solver has been shown to be an effective device for two different problem areas (trigonometry and symbolic logic). Admittedly, these areas contain psychologically similar problems, but even a device that handled only mathematics and related topics would be extremely important. Polya (1954) has presented a persuasive argument that problem-solving rules exist for these areas.

As would be expected, problem solving by use of a General Problem Solver is a slower process than problem solving using an area specific device. But it is almost certainly a faster method than problem solving using an even more flexible self-organizing random net.[4] The discovery of general problem-solving procedures is an important goal in itself. A typology of problem-solving areas, categorized by the processes which were applicable within them, would be extremely interesting.

Self-organizing systems are not only general, they improve with practice within a given problem area. Actually, what they do is reorganize their internal information processor so that it is more efficient in producing the kind of input-output mappings that are being required of it. Can a similar improvement with practice be expected of predesigned artificial intelligence systems?

The answer is yes, but the improvement is of a different type. Most of the currently operating predesigned systems do not learn in the sense of reorganization of internal transformations on the data, but they can be educated. Once a system has proven a particular result, it can store the result for later use as a "known" in constructing a proof. This procedure is analogous to a geometry student's applying the Pythagorean theorem to solve a particular problem; he does not have to rederive the theorem every time it is used. In general, the ability to store previous results will cause a system to improve its problem-solving ability as it gains more experience with the problem-solving area.

Newell et al. (1959b), in a semispeculative paper, have pointed out that this is not the only way in which a predesigned system could improve its performance. If truly general decision procedures were to be discovered, the problem of improving the present design of a predesigned system could be presented to such a system as a problem. The resulting change in the system to be improved, although Newell, et al. refer to it as "intelligent learning," is really more of a logical analysis using inductive and deductive reasoning. The improved system should reach its optimal internal state more rapidly than a system changing in the blind (although feedback-controlled) manner envisaged in most self-organizing systems. Theoretically, there is no limit to the level at which "intelligent learning" could be carried out; we could presumably redesign the redesigner of a system to be redesigned. Practically, the thesis assumes that the original designers know good rules for designing artificial intelligence systems. It is rather doubtful that anyone knows such rules for problem solving, in the most general sense. Newell et al. report interesting preliminary results with their particular deductive learning system. Their proposal is certainly worth investigating, but it is a conjecture at this time.

No system is completely random. Random reorganization must operate within certain rigidly stated constraints. Indeed, one of the most important reasons for constructing an experimental model of a random reorganization system is to ensure the designer that the system can work at all. Within systems that we would consider predesigned, random choices may be allowed at certain points. This randomness may or may not drop out as the system acquires more information about its environment.

Since the distinctions of this section—random versus predesigned, specificity versus generality, flexibility versus speed—all imply continua and compromise, no definite answer can be given to the question "What sort of system ought to be used?" The answer depends on the purpose of the user and the amount of information he has about the problem area before he builds his artificial intelligence.

## 3    Algorithms and heuristics

In the abstract presentation a problem is solved when an adequate path is found from a possible problem (stimulus) to a possible solution (response). An artificial intelligence system is nothing more than a set of instructions for selecting such a path. What are some of the requirements that we can place on the instructions?

The first thought that comes to mind is that they ought to work. Given the problem, the system should always find the solution. Any computing system which has this characteristic, regardless of whether or not it is called an artificial intelligence, is called an *algorithm*. For a concise definition we say that an algorithm is a search method which, with certainty, will produce the correct response for any stimulus in the set of possible stimuli. (Throughout this section, the terms stimulus and problem, and response and solution, will be used interchangeably.) Notice that nothing has been said about the cost of finding an answer, and for that reason artificial intelligence systems may not always be "better designed" if they are algorithms.

The undesirability of algorithms may be illustrated by example. Newell and Simon (1957) proposed, somewhat facetiously, a "British Museum" algorithm[5] for solving problems in symbolic logic. Starting with the "given" theorems of a problem, we could generate all their implications, at random, then all of the implications of the implications, etc. until the "to prove" was produced. This method is certain to produce a proof to any solvable problem. But, as Newell and Simon point out, it might take hundreds of years on the fastest computer imaginable. Their alternative, the Logic Theorist, applies rules that will not solve every problem presented to it, but will usually produce a proof in a reasonabe time.[6]

Newell and Simon refer to such rules as *heuristics*. They define a heuristic as a method which may solve a problem within a reasonable limit on computing cost. Polya gave a similar definition.

Heuristic reasoning is reasoning not regarded as final and strict but as provisional and plausible only, whose purpose is to discover the solution of the present problem.

Polya, 1957, p. 113.

Both definitions stress the probabilistic nature of heuristic methods, they "typically work" (Polya).

Suppose that several artificial intelligence systems are proposed as methods for solving a particular class of problems. Each system has its own cost and probability of achieving solution. How do we decide which one to use? As might be expected, there is no general answer. There is a general policy for making such decisions.

Deciding to use an artificial intelligence system is equivalent to purchasing advice. Before we present the problem to the system, we know *at least* that the solution is one of a set $A$ of possible solutions. (If we do not know this, we cannot specify the problem in sufficient detail to design a machine to solve it.) We may even be able to state the probability of a particular answer's being correct, without examining the problem at all. Suppose a blind man must decide how a fair coin has landed. He may choose either possible response, with a probability of being right of .5. Or, he may ask advice from friends who suffer from varying degrees of myopia. The conditional probability of his giving the right answer, given advice from his friends, is a measure of the performance of the system "blind man and friends." We can compare this to the performance of the simpler system, "blind man," to determine how much he should pay his friends for their aid.

Marschak (1960) showed that buying advice has certain peculiar features which determine the amount that should be paid for it. Advice is not of use in and of itself, it is an aid in decision making. A particular decision is made as the result of applying a policy to a particular situation. The expected value of the decision is, roughly, the average reward that the decision maker can expect if he makes decisions according to a given policy over an infinite sequence of experiments. Through the aid of advice the decision maker hopes to increase this quantity.[7] Marschak pointed out that the amount of this improvement may not be identical, or even monotonically related to, the amount of uncertainty as to the true state of nature (in our case, the actual solution) which the decision maker has. Measures of the amount of uncertainty (such as Shannon's measure (Shannon and Weaver, 1949), discussed in Chapter 4) reflect the distribution of probabilities over the set of possible alternatives, without specifying which alternatives have which probabilities. They measure mathematical, but not semantic, information. In Los Angeles there is smog in the air approximately 1 out of every 2 days. Severe earthquakes occur less often than once every 10 years. In terms of a quantitative measure of information alone, the advice that tomorrow will be a smog-free day transmits more information than the advice that there will be no earthquake tomorrow. This is true for the average signal for smog versus the average signal for earthquake. Most residents of Los Angeles would prefer to have a perfect predictor of earthquakes than a perfect predictor of smog!

The same considerations apply to the choice of artificial intelligence systems. Some problems are such that answers are either right or wrong. Proof sequences in symbolic logic cannot be almost true. In dealing with such problems, the value of a particular artificial intelligence system can be determined by calculating the probability that it will produce the correct answer. This figure, and the cost of the system, can be compared to the cost of having a wrong answer. Selection or rejection of the system can be based on these criteria.

Other problems are not of this type. An answer might be partially correct. In concept learning, a system might develop a categorizing rule that worked for 90% of the cases to be categorized. (Experimental examples of such concepts were given in the studies by Bruner, Goodnow, and Austin, 1956; Gormezano and Grant, 1958; and Reed, 1946.) The best medical diagnosticians cannot claim to have learned infallible rules for categorizing their patients. In choosing artificial intelligence systems to attack such problems, we ask not what is the probability that the best solution will be chosen, but what is the average value of the solution that is chosen? This value must be determined by some measure over the set of problems which the system may encounter.

We must also consider the cost of obtaining a solution. This cost may vary from problem to problem in a given problem area. We can write an extremely general equation to illustrate the relation between the two. Let $V_{ij}$ be the value of the solution proposed by the $i$th artificial intelligence system on the $j$th problem. Similarly, let $C_{ij}$ be the cost of that advice. One criterion for selecting an artificial intelligence system would be to choose the system $i$, within the set of systems $I$, that maximized the quantity

$$(7.3.1) \quad E(V_i) = \sum_j (V_{ij} - C_{ij}) \cdot (\text{probability of encountering problem } j)$$

The difference $(V_{ij} - C_{ij})$ over each problem must be considered, instead of the separate sums, $\Sigma V_{ij}$ and $\Sigma C_{ij}$. Value and cost may be correlated, either positively or negatively. Newell and Simon (1957) observed that when the probability of the Logic Theorist's obtaining a solution was high (in fact, 1), the cost of obtaining that solution was usually low. It took the system a long time to discover that it could not solve a problem. Even in algorithmic systems, the cost and value of (here, perfect) advice may covary.

Throughtout this discussion, maximizing the average value of the advice received from a system has been stressed, which may be an inappropriate condition. The general problem is one in which the decision maker has a set of alternatives (choose or reject given systems). Each choice, taken together with a particular state of nature (sequence of problems that will be presented to the system), will specify a payoff in terms of cost and value of computation. The considerations that apply to general decision-making problems (Luce and Raiffa, 1957) apply here.

## 4    Moving toward a solution

Ashby (1961) proposed a "crucial" test for any machine that claimed to be intelligent—is it capable of rapid selection of an appropriate solution for the problems it faces? An artificial intelligence system is supposed to select an adequate path from a problem to a solution (stimulus to response), and ought to do this in an efficient manner.

Ashby himself had shown (Ashby, 1960) that any machine that can monitor its own internal state is capable of some efficiency in selection. He did this by discussing the following (slightly modified) example.

A machine determines which input-output mapping it will use by observing the simultaneous setting of $N$ independent counters. If a counter is to be reset, its new value is determined randomly. Any counter will be reset to its appropriate value with probability $p$. The system, however, will not have found the correct mapping until all counters are correctly set. Ashby suggested three methods by which this system could, through monitoring its own internal state, find the correct solution. The first was complete randomness. Whenever the system is informed that it has produced an incorrect solution, it resets all counters. The expected number of times the system should have to reset itself in this method of operation is $(1/p)^N$, which is a very large number if $N$ is at all large. Since $N$ may be thought of as the number of small decisions needed to solve a complex problem, we can see that such a system would not arrive at a solution of a difficult problem in a reasonable time. In the second method of operation performance is better, but not sufficiently improved. In this mode, Ashby would have the system set one dial at a time, resetting each counter until it was correct. The expected number of settings required would be $(N/p)$, a linear function of $N$. Only in the third mode of operation would the machine give an acceptable performance on complex problems. In the third mode, Ashby's system is informed which counters are correctly set. It then resets only the incorrect counters (again, randomly), until the correct mapping is discovered. The expected number of resettings $R$ in this case is[8]

$$(7.4.1) \qquad R = \frac{1}{p} + [-\log (1 - p)] \log N$$

Granted that a dramatic improvement in solution time has been achieved, the solution itself raises new problems. Minsky's (1961a) objection, previously cited, is relevant. How is the system to know which of its subdecisions were correct? The nature of the problem may prevent evaluation of serial decision making until the end of the series is reached. How, then, do we distribute the credit for making a right or wrong decision? These are valid questions which are not easily answered.

An intelligent machine must be able to do more than observe its own internal state. It ought to be able to observe where it is located in the problem-solving environment. The analogy to a map is frequently given. It is not enough to know that the solution offered is not correct, we should know what are the differences between the solution offered and desired. The simplest such information is the relative distance between two offered solutions. Suppose an artificial intelligence produces two responses and keeps a record of how the responses are produced. If one solution is better than the other, although neither were adequate, it would be a good heuristic to assume that the processes unique to the better response were desirable.

The way a predesigned artificial intelligence moves through its environment is to apply operators to its present solution to transform it into a new solution. For instance, in Slagle's (1961) system for solving calculus problems, the expression $\int Af(g) \, dv$ will be changed into $A \int f(g) \, dv$. Every system, including a random system, has operators that it can apply in a search for a solution. If the system is to satisfy Ashby's criteria for intelligence it must apply these selectively. There are two questions that must be answered: Can the operator be applied at all? Will the application of this operator (probably) result in a move toward solution? To do this, the artificial intelligence must have concepts. In progressing through the space of possible solutions the problem-solving mechanism must continually evaluate the difference between the available and desired results. Newell, Shaw, and Simon (1959a) suggested that differences could be used to describe the overall situation. The problem solver could have a concept, based on differences, of situations in which the application of operator $x$, $y$, $z$, etc. usually reduced the differences.

Again an analogy may be made to geographical problem solving. I am in my office in Los Angeles, and I wish to go to Boston. This is a situation in which great distance must be reduced. What reduces great distance? An airplane. Can an airplane be applied to me? No, I am not at the airport. What is the difference between my current situation and the airport? A medium-length distance. What reduces medium-length distances? An automobile. Can I apply an automobile? No, I am not in the parking lot. What is the difference between my current situation and the parking lot? Small distance. What reduces small distance? Walking. Can I apply walking? Yes, execute this operator and proceed. Situations can be described in terms of their absolute characteristics and in terms of differences noticeable when they are compared to other situations. For every difference that may have to be reduced, there should be at least one operator that can reduce it. For each possible difference the system must have a concept, based on the description of operators, that it can use in selecting the appropriate operator. For every operator there must be a concept, based on absolute characteristics of situations, that the system can use to determine whether or not the operator can be applied. The artificial intelligence can then make an intelligent selection of responses.

Deciding whether or not an operator can be applied is often a straightforward question. For instance, we know that, now and for all time, we can find the logarithm of $x$ only if $x$ is a positive real number. We can specify rules for deciding whether or not a particular operator can be applied to a situation. It is much harder to specify when a machine should decide to apply a particular operator, although several other operators could be applied. Specifying a decision rule to answer this question is equivalent to stating how to decide on a good move in problem solving. If a machine is designed to attack problems that are at all complex (e.g., symbolic logic, chess, and even concept learning) we will not be able to specify all the situations in which the machine will have to make a choice. We may not even be able to partition the universe of possible choice points into useful classes of choice situations. The best approach we can take is to provide the machine with heuristic rules for selecting the operation that will probably move it closer to a solution. But "moving closer to a solution" is a slippery definition. A truly intelligent machine should have several ways of evaluating this phrase and should be able to choose among them. Newell, Shaw, and Simon (1959b) point out that a machine that could generate alternate descriptions of the choice situations it encountered and then choose among these descriptions would be an "intelligent learner." As it gained experience, it would become a

better problem solver because it would discover better ways of looking
at its environment.

## 5    *The computer and the system*

The foregoing discussion stressed the information-processing capacities of an artificial intelligence system without considering how
the system was to be constructed. In practice, information processing
systems can always be envisaged as (perhaps complex) electrical switching circuits (McCulloch and Pitts, 1943). Such circuits can be constructed by programming a digital computer.

Why construct such switching circuits at all? From our prior sketch
of artificial intelligence systems, which was conducted at an abstract
level, we might conclude that system performance could be predicted
by analysis. In theory this is true, but in practice it is not. The task
of computing the performance aspects of a complex information
processing system may be so formidable that it is simpler to build and
experiment with a pilot model. One of the conclusions reached by
constructing the model may be that the system will not work—this,
in itself, can be highly interesting (e.g., the study of Hebb's (1948)
theory by Rochester, et al., 1956). The availability of large digital
computers has permitted such empirical studies. Minsky (1961*b*) considers this so important that he doubts that artificial intelligence research can be carried on to any extent without the computer. Considering the British results, this is doubtful. But it cannot be denied
that the digital computer helps a great deal. Since it is such a common
tool in the field, some of its operating characteristics should be considered.

Digital computers are divided into four basic units; input, output,[9]
computing, and storage devices. Information is stored in the computer
in *words,* which are really ordered sets of $n$ digits of a specified
modulus (usually binary). In the computer's storage unit (conven-
tionally, the "memory unit") are a large number of discrete locations.
Each location is addressed, much like the street numbers of houses.
The contents of one location constitute a word. Each word is referred
to by its location number. Thus the statement that "number seven
equals twelve" means that there is a location, numbered seven, which
has some arbitrary number of decimal digits, all of which are zero
except the last two, which are the digits 1 and 2.

Digits can be thought of as code symbols. Normally we think of
digits as symbols for numbers, but this is not necessary. They can serve

as codes for any symbol or "natural language" word. The computer can be instructed to recognize a symbol as a number if it occurs in some positions and as a word or operation if it occurs in others.

The computing unit is prewired to operate on some two hundred or less prespecified coded symbols. These symbols are placed, as parts of words, in the storage unit. When the computing device receives one of these pre-specified codes as an instruction, it performs a particular operation on an indicated symbol, or operand. The operand is specified by stating its location in the memory device. For instance, suppose a computer is built to interpret the first three digits of an instruction as a code symbol for an operation and the next four as the location of the operand. When the word 0011000 is sent to the computing device, it will be interpreted as a command to numerically add (001 . . . .) the symbol in location 1000 into the accumulator (a special buffer register). The symbol 0021000 might be interpreted as subtraction of the same symbol from the contents of the accumulator.

Before computation is begun, certain locations are designated to hold the words to be interpreted as instructions. These locations can be signaled to the computer in two ways. The simplest way is to have a convention which specifies that instructions always begin at location $x$ in the memory unit and continue at intervals of $y$ locations (for engineering reasons immediately adjacent instruction locations may not be desirable in some computers) until there is an instruction to halt. Another way to specify the locations is to introduce the convention that certain digit positions of each instruction symbol will contain the address of the next instruction. Under either convention the programer needs to specify only the first instruction location; everything else can be done automatically.

Either convention permits execution of a long, complicated, necessarily specific set of instructions. Since branching instructions (e.g., go to location $a$ if location $x$ has a contents numerically greater than location $v$'s, otherwise go to location $b$ for the next instruction) are permitted, the possible list of instructions is quite flexible. Because of branching, the actual sequence of instructions that will be executed on a particular series of computations depends somewhat on the input data. A most interesting feature of the second method of specifying instructions is that we can, in principle, compute a number and store it in the "next location" section of some instruction. Although normal arithmetic computations do not require (and indeed, avoid) this procedure, it is important in artificial intelligence programing.

Taken as a whole, a list of instructions is called a program. The human operator does not need to specify the location of every instruction in a program, nor does he need to use the digit-words that will be interpreted by the computing unit of the machine. Most modern computers can be programed in a language that is more natural for humans. Modern computer languages, such as ALGOL, a language that can be used on many machines, or International Business Machines' FORTRAN, are very similar to conventional algebraic notation. The user writes his program in FORTRAN, ALGOL, or some other human-oriented language. It is then automatically converted into the sequence of digits that will actually control the computer. Such languages are called *source languages*. They may operate by *compilation* or *translation*.

Compilation is a process by which a human-oriented source language like FORTRAN or ALGOL is received *as input* for a special computer program, the *compiler*. This is a program stored in a computer like any other program. The output is a new program written as a set of machine instructions. At some later time this new program may be loaded into the computer, without the compiler, and used to process data. Thus, compilation is a two-pass operation, similar to reading a translated book; first the book must be translated.

The second method of converting source language into machine programs is by the use of an *interpreter*. Like the compiler, the interpreter is a special program which receives the user's program as input. It selects the corresponding machine instructions for each step in the user's program, one at a time, and executes them immediately. It does not produce a machine language program for later use. Thus the interpreter is just what the name implies. The user "speaks" a word in source language, which is immediately interpreted into machine language.

Compiled programs do not have to share machine space with another program at the time they are executed; interpreter programs do. The interpreter itself is in the computer at execution time, which can result in a sizable reduction in the available machine space.[10] Compiled programs are much faster at execution time, since they do not require translation every time a part of the user's program is re-executed. The interpreter does not require a two-stage operation, and, it relieves the user of any need to understand machine language, since modifications of the original program are also written in source language. This is a great advantage if a very complex program is being written but is not planned to be a "production program" to be used over and over after it has been tested. If a program is to be used many times, compilation is usually preferable.

For further discussion of computers and programming, the reader is referred to McCracken's (1957) text, the technical handbook on data processing by Grabbe, Ramo, and Woolridge, (1959), or the manual by Newell (1961).


## 6   *List processing*

Modern digital computers are primarily devices for solving problems in numerical computation. One of the chief reasons for developing computers was to be able to solve large systems of simultaneous differential equations. A major use today is to process statistical and accounting data. In such applications there is no need to find out *how* to solve the particular problem at hand. The human programmer knows how to solve the problem. All the computer provides is a device for performing certain simple arithmetical computations very rapidly. The internal organization of digital computers has been designed to facilitate such computations.

The problems encountered in artificial intelligence research place much greater emphasis on the discovery of a solution method, and less on carrying it out. There is no reason to believe that the optimal artificial intelligence "hardware" is also optimally suited for numerical computation, or vice versa. (It can be proven, however, that the digital computer is a sufficient device for realizing computations in either field. The proof rests on the fact that Boolean logic statements can be realized upon a digital computer.)

Newell, Shaw, and Ellis (1959) and McCarthy (1960*a*, 1961) considered the capabilities that an artificial intelligence system ought to have. They have concluded that a digital computer should be reorganized as a *list-processing* device—a type of computing machine originally developed by Newell and his associates. List processing can be done by the use of a special interpreter and requires no hardware modifications. Two such interpreters are in general use today, Information Processing Language V (IPL-V) (Newell, 1961) and List-Processing Language (LISP) (McCarthy, 1960*b*). These interpreters, in effect, create a machine in which the logic of data storage and computation is the interpreter's and not the computer's.

The principal difference between list processing and normal programming is in the method used to refer to items in memory. Digital computers refer directly to the location of a symbol. In list processing symbols are stored on lists of symbols. The name of the list is the name of the location of the "head," or first symbol on the list. As part of its contents this cell contains the address of the cell that contains the first symbol on the list. The cell containing this symbol also contains the address of the cell containing the second symbol, etc., until the cell containing the last symbol on a list is reached. In this cell the "next location" is replaced by a list termination symbol. The head cell may contain a symbol that is the name of an associated list, or its contents may represent other information. Since the name of a list is a symbol, and may be stored in the head or body of other lists, a complex *list structure*, or cross referencing system between lists, can be developed. Information is found by searching lists until the required symbols are found. Several entries may be provided to a single piece of information by placing a symbol on more than one list. Symbols can be reached indirectly by locating other symbols known to be associated with them.

Another advantage of list processing is that it can be used to program a computer for recursive computation. The details of how this is done need not concern us. [The technique has been explained by Newell (1961).] What we are concerned with is the idea of a recursive operation, since such operations are quite important in artificial intelligence research.

A recursive operation is one in which the function being computed contains itself as a subfunction. This means that the original function must, if it is to be nontrivial, contain three separate types of functions; test functions, argument generating functions, and value computing functions. Consider a main function $f$ with test, argument-generating, and value-computing functions $t$, $g$, and $h$. For simplicity, assume that all functions of one argument $x$, and that $t(x)$ is either 1 or 0. If $f$ is recursive, it can be expressed as

(7.6.1) $$f(x) = h(x) \quad \text{if} \quad t(x) = 1$$
$$f(x) = f(g(x)) \text{ otherwise}$$

The value of $f(x)$ is conditional upon the value of $t(x)$. If $t(x)$ is not 1, then $f$ of the modified argument $g(x)$ must be computed *recursively*, within the general context of computing $f(x)$.

Recursions may be concatenated beyond this simple example. For instance, $h(x)$ might also be recursive. In artificial intelligence systems quite complex recursive operations are found.

McCarthy (1960a, 1961) has developed a notation for expressing recursive operations. We shall present an abbreviated discussion of it to illustrate how problems that are not normally described as mathematical can be presented to a digital computer. We shall not attempt to describe the mechanics of McCarthy's (1960b) computer language for putting his notation into a machine language computer program, nor shall we be concerned with the details of the syntactical structure of his formalisms. (McCarthy uses the Lambda notation first proposed by Church (1958), but we shall ignore the method by which he distinguishes between bound and free variables.) The reader will be able to see how the discussion of McCarthy's notation fits into the study of concept learning if he attempts, while reading the following paragraphs, to answer the question "What is the relation between McCarthy's notation and the graphic TOTE representation of Miller, Galanter, and Pribram (1960)?"

McCarthy expresses a computation $C$ by an ordered set of pairs.

$$(7.6.2) \qquad C = [(p_1, e_1), (p_2, e_2), \ldots (p_n, e_n)]$$

The value of $C$ is determined by evaluating, in order, the pairs $1 \ldots n$. The symbols $\{p_i\}$ represent the values of subcomputations which correspond to the computation $t$ in equation 7.6.1. Every $p_i$ is assumed to have value 1 (true), 0 (false), or to be undefined. In computing, $C$ is assigned the value of subcomputation $e_i$ as soon as a $p_i$ is found which has value 1. The symbols $\{e_i\}$, then, represent computations corresponding to $g$ or $h$ in equation 7.6.1. Formally the value of $C$ is defined by

$$(7.6.3) \qquad C = e_j \ \text{if} \ p_j = 1, \qquad j \leq n$$
$$\text{and} \ p_i = 0, i = 1, \ldots j - 1$$

If no $p_i$ has value 1, or if some $p_j$, $j < i$, is undefined, then $C$ is undefined.

Recursive functions may be written in this notation. Equation 7.6.1 is rewritten as

$$(7.6.4) \qquad f(x) = [(t(x), h(x)), (1, f(g(x)))]$$

Notice that the constant 1 occupies the $p_2$ position in equation 7.6.4, thus insuring that $f(x)$ will be defined. The function still might involve a nonterminating recursion.

We can express the problem of going from place to place by McCarthy's notation. The problem of going from Los Angeles to Boston (section 4) is a specific example of the general problem of going from place to place. In moving, the place at which the person is located ($X$, below) is made equal to the place at which the person wishes to be ($Y$, below).

$$(7.6.5) \qquad \text{MOVE} \ (X, Y) = [((X = Y?)X), (((X - Y) = \text{LONG?}),$$
$$\text{FLY} \ (X, Y)), (((X - Y) = \text{MEDIUM?}),$$
$$\text{DRIVE} \ (X, Y)), (1, \text{WALK} \ (X, Y))]$$

where the English words have their usual connotation. The operation

MOVE is not explicitly recursive, since MOVE $(A,B)$ does not appear on the right-hand side. MOVE would be implicitly recursive if MOVE were a subroutine of FLY, DRIVE, or WALK. Suppose FLY were

(7.6.6)     FLY $(X, Y)$ = $[((X =$ AIRPORT?), TAKEPLANE $(X, Y))$
            $(1,$ TAKEPLANE (MOVE $(X,$ AIRPORT$), Y))]$

The reader can now see the close resemblance between the analyses of McCarthy and Miller et al. McCarthy's notation can be used for the algebraic expression of TOTE units. By the use of list processing, the algebraic expressions can be placed on a digital computer, thus making it possible to use TOTE analyses to predict behavior in a dynamic model.

In list processing, data is stored in a rather different manner than it is in conventional programming. The distinction between data and stored program that is usually found in numerical analysis disappears. Everything, including the program itself, is stored as a list. The program list can be treated as a piece of data by other programs, including its own subroutines. This gives the program a capability for modifying itself, providing that the programmer specifies how such modifications are to take place.[11]

By convention, data can be stored on two types of lists; ordinary lists and description lists. A description list is a list that is attached to another list to specify information about it. There is a close parallel between description lists and the idea of descriptions of objects (Chapter 2). Description lists have dimensions (called attributes) and values. The description list alternates symbols which specify the type of information (attributes) and symbols which specify the information itself (values). Thus, as a value, an identical symbol may mean different things depending on the attribute with which it is associated. As an example, think of the different connotations of "red" as the name of the color of a traffic light and as the name of a political belief. Since values can be the names of lists, the attribute of a particular symbol may be used to provide entry to an extensive structure of information. In addition, description lists may, themselves, have description lists. A compounding of lists in any manner is called a list structure. The name of the list structure is the name of the list which provides the highest-order entry point to all lists. By "highest order" we mean that by entering this list, a path can be traced, via sublists, to any point in the structure.

Suppose we have a list called "PRESIDENTS" which has added to it, in order, the names of each of the Presidents of the United States. The name of each President would be the name of a list structure description list with attributes that corresponded to his immediate relations and values which in turn corresponded to the name of the person who bore that relation to him. Suppose that in 1962 we wish to answer the question, "What is the name of the daughter of the current President of the United States?" Select the last symbol on the list PRESIDENTS. Find the value of the attribute DAUGHTER for this symbol. The symbol thus found, CAROLINE, would be the correct answer. Notice that exactly the same program will work for the President in 1967, although the author does not now know his name, and cannot reserve spaces in advance for the necessary information. The unlikely event that Mrs. Kennedy might have quintuplets in 1963 makes no difference to this program!

Although the example may be frivolous, the principle is not. An artificial intelligence system ought to be able to handle unforeseen but possible conditions.

Set theory was central to the earlier discussion of concept learning. An artificial intelligence system ought to be able to manipulate sets, since these manipulations have such general applicability. Writing artificial intelligence programs in list-processing languages has the advantage that these languages can be thought of as being a special set-theoretic notation. A list may be equated with a set; the symbols on the list (not the cells on the list) become the elements of the set. The basic operations of union, intersection, inclusion, and identity may be made to refer to lists of common and unique symbols on specified lists or list structures.

Ordered, finite sets are also easily expressed in list-processing languages by the simple device of making the position of an item on a list an important piece of information.

Relations can also be expressed. Suppes (1957) discussed relations as sets of ordered $n$ tuples. The $j$th domain[12] of the relation is the set of all items which may appear in the $j$th position of an $n$ tuple in the set of all allowable $n$ tuples. Both sets must be specified, because the set of $n$ tuples defining the relation may not be the same as the set of all possible $n$ tuples that could be created from the $n$ sets of $j$ domains. For instance, take the binary relation "A bigger dog than." The symbols terrier and collie must appear in the first or second domain, since the set of $n$ tuples of the relation has a subset; (Collie, Pekingese), (St. Bernard, Collie), (Terrier, Pekingese), (St. Bernard, Terrier). However, the $n$ tuple (Terrier, Collie) is not a member of the set defined by the relation.

List structures could be used in several ways to represent relations. For example, the main list of the structure could be a list defining an

ordered set, or $n$ tuple, that is an element of the relation. The names
of the lists representing the sets defining the $j$ domains could appear
as values of the appropriate attributes of a description list of the
main list. These lists would be lists of symbols that might appear in
the $j$th position of an $n$ tuple on the main list.

## 7    The logic of simulation

We have discussed artificial intelligence without reference to human
problem solving. If we are going to define "concept" in symbolic
terms, could we not build an automatic concept-learning symbol-
manipulating device? The answer is yes, but that it is difficult to build
an efficient one. When we try to devise an artificial concept learner,
we may come away with more respect for human data-handling capabilities. Humans learn complex concepts under an amazing number
of constraints (e.g., imperfect memory). When we place the same
handicaps on an artificial intelligence system the design problem is
compounded.

Since the data-processing machines available today have entirely
different limitations than do biological problem-solving systems, why
bother to try to design a "computer" model of artificial intelligence
that can operate under human constraints? The practical answer is
that man is the most efficient solver of inductive problems known
today. There are many information processing systems in which people
cannot be replaced. With his abilities, man also brings his limitations.
For instance, human medical doctors are our best diagnosticians of
illness. However, in some situations (notably army induction centers)
the doctors are overwhelmed with data. An ideal examining system
would couple the diagnostic skill of the human with the "brute force"
data-handling capability of a computer. In fact, if we built an inductive reasoner as good as man, it should not be too hard to improve
it. And surely there are inductive problems for which man has been
unable to find a solution.

Extending our information processing capacity is not the only reason
for creating a human simulation system. Such a device might aid us
in understanding how man performs. Before we could create such a
system, we would be forced to state how people behave. The construction of the device would then force us to develop a rigorous theory
of human psychological processes.

Computer program models stand in exactly the same relation to
data and scientific explanation as do mathematical, physical, or any

other types of model (cf. Bergmann, 1944). Ashby (1956) has presented a "black box" supplement to the logic of science analysis which is particularly suited to simulation. Suppose an engineer is faced with a sealed black box. On its outside face are two sets of dials. The engineer may alter one set and observe the readings on the other, but he must not open the box. Suppose further that there are so many settings possible that it would be impractical to record all of them. How is the engineer to predict the "output" dials, the ones that move in response to his setting? (Note that it is arbitrary which set of dials he chooses as output at any one time.) Ashby suggested that the engineer should build a second box, with identical dials and *known* connections between them. Let us refer to this as the transparent box. The transparent box can be tested to see if for some sample of input settings the output settings are identical to the output settings of the black box. It is not necessary for the engineer to actually set the dials on the transparent box. He knows how it works, so he can predict what the output settings will be for any input setting. But in a given case it may be easier to observe the performance rather than to calculate it. The question is one of economy, not of logic. The engineer is entitled to say that he has "explained" the workings of the black box insofar as the transparent box mimics black box performance. Strictly speaking, the engineer can offer this explanation only for tested input settings. However, as the mimicking procedure extends over a larger sample of possible inputs, the engineer is bound to develop subjective confidence in his transparent device. Indeed, Watanabe's analysis can be applied to the result of the mimicry.

In one sense, the engineer never explains the inner workings of the black box. He cannot claim that he has a physical duplicate of the mechanisms which change input into output settings. He has constructed a model which is accurate only in the sense that it produces the same mapping of input dial to output dial as the black box, although an entirely different physical process may be in use.

Ordnance research has provided an example which shows the advantages and limitations of this approach. During World War II there was great interest in the development of a bomb that would correct its trajectory after being launched from an aircraft. A noted scientist presented a (literally) black box which he alleged to contain a guidance device. A small box received, as input, a signal indicating the deviation between desired point of impact and point of impact if the present trajectory were continued. After a short delay it emitted a signal which could be used to correct the trajectory. To the cyberneticist this was a simple, negative feedback computing device. Several such error-compensating radars were available and could be used as "transparent boxes," explaining the behavior of the scientist's device. But mechanical engineers were not satisfied with this explanation. The technology of the mid-1940s could not produce a transparent box that was functionally equivalent to the black box unless it used devices of great size and expense. The transparent boxes available were certainly not expendable. Yet the scientist claimed that his device was a practical method of guiding explosives. (There was another, extra-logical problem. The reputation of the scientist suggested that the device was not electronic.)

The black box contained a pigeon. Further details of this problem, and its ultimate fate, have been reported in the unclassified literature (Skinner, 1960).

An information flow model of Skinner's warlike bird did not have to peck at a screen. It had only to emit a signal indicating where the pigeon would peck. In mathematical terminology, there need only be a one-one mapping from "model" output to "black box" output. Exactly the same logic can be used for input states. *So long as no information is lost in the translation,* the inputs and outputs to the black box may be translated into inputs and outputs convenient to the "transparent box." The two boxes are said to be homologous machines.

We can regard a simulation study as an attempt to develop theorems. For clarity, we shall discuss a hypothetical computer simulation. The initial program represents the postulates, the input data represent the special condition, the interaction of the two produces a theorem. Obviously there is a formal similarity between mathematical models and computer models; they both involve the manipulation of symbols in accordance with prespecified rules. The advantage in realizing a model as a computer program is that by doing so, models may be designed and conditions investigated that would require calculation far beyond the capabilities of humans.[13] In particular, the computer's ability to explore rapidly all the consequences of a few specific postulates is attractive to the theorist. The postulates may be stated in the more general notation of symbolic logic and set theory instead of conventional mathematics and still be computable in practice.

The computer's ability to deal with complex calculations has appealed to several investigators who wished to test basic assumptions about the organization of the nervous system. The studies that have been reported all appear to have been influenced largely by the work of Hebb (1949) and Pitts and McCulloch (1947). Hebb speculated that all the complex behavior of the nervous system could be accounted for by a few basic assumptions about the growth of nerve networks. The ramifications of these assumptions were too complex to explore by hand computation. Rochester, Holland, Haibt, and Duda (1956) programmed a computer to carry out the calculations. They found that, as originally stated, the assumptions were unworkable. They also found that reasonable behavior could be obtained from Milner's (1957) modification of Hebb's theory. Rosenblatt (1961; Block, 1961) has also conducted extensive studies of somewhat different assumptions concerning the growth of nerve nets.

The motivation of such studies is to show that an initially random nerve net can, given certain postulates concerning change of its structure, develop into a highly organized system for transforming input to output data. Inside the digital computer each "nerve" is represented by a set of numbers specifying the current state of its parameters. When a stimulus is presented, all computations are carried out (in a linear sequence since the computer is a linear device) as numerical operations. At the end of the sequence of computations the state of the system is evaluated and the next sequence begun. Von Neumann (1958) suggested that this may demonstrate the basic difference between a computer and a brain; in the biological organism the computation is a truly parallel operation (with the possibility of interaction between computations, as in Kohler's (1940) field theory of brain activity) using analog computational methods. In addition, the sheer number of units in biological systems—much greater than the number of neurons that can be represented within a modern digital computer—limits the realism of the simulation. Any behavior which, in the living brain, depends on the number of neurons cannot be represented in the simulation.

For these reasons Block (1961) stated that the best we can hope for is a demonstration that an initially randomly connected "black box" will eventually organize itself so that it demonstrates interesting behavior. If the fundamental laws of its growth did not violate known neurophysiology, it might be a model of the brain. Green (1961) [14] maintained that this was not enough. To display interesting behavior, random sets either take too long or have to be modified so that they are no longer random. If by "interesting" we mean the simulation of a complex behavior such as concept learning, the foregoing is probably true, but considering the necessary engineering limits on the construction of random nets, this may be too rigorous a criterion. If we could specify the basic operations required in concept learning (or any cognitive activity) and then show that a random net could construct the basic functions, we would have an extremely useful proof. At present this proof is premature because we do not even know the identity of the basic functions.

Other computer simulation studies have been aimed at discovering these very functions. The work has been by no means restricted to concept learning. In fact, most of the research in the area stems from the work of Newell, Simon, and Shaw on deductive logic (Newell and Simon, 1957; Newell and Shaw, 1957). They explained the rationale of their work in an article describing the possible form of an information processing of human problem solving (Newell, Shaw, and Simon, 1958). Although we could wait until we knew what functions a random nerve net of some form could produce, Newell et al. maintained that there was no need to do this. They proposed to investigate the implications of complex rules for information processing by programming them and experimenting with the resulting program. Ideally, such investigations would identify operations derivable from a neurophysiological model of learning. The routines of a program are essentially, TOTE units—symbol-manipulating devices. A strategy is the same thing. Miller, Galanter, and Pribram (1960) have acknowledged the powerful influence that Newell and his associates had on their thinking, and Bruner (1960), although his analysis antedates that of Newell et al., has agreed that the programming approach is a powerful tool in the analysis of strategies and their implications.

Although many theorists interested in complex mental processes [e.g., Hovland (1960), Taylor (1960), and Bruner (1960)] accepted the computer model as a fruitful technique, questions have been raised. Kendler (1961), in discussing the deductive model of Newell et al., pointed out that the argument for simulation rested on similarities between human behavior in previously investigated situations and certain aspects of a program's performance. Kendler evidently felt that this was not enough. "They add nothing to our further understanding of the living mechanisms, but they do provide a better understanding of the computer." (Kendler, 1961, p. 452.) Kendler further suggested that, in spite of the rather disparaging view of Newell et al. of associationist theories (such as Hull's), all they had done was to rediscover the mediating response via mathematics and cybernetics. Kendler completed her review of information processing in concept learning by suggesting that analysis by subjectively discovered TOTE units represented a return to introspective psychology. This would generally not be considered progress.

There appear to be two separate objections. In discussing Miller, Galanter, and Pribram's "subjective behaviorist" approach, Kendler was presumably unsatisfied with the sources of TOTE units. These units are admittedly introspectionist guesses. A scientific model, including an information processing model, stands or falls on its ability to handle the data of its field. The inspiration that led to its construction is irrelevant. At present the TOTE analysis does consist of rather unconnected guesses. Eventually, it is hoped that information processing models in different fields (e.g., problem solving, concept learning, verbal learning) will be related to each other through the existence of common or complementary functional units. Considering the fact that the rigorous information-processing approach to psychology is only a few years old, a criticism that it has not produced a full fledged theoretical system seems premature. On the other hand, the proponents of information processing models cannot yet claim to have proven that their approach is anything more than possible.

Kendler also objected that the models have not yet provided theorems which could be tested in new experiments. Although the utility of information processing models will be determined in part by the number of new experiments they generate, it will also be determined by their ability to handle data from previous experiments. Three criteria can be applied: Do the information processing models provide a more parsimonious explanation (i.e., fewer assumptions) of same data than do previous models? Do the models have a wider range over different experiments, thus tying them together in a neater way? Do they make more detailed predictions within a given setting? At present the answer to these questions appears to be "no," "maybe," and "yes." Compared to their competitors (e.g., mathematical models of discrimination), information-processing models have generally required more unproven assumptions. The range of applicability of models varies widely, from Feldman's (1961) model of behavior in the binary choice situation to Newell, Shaw, and Simon's (1959a) "general problem solver." Information-processing models usually give a more detailed description of the presumed process by which the response was developed. This makes it possible to distinguish between smaller sets of responses. For instance, instead of predicting that a subject will be right or wrong, a prediction may be generated concerning the kind of wrong answer.

Notice that the criterion for validation has changed from that used in discussing nerve net models. We no longer ask that the components of a model be based on plausible neurological assumptions. Instead, we attempt to develop a minimum set of functional units (TOTES or subroutines, depending on the terminology) such that, when a computer is programmed in accordance with these units, its input and output can be put in a one to one relation with certain stimulus-response aspects of a human experimental situation. As we relax the requirement of biological plausibility, we should increase the stringency of our requirement that the computer program actually mimic observed human performance. It must be admitted that present computer models have not been as stringently tested as they should be. Too few theorems have been validated. This is Kendler's strongest objection. Given a set of observed stimuli and responses, it is probably always possible to write some computer program to reproduce them. Some element of prediction is needed.

REFERENCES

Ashby, W. R., 1961. What is an intelligent machine? *Proc. Western Joint Computer Conf.* **12**, 275–280.

Ashby, W. R., 1956. *Introduction to Cybernetics.* New York: Wiley.

Ashby, W. R., 1960. *Design for a Brain* (2nd ed.). New York: Wiley.

Bergmann, G., 1944. An empiricist's system of the sciences. *Sci. Monthly,* 140–148.

Block, H. D., 1961. Analysis of perceptrons. *Proc. Western Joint Computer Conf.,* 281–289.

Bruner, J. S., 1960. Individual and collective problems in the study of thinking. *Ann. N. Y. Acad. Sci.,* **90,** 22–37.

Bruner, J. S., J. J. Goodnow, and G. A. Austin, 1956. *A Study of Thinking.* New York: Wiley.

Bush, R. and F. Mosteller, 1951. *Stochastic Models for Learning.* New York: Wiley.

Church, A., 1958. *Introduction to Mathematical Logic,* Princeton: Princeton University Press.

Estes, W. K., 1950. Toward a statistical theory of learning. *Psychol. Rev.,* **57,** 94–107.

Feldman, J., 1961. Simulation of behavior in the binary choice experiment. *Proc. Western Joint Computer Conf.,* 133–144.

Gelernter, H. L., 1959. Realization of a geometry theorem proving machine. *Proc. UNESCO Conf. on Information Processing.* Paris: UNESCO House.

Gormezano, I. and D. A. Grant, 1958. Progressive ambiguity in the attainment of concepts on the Wisconsin card sorting test, *J. exp. Psychol.,* **55,** 621–627.

Grabbe, E., S. Ramo, and D. Woolridge, 1959. *Handbook of Automation, Computation, and Control. Vol. 2.* New York: Wiley.

Green, B. F., Jr., 1961. Computer models of cognition. *Psychometrika,* **26,** 85–96.

Hebb, D. O., 1949. *The Organization of Behavior.* New York: Wiley.

Hovland, C. I., 1960. Computer simulation of thinking. *Amer. Psychologist,* **15,** 687–693.

Ittner, W. and C. J. Kraus, 1961. Superconducting computers, *Sci. American,* **205,** 125–136.

Kendler, T. S., 1960. Concept formation. *Annu. Rev. Psychol.,* **12,** 447–472.

Kochen, M., 1960. Experimental study of "hypotheses formation" by computer. *Proc. 1960 London Sympos. on Information Theory.*

Kohler, W., 1940. *Dynamics in Psychology.* New York: Liveright.

Luce, R. D. and H. Raiffa, 1957. *Games and Decisions: Indroduction and Critical Survey.* New York: Wiley.

Marschak, J., 1960. Remarks on the economics of information. In *Contributions to Scientific Research in Management*, Berkeley: University of California Press.

McCarthy, J., 1961. A basis for a mathematical theory of computation, preliminary report. *Proc. Western Joint Computer Conf.*, 225–238.

McCarthy, J., 1960a. Recursive functions of symbolic expressions and their computation by machine. *Communication of the Assoc. for Computing Machinery*, 3, 184–195.

McCarthy, J. (ed.), 1960b. The LISP-I Programmer's Manual. M.I.T.

McCracken, D. D., 1951. *Digital Computer Programming*. New York: Wiley.

McCulloch, W. and W. Pitts, 1943. A logical calculus of the ideas imminent in nervous activity. *Bull. Math. Biophys.*, 5, 115–137.

Miller, G., E. Galanter, and K. Pribram, 1960. *Plans and the structure of behavior*. New York: Holt.

Milner, P. M., 1957. The cell assembly, Mark II. *Psychol. Rev.*, 64, 242–252.

Minsky, 1961a. Steps toward artificial intelligence. *Proc. of The Institute of Radio Engineers*, 49, 8–30.

Minsky, 1961b. A selected descriptor indexed bibliography to the literature on artificial intelligence. *Proc. Institute of Radio Engineers*, 49, 39–55.

Newell, A. (ed.), 1961. *Information Processing Language V. Manual*. Englewood Cliffs, N. J.: Prentice-Hall.

Newell, A. and J. C. Shaw, 1957. Programming the logic theory machine. *Proc. Western Joint Computer Conf.*

Newell, A., J. C. Shaw, and T. Ellis, 1959. A command system for complex information processing. *Rand Corp. Tech. Rep.*

Newell, A., J. C. Shaw, and H. A. Simon, 1955. Current developments in complex information processing. *Rand Corp. Tech. Rep.*

Newell, A., J. C. Shaw, and H. A. Simon, 1958. Elements of a theory of human problem solving. *Psychol. Rev.*, 65, 151–166.

Newell, A., J. C. Shaw, and H. A. Simon, 1959a. Report on a general problem solving program. *Proc. 1st International Conf. on Information Processing*. Paris: UNESCO House.

Newell, A., J. C. Shaw, and H. A. Simon, 1959b. A variety of intelligent learning in the general problem solver. *Rand Corp. Tech. Rep.*

Newell, A. and H. A. Simon, 1957. Empirical explorations of the logic theory machine: a case study in heuristics. *Proc. Western Joint Computer Conf.*

Pitts, W. and W. S. McCulloch, 1947. How we know universals: the perception of auditory and visual forms. *Bull. Math. Biophys.*, 9, 127–147.

Polya, G., 1957. *How to Solve It*. New York: Dover.

Polya, G., 1954. *Mathematics and Plausible Reasoning* (2 vols.). Princeton: Princeton University Press.

Rochester, M., J. Holland, L. Haibt, and W. Duda, 1956. Test on a cell assembly theory of the action of the brain, using a large digital computer. *Institute of Radio Engineers Trans. Information Theory*, PGIT-2, 80–93.

Reed, H. B., 1946. The learning and retention of concepts. I. The influence of set. *J. exp. Psychol.*, 36, 71–87.

Rosenblatt, F., 1961. *Principles of Neurodynamics*. Cornell Aeronautical Laboratory Report.

Selfridge, O., 1959. Pandemonium, a paradigm for learning. In Blake and Utley (ed.), *Proc. 1958 Sympos. Mechanization of Thought Processes*, London: H. M. Stationery Office.

Shannon, C. and W. Weaver, 1949. *The Mathematical Theory of Communication.*
Champaign: University of Illinois Press.

Siegel, S., 1959. Theoretical models of choice and strategy behavior: stable state
behavior in the two choice uncertain outcome situation. *Psychometrika*, **24**,
303–316.

Skinner, B. F., 1960. Pigeons in a pelican. *Amer. Psychologist*, **15**, 28–37.

Sluckin, W., 1960. *Minds and Machines*, Baltimore: Penguin Books.

Slagle, J., 1961. SAINT, A symbolic automatic integrator. *M.I.T.–Lincoln Lab.
Technical Report.*

Suppes, P., 1957. *Introduction to Logic.* Princeton: Van Nostrand.

Taylor, D. W., 1960. Toward an information processing theory of motivation.
*Proc. Nebraska Sympos. on Motivation.*

Turing, A. M., 1950. Can a Machine Think? *Mind.* (Reprinted in Newman, J. R.)
*The World of Mathematics Vol. IV.* New York: Simon and Schuster, 1956.

Von Neumann, J., 1958. *The Computer and the Brain.* New Haven: Yale University
Press.

Wang, H., 1960. Toward Mechanical Mathematics. *I.B.M. J. Research and Development,* **4**, 2–22.

Weiner, N., 1948. *Cybernetics.* New York: Wiley.

FOOTNOTES

1. David Brinkley, on the "David Brinkley Journal," NBC-TV, November 22,
   1961.
2. It may be difficult to discover the optimal internal state. Its determination becomes an important problem if changes must take place in a continuous space
   and if there are locally optimal points in this region. The problem is further
   discussed by Minsky (1961a) and Selfridge (1959).
3. Minsky (1961a, b) has reviewed the field from a somewhat different point of
   view. He has provided an extensive bibliography.
4. An empirical test has never been made and is difficult to envisage.
5. So called for the contention that a monkey, if given the time, would eventually
   produce all the books in the British Museum by playing with a typewriter.
6. Wang (1960) has shown that in symbolic logic there is an algorithmic proof
   method which operates with reasonable speed. Newell et al. were primarily
   interested in artificial intelligence methods, not in the proof of theorems in
   symbolic logic.
7. We purposely avoid stating what the decision policy is. A great many considerations will enter into this, including the decision maker's estimate of whether
   or not he is playing a game against a rational opponent (Luce and Raiffa,
   1957).
8. This result was obtained by analyzing Ashby's (1960, p. 151) third case as a
   linear difference equation.
9. Input and output devices will not be further discussed. They are irrelevant to
   the logical problem, although they may become major technological bottlenecks
   in the construction of artificial intelligences.
10. LISP, an interpreter program with a compiler option, is a program used in
    many artificial intelligence studies. It occupies approximately 40% of the avail-
    able space of the IBM 7090 computer, one of the largest now available. IPL V,

a similar interpreter with a less human-oriented source language, occupies less than half the space.

11. LISP and IPL V use different procedures to do this.
12. The terminology used here is different from Suppes.
13. In spite of their speed, computers may not be fast enough for some problems. Kochen (1960) has given an example of a concept-learning problem in which this is true.

# 8

# An information-processing model of concept learning

## 1.  Introduction

There are many possible models that could be classified as "information processing." Analysis of human concept learning requires a particular model, one in which there is an adequate simulation of human performance. What should the characteristics of this model be?

The late Sterling Professor Carl Hovland, of Yale University, aided by his students and associates, conducted a series of studies to answer this question. At first they concentrated on experiments that established contrasts between human performance and the performance of Hovland's (1952) hypothetical perfect (and unbuildable) concept learner. As a result of this research, some of the operators needed in a simulation model were specified (Hovland and Hunt, 1960). An information-processing model was constructed (as an ILP-V digital computer program) and some hypothetical experiments performed (Hunt and Hovland, 1961). It had been hoped at first that this model could be used to simulate a large number of experiments already reported in the literature of experimental psychology, but this proved impossible. In some cases the original investigators had left uncontrolled variables which, according to the model, were of crucial importance. In other cases it appeared that subjects had been presented with problems with trivial information processing aspects. Presumably, any difficulty the subjects had was due to the extremely rapid rate of presentation of stimuli (usually less than 10 seconds per stimulus), which would have changed the problem from one of conception to one of perception.

A second goal of the project was to investigate the effects of introducing alternate procedures in different sections of the complex model. Here major emphasis was on experiments using the information-processing model. The work fell more in the field that Amarel (1960) has called "experimental engineering." A model containing several alternate ways of performing different operations was presented with different types of problems. The model's ability to obtain solutions and the manner in which the solutions were obtained were the principal variables of interest. As in the other work, an attempt was made to relate engineering and psychological experiments. In some cases psychological experiments were conducted to develop new parallels between the model's performance and human data.

No single, all encompassing model of human performance was ever developed. After evaluating the results obtained in a series of small studies, however, the current author believes that several conclusions can be reached about the performance of such a model. The conclusions fall into two, not always exclusive categories; requirements for an information processing model, and research techniques for realizing and analyzing such a model. The conclusions will be presented in this chapter. They are entirely those of the author and do not necessarily represent the views of Hovland or any of his other associates.

## 2   Analytic and research techniques

The first conclusion is not surprising; it is possible to develop an information-processing theory of concept learning. In so doing, it has proven desirable to realize the model as a computer program. List-processing techniques were used to program the necessary set theoretic formulas and, as will be seen, to construct a decision tree. List processing is not necessary, however. Kochen (1960) developed a concept-learning system that was programmed in machine language.

Programming proved to be an expensive way to theorize. A great deal of time was devoted to programming after the theoretical decisions had been made. Also, as is typical of many simulation studies, the model tries to make a digital computer perform a task for which it is not optimally designed. As a result, simulation studies required a large amount of computing time. Since computer time is valuable, the experimenter should be able to show at least that his results might be able to justify the expense. Obviously no general statement about when to use a computer program is possible. But it does not seem a worthwhile scientific strategy to invest effort in a complex simulation study until mathematical analysis has been pushed as far as it possibly can be. When the same level of precision can be attained by either method, analysis should always be preferred to simulation.

Simulation models are the most useful when a single simple principle leads to such complex computations that mathematical analysis is impossible. Experiments with the model revealed that such a principle was involved in concept learning. Although the model had originally been written as a statement of manipulations of sets, an examination of the concepts it developed when given different logical types of problems indicated that they could be regarded as trees of sequential decisions. At least to the author, this was an unexpected result and demonstrated how simulations may reveal unanticipated theorems in a complex model. It was interesting because decision trees have been used explicitly in models of concept use (Banerji, 1960), verbal learning (Feigenbaum, 1959, 1961), and decision making (Luce and Raiffa, 1957).

A decision tree is a line graph. Line graphs are networks constructed by defining a set of points and a set of lines, each line connecting two points. Decision trees are representations of a series of decisions by what Riordan (1960) has defined as a planted, rooted tree. A single point is arbitrarily designated as the starting point or *root*. This point could be connected to another point by means of a line segment. To fit Riordan's definition of a planted tree, the root must be connected to only one other point outside the tree. In the trees constructed by the concept-learning model, the concept is represented by a tree whose roots are not connected to any point outside the tree. Each point, or *node*, in a tree has exactly one connection to a point closer to the root (i.e., a node is attached to only one other node which is separated from the root by fewer line segments than the original node). If node $a$ is closer to the root than node $b$, then $a$ is higher than $b$.[1] Unless a node is an endpoint, it is connected to two lower nodes and, through them, to any number of still lower nodes. Endpoints are nodes connected to a higher node and to *no* lower nodes. An $n$-ary tree is one whose nodes are connected to $n$ lower nodes. We shall deal with binary trees exclusively. A *path* is a collection of lines from the root to an endpoint.

A binary tree is represented in Figure 8-1. Roots and endpoints are distinguished, and paths are defined by their endpoints. The length of a path is the number of line segments in it. A stem is defined by stating the highest node in the collection of lines making up the stem. In Figure 8-1 an example of a stem is given. Every stem is itself a planted, rooted tree, whose root is one of the two branches of the next highest node in the decision tree. Stating this node and branch is equivalent to defining the stem. The height of the tree is the length of the longest path. The diameter of the tree is defined by the greatest distance (number of line segments) between two endpoints. We could similarly define average height as the average length of a path and average diameter as the average distance between two endpoints.

If Figure 8-1 is to represent a decision tree, decisions should be involved. The technique of representing sequential decisions by trees

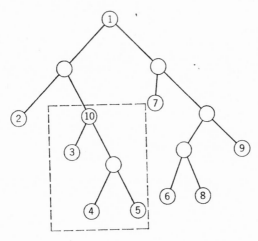

Figure 8-1. A planted, rooted binary decision tree.
Point 1 is the root; points 2–9 are endpoints;
point 10 is the highest node of the stem enclosed
in dots. Height of tree = 4; diameter = 8.

is a familiar one in game theory, where strategies are so represented
(Luce and Raiffa, 1957). The use of trees in concept learning is little
different. A test is associated with each node. Information to be tested
is assumed to be available at all times. (The information could be the
result of previous tests.) Depending on the result of the test, a particular branch to a lower node is taken, and the process is repeated
until an endpoint is reached. At each endpoint one of the alternatives
available to a decision maker is specified. Reaching an endpoint in
the model is equivalent to taking this action.

An example of such a tree is given in Figure 8-2. This figure demonstrates the identification of playing cards as members of one of four
classes, depending on their value (face card or number) and suit.[2]
Figure 8-2 demonstrates two important features. One is the convention,
which we shall follow throughout, of assigning the left-hand branch
of a node as the path to be followed if the node's question is answered
affirmatively, the right-hand side as the path if the question is answered
in the negative. We shall refer, respectively, to a positive and negative
branch. A positive path below node $x$ will mean the path from node $x$
to an endpoint which contains as line segments only positive branches.

The second feature illustrated by Figure 8-2 is that different trees
may be used to make the same ultimate discrimination. These trees
may vary in complexity. If measures based on a decision tree are to be

used to describe concept learning or any other psychological process, the manner of constructing the tree will be of considerable importance. Different construction techniques will produce different trees to handle the same data.

In concept-learning studies we are concerned with decision trees that make tests on the descriptions of objects. Each node of the tree is associated with a test to establish whether an object is (or is not) included in a set of objects defined by a particular descriptive statement or string of statements. Arriving at an endpoint is equivalent to assigning the object under consideration to a subset of objects defined by the intersection of the sets defined by higher nodes of the branch. For instance, in Figure 8-2 class *D* is the set of all cards that are black, not clubs, and not face cards.

If the decision tree is an adequate representation of the concept of a particular name, the sets defined by the endpoints will all be either subsets of the denotation of a name or subsets of the complement of

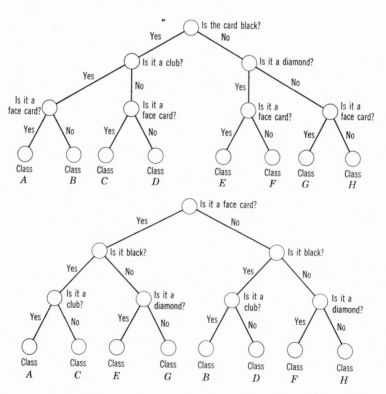

Figure 8-2. Two decision trees for grouping playing cards.

the denotation. Arrival at an endpoint will be sufficient to establish whether or not the name can be applied to the object under consideration. Arrival at an endpoint is also equivalent to assigning an object to some set $e_i$ of objects having a given description (see Chapter 2). Obviously there is a close interdependence between the use of a description and a decision tree.

## 3     *Requirements for a simulation model: object description*

A concept-learning simulation must provide for an alternate description of the objects to be categorized. As we pointed out in Chapter 2, several concepts may be associated with the same name, depending on the description of the objects. If the concepts define equivalent sets in the universe of objects, there is no problem, since the concepts will be functionally identical. In the typical concept-learning situation, however, an hypothesis must be developed from a sample of the universe. The possibility exists that there will be two or more concepts, based on different descriptions, which are equivalent for the sample but not for the universe. This happened in the experiment by Hunt and Hovland (1960) in which the "learning sample" could be categorized by rules based on a particular set of dimensions or dimensions which were defined in terms of the relations between the values of dimensions of the first description. In that experiment, approximately half of the subjects used each description.

Establishing a description is, itself, a two-phase process. In the first phase dimensions and values are defined; in the second a subset of dimensions and values are selected as a focus of attention. Either of these phases could come first. Although it should be relatively easy for an experimenter and a subject to come to an agreement on the definition of dimensions and values, it is more difficult for them to agree on a focus of attention unless the stimuli are quite simple or the experimenter is willing to state, in advance, the relevant dimensions.

The act of describing stimuli is really a problem in perception. As we saw in Chapter 4, this field has no systematic theoretical development. Therefore, we cannot expect to develop any model of concept learning which contains within itself a method for developing descriptions. At best, we can provide a set of a priori methods of computing descriptions and scanning them. It is not at all clear what these should be. In their model, Hunt and Hovland (1961) provided two alternatives: either accept a predefined formal description, or calculate the values of dimensions based on "equality-inequality" or (for dimensions with numerical values on a common scale) "equal, greater, or less than" relations between the values of dimensions of the formal description. They also suggested that certain dimensions such as color and shape of figure in a figure-ground relation should always be perceived together. In other words, a computer simulation should provide for the grouping of stimulus elements according to the "laws of perception." Until these laws are stated more accurately, we can do this only for a limited class of pretested stimuli. This, of course, is not really a useful simulation, since it is simply a way of expressing what we already know. But it may help in preparing data for the next major phase of concept learning, the discovery of a solution.

Unless we know the entire life history of a subject we cannot predict how he will initially describe stimuli. But we may be able to predict how he could, or should, change his description of objects as he gains information during a particular concept-learning problem.

There is one situation in which the concept learner can be positive that he should change his description. If two apparently identical objects are observed, but one can be assigned a name and another cannot, the current description cannot be relevant to the concept of that name. Kochen (1960) has referred to this situation as a *primary inconsistency*. Primary inconsistencies imply that either there is some way of discriminating between objects which is not reflected in the current description or that the concept of the name is a probabilistic one. By definition (Chapter 2), the second situation has been ruled out of concept learning.

The occurrence of a primary inconsistency does not specify the way in which the description must be changed to make it relevant. Referring back to the formal description of relevancy, we see that primary inconsistencies indicate that one of the subsets of conceivable objects $c_j \subset C$ has a nonempty intersection with the set $P$ of objects that can be assigned a name (the denotation of the name) and with the set $\bar{P}$ of objects that cannot be assigned the name (the complement of the denotation). This could happen in one of two ways. In the current description $\phi$, one of the relevant dimensions $\Omega_l$ of the possible description space $\Omega$ might be disregarded. Alternately, one of the dimensions of the current description might represent a derivation from two more molecular dimensions. This abstracting process might have produced an irrelevant description from a relevant one. For instance, if a basketball coach was interested in absolute height he would not describe his players in terms of their height-weight ratios. Unless the learner has exacted a promise from the experimenter, or from nature, that certain definitions of dimensions and values are relevant,[3] he does not know whether he should recompute his entire description or merely alter his focus of attention. It may be that different psychological processes are involved in each change.

A heuristic guide for changing descriptions may be used. The learner might know that a usable concept would have to be represented by a simple tree (e.g., of maximum path $n$). While using a description the learner could observe the complexity of the tree being developed. If it began to approach or exceed the allowed complexity, changing the description would be rational. If the current description was not relevant, nothing would be lost. If it was, there still would be negligible loss, since either there would have to be another relevant description in which the concept could be defined more simply, or the problem would be beyond the information processing capacities of the learner. Notice that the learner should consider why he is failing to solve a problem before he changes his description. Changes based on the maximum complexity guide should, to be useful, impose a simpler structure on the environment (i.e., reduce the number of dimensions), whereas changes based on the primary inconsistency guide should generally make available more information about the stimuli. This would require a more complex description.

## 4    Selection of positive instances

Given a particular description, the model must be provided with a technique for discovering an adequate concept. This involves the establishment and checking of a tentative answer.

We can further this development of an hypothesis in concept learning by designating a particular class of objects as "positive instances" and then discovering certain aspects of the descriptions of objects common to all the positive instances. In the checking phase instances outside the set of positive instances are examined to make sure that the hypothesis does not classify any of them erroneously. In learning to name animals, we discover how to tell "dogs" from "not dogs," not dogs from horses, dogs from cows, and dogs from pigs.

The decision to follow a "positive focusing" plan was drawn more from psychological research than from computer simulation. The dominant strategies used by Bruner, Goodnow, and Austin's (1956) subjects involved developing hypotheses from positive instances, even when this strategy was not the most efficient one. Further evidence for asymmetrical treatment of positive and negative instances was obtained in an unpublished study by Bregman and Hovland, cited in Chapter 5, and by Wallach (1959). Hovland (1952) pointed out that, on the average, positive instances transmit more information, so this strategy can be defended as rational.

On the other hand, human subjects do not always accept an experimenter's definition of "positive instances." It is logically correct, and may be simpler, to define the concept of a name by stating (*a*) the concept that defines the *complement* of the denotation and (*b*) the fact that the complement of the denotation is being defined. This device can be especially useful when the subject is attempting to learn a disjunctive concept. (Bruner et al. and Wells [1962] observed such behavior.) The ability to change the definition of positive instances should be contained within the model.

This capability was included in Hunt and Hovland's model. At any one time their system sought to develop discriminations between the positive and negative instances. Different options could be exercised to define these sets. The first was to make the set of positive instances equivalent to the denotation of the name whose concept was to be learned. The second was to make it equivalent to the complement of the denotation. The third and fourth procedures could be utilized if there were several concepts to be learned. First the model selected the *largest* (or smallest) denotation of any name whose concept was to be learned and developed a concept for that name. Then it removed all objects in the denotation of that name from the universe of objects to be categorized, and repeated the procedure until all concepts were learned. This strategy reduces the amount of data to be handled. If the largest denotations are handled first, the fastest data reduction is achieved. At the same time, it increases the number of positive instances considered during the early stages of concept learning. Considering the smallest denotation first reduces the number of positive instances to be examined early in the problem but does not achieve as rapid a reduction of data.

Do we ever define concepts this way? Apparently we do. Health, for instance, is not defined by the presence of particular stimulus elements, or by a definition of "unhealthy," but rather by the absence of relevant characteristics of particular ailments.

## 5    The development of decision trees

After positive instances are selected, the model must have a procedure for defining a concept based on them. By combining our criteria

for a model and our knowledge of the psychology of human concept
learning we can place some requirements on this procedure. In the
interests of theoretical parsimony, only a few simple tests on input
data should be used. These tests could be applied recursively. To
agree with our empirical knowledge, the model should reach an answer
more rapidly if a conjunctive concept is to be learned. Ideally, the
mechanics of reaching this answer should be compatible with models
of information processing in other areas of human behavior.

In Hunt and Hovland's model a *conditional focusing* routine was
included to give the model the capability of attaining disjunctive concepts. Although originally conceived of as a recursive formula using
an algebra of sets (an analysis based on McCarthy's (1960) discussion
of feasible computation in list processing), it was found upon experimentation, to develop "concepts" that were identical to a decision tree
structure. (This is not a new discovery. R. B. Banerji pointed out in
correspondence that decision trees can be represented by an algebra
of sets. The fact remains that, in this particular case, the computer
simulations had heuristic value in pointing out the applicability of a
particular technique.) Further examination of these answers showed
that, with a single modification, the conditional focusing routine could
be made to favor conjunctive hypotheses when offered a choice.

First we shall describe the original conditional focusing routine as
a procedure for developing a decision tree. An equivalent description
as a recursive function operating on sets was given by Hunt and Hovland (1961). Then some of the suggested modifications will be discussed.

Figure 8-3 represents the flow diagram for conditional focusing.
Initially the routine must be given a list of positive instances, a list
of negative instances, and the name of the current node. At the beginning of a problem the node would be the name of the root of the
tree, the two lists would contain all positive and negative instances.
These may be modified during recursions within the main routine.

The first step (in Figure 8-3) is to determine whether the input node
is an endpoint. If it is, one of the two lists of instances will be empty.
The node may be associated with the name of instances on the nonempty list (1) and the routine terminated.

If the two input lists are not empty, a test must be made to distinguish between them. First, all descriptive elements common to *all*
instances are removed (2), since they could not provide discriminating
information. Then the descriptive statement most commonly found
to be applicable to positive instances is located (3). The test to be
associated with the node is a test for its applicability. All objects to

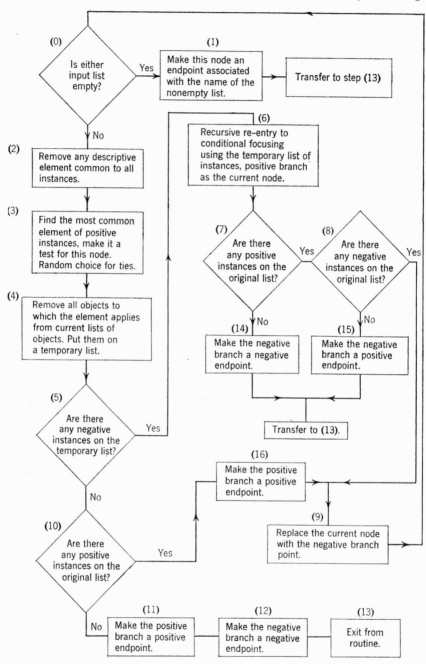

Figure 8-3. Conditional focusing.

which this statement can be applied are removed from *both* positive and negative lists (4). In psychological terms, this is equivalent to selecting some objects for special attention; these objects are the "most typical" positive instances by a crude criterion. "Glaring examples" of negative instances that are like typical positive instances (by the same criterion) receive special attention at the same time. If there are *no* such glaring examples, a positive result for this test is sufficient, *at this node*, to distinguish positive from negative instances. Therefore, the node at the end of the positive branch of the original node may be made an endpoint associated with the name of the set of positive instances (steps 5, 10, and 16). The negative branch can be made an endpoint, however, only if there are no more positive instances left on the original list (steps 10, 12, 13); otherwise the test developed at step 3 is a sufficient but not necessary condition to distinguish positive from negative instances. Thus the node at the end of the negative branch should contain further tests to distinguish between the instances not classified by the test at the original node. Elaboration of the tree along the negative branch is accomplished by replacing the currently active node with the node at the end of the negative branch (9), and then returning control to further processing of the remaining instances (0).

What if the "most common element" of positive instances also appeared on some negative instances, if there were "glaring examples"? If this happened, the node at the end of the positive branch, instead of being an endpoint, should be a further test, or entry to a tree of tests, which discriminated between instances on the temporary lists defined in step (4). Such a test is accomplished by a recursive entry to the conditional focusing program, using the temporary lists as the instances to be processed and using the node at the end of the positive branch as the active node (steps 5, 6). Further recursions may be made within this recursion, leading to an elaborate tree. Whenever the process terminates the program will return control to the next higher level. Recursion will then proceed down the original negative branch. First a test is made to see whether or not the negative branch can be used as an endpoint [i.e., check to see if only one type of instance remains to be classified (steps 7, 8, and 14 or 15)]. If it cannot, a tree is elaborated, with its root at the right branch.

As an illustration, let us observe the performance of the conditional focusing routine on the Shepard, Hovland, and Jenkins (1961) "Type II" problem presented in Table 8-1. First, the frequency of descriptive elements on positive instances is counted. All six statements (large, small, black, white, circle, triangle) appear an equal number of times,

*Table 8-1   A Type II problem*

| Positive Instances | Negative Instances |
| --- | --- |
| Large, black circles | Large, black triangles |
| Large, white circles | Large, white triangles |
| Small, black triangles | Small, black circles |
| Small, white triangles | Small, white circles |

so one is chosen at random. Suppose "large" is chosen. At the first node (the root), instances will be divided into "large" and "small" objects. At the positive node immediately below the root, a discrimination will be made between (large, black circles) (large, white circles) and (large, black triangles), (large, white triangles). A discrimination on "large" is not permitted. The most common element over positive instances in the subproblem is "circles." This discrimination separates all positive from negative instances. Similarly, on the right-hand (negative) branch, the discrimination based on "triangle" separates positive and negative instances in the subproblem based on "small" objects.

Suppose the initial random choice had been of a discrimination based on the irrelevant element "white" instead of the relevant "large"? The model has no way of determining the relevancy of a test until it is made. What would happen is that the tree of Figure 8-4 would be duplicated at either node below the irrelevant test. This decision tree is indicated in Figure 8-5.

Either of these trees can be contrasted to the simple tree for the Type I problem of Shepard et al. In a Type I problem all positive instances have one value (e.g., large) in common that is never found on negative instances. The "tree" would be a root, containing the question "Is object large?" and two endpoints.

As presented, the conditional focusing routine is an algorithm for

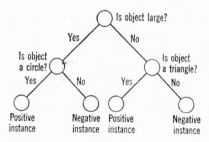

Figure 8-4. One possible decision tree for the Type II problem.

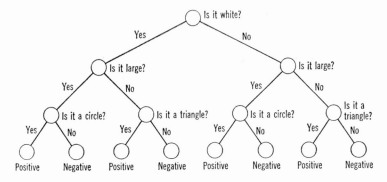

Figure 8-5. Second possible decision tree for the same problem.

producing answers. Clearly this will not do as a simulation. Hunt and Hovland suggested that it could be made a simulation by arbitrarily limiting the number of recursions permitted. This limited the maximum length of a path. Using an arbitrary limit, the performance of the program was compared to human performance in attacking five concept-learning problems varying in complexity from a two-dimensional conjunctive concept to complex disjunctions.[4] Although there was reasonably good agreement between the accuracy of classification of objects made by the model and by the humans, performance differences were noted. The variability of answers given by humans was not approached. The complexity of the tree grown for conjunctive problems did not reflect the ease with which subjects solved these problems. Although subjects did initially concentrate on positive instances as defined by the experimenter, they were ready to shift their definition. The model was not designed to shift so rapidly.

Two modifications of the conditional focusing routine should be effective in producing the required behavior. Interestingly enough, they also might improve the performance of the routine as an artificial intelligence, since they result in a less complex tree for a given problem.

A check for possible conjunctive answers was introduced in a later study by Hunt (1962). This alteration, which has been placed between steps (0) and (2) of Figure 8-3, is indicated in Figure 8-6. What it does is determine what set (if any) of descriptive statements can be applied to *all* positive instances. This set is called a *focus*. A check of negative instances is made to determine whether any negative instance contains the focus in its description. If there is no such instance, a test for the presence of the focus is sufficient to distinguish between all positive

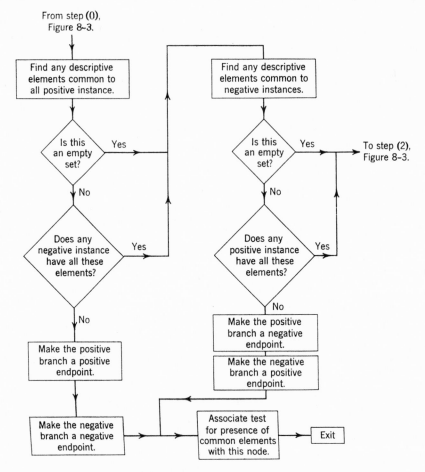

Figure 8-6. Modification of conditional focusing for a rapid solution of conjunctive problems. From step (1), Figure 8-3.

and negative instances, so both branches from this node may go to endpoints. If no focus can be found using positive instances, the procedure may be repeated using negative instances to develop the focus. If this also fails to find a focus, the main computation is entered at step 2.

At first glance such a modification appears to increase computational complexity greatly. Actually it does not; the calculations depicted in Figure 8-6 are not as time consuming (especially in list-processing languages) as the computations of step (2) of Figure 8-3.[5]

All the computing in Figure 8-6 can be done by using a single operation for selecting identical descriptions. The description of the first instance on a list is copied, and the copy is matched to the description of each successive instance in that list. If the values of a dimension on a copy and an instance do not agree, the dimension is removed from the copy. If any dimensions and values remain in the copy after the list of instances has been scanned, the copy is itself a statement of common descriptive elements. An analogous procedure can be used to match for nonidentity when negative instances are being examined. It seems reasonable to assume that a matching procedure would, in biological organisms, be more rapid than the counting procedures required by step (2) of Figure 8-3. A recent proposal for a computer memory device (Kiseda et al., 1961) suggests that matching could be achieved economically in future computer systems.

To avoid unlimited and impractical recursions we can introduce an entry parameter. Before entering the main computation at step (2), Figure 8-3, a stochastic decision could be made. With probability $(p)$, the program would terminate conditional focusing and return control to the next higher branch. This single parameter $p$ would place a "stochastic limit" on the height of the branch of a tree that could be developed. For any $p < 1$ there could be found a number $x$ such that the probability of developing a path of length $x$ was arbitrarily small. In effect, this limits the complexity of the concepts which the model will try to develop. It serves as a guard against the selection of irrelevant tests.

Limiting the depth of a recursion offers several ways of obtaining interesting new behavior. A random signal to stop recursions could be interpreted as a signal to re-examine the choices made previously, or it could be seen as a signal to alter the description of objects. The choice between these two alternatives might be determined by a random decision.

There is no reason why choice to continue recursion must depend on a constant or a random parameter. The value of $p$ could be an increasing function of the depth of the recursion, so that the more complex the tree, the greater the chance of a stop signal. It could also be determined by the ratio of positive to negative instances at the current node. Either of these relations would allow the model to limit the complexity of the answer because of cost of computation or because the discriminative power to be gained by further computation was known to be small. In our discussion of algorithms and heuristics, we saw that a good artificial intelligence considers both these variables.

## 6    *Relation to stimulus-response theories*

We have presented a picture of a three-phase concept-learning model: perception, about which we can say very little, definition of positive instances, and answer development by the "decision tree" technique. Can the manner in which the various steps of concept learning are assembled be specified? In so specifying, can we trace a connection between information processing and stimulus response theories of concept learning?

It is possible to make a serial analysis of each step in the model's concept-learning process. We could think of each of these steps as an instrumental response and discuss the process of learning a particular chain of responses to the stimuli created by previous responses. This would be consistent with the analysis of thinking presented by Maltzman (1955), Kendler and Kendler (1962), Goss (1961), and Osgood (1953). But this poses problems in specifying the order for each class of responses and in specifying rules by which ineffective responses are changed.

We can only observe the initial stimulus and final response. If we could specify either a logical order for the intervening (mediating) responses or a correspondence between particular orders and possible observable stimulus-response relations, we could infer the order of mediating responses. But in concept-learning studies neither course is possible. Exactly the same set of answers will be produced if the order of applying mediating responses is: (*a*) define dimensions, select instances on which attention can be focused, and attempt to develop an answer or (*b*) select a subset of instances on which to focus attention, define dimensions within these instances, and attempt to develop an answer. It might be possible to infer the order *if* we knew the rules for changing responses. In particular, stimulus-response theories usually assume that the effects of reward or nonreward are distributed backward over stimulus-response bonds in a manner determined approximately by a negative exponential function. (The effect of a reward on the response which lead to it is assumed to be a negative exponential function of the time between response and reward.) If such a redistribution of response strength actually did portray the rules for changing components of a chain of responses in concept learning, could we not determine the order of application of each type of response by observing which types of responses were the most labile both within and across problems?

Apparently not. The probability that a particular response will occur depends on both its own response strength and the response strength of other possible responses in the same hierarchy (Hull, 1943). Therefore, a particular response might be continued, although it had participated in a series of fruitless chains of responses and was quite close to the point of nonreward, simply because it had no strong competitors in its habit family hierarchy. An organism operating on strict S-R principles for changing solution procedures might be led into extremely stereotyped behavior. Wertheimer (1959) maintained that this possibility was so likely that an S-R analysis of intelligent behavior could not be adequate. Instead, he argued, a model of "good" productive thinking must provide for an alteration of the problem solver's attack on a problem based on an understanding of the relations between the elements of the problem.[6] Although it might be possible to build such "understanding" into an S-R mechanism, the resulting model would probably be unwieldy. If we equate deductions of inferences from the information obtained while making a fruitless attempt at solution to Wertheimer's "understanding," a rational reselection of subresponses may be achieved. This can occur in an information-processing model.

In the proposed model two types of information can be extracted from failures to develop a decision tree. A primary inconsistency (section 3) may be discovered. As was pointed out, this inconsistency can be interpreted as a signal to expand the description. Failure may also occur because the decision tree being developed has become too complex. This is a heuristic signal that the description should be simplified or carried to a higher level of abstraction. Alternately, some modification in the tree-growing procedure might be possible. Several "rational" cues, such as the extent to which the tree had already been developed to satisfactory endpoints, could be used to guide the decision to make a given modification. An adequate concept-learning model should contain a mechanism for using such information. It could fall back on random choice, perhaps based on response strengths, *after* its mechanisms for making rational choices were exhausted. By use of the computer programing technique a large number of possible "mixed" models of rational choice and habit strength can be investigated. Such models may appear as a "second generation" of information processors.

7    *Memory and transfer: unsolved problems*

The discussion of the present chapter has been oriented toward simulation of a subject who receives all available information and then develops a concept. No mention has been made of either a learner who continuously receives information from the environment and reacts to it, or of one who improves his performance from problem to problem. Yet both situations must be faced in the design of simulation models or artificial intelligences.

An artificial intelligence model of concept learning which continuously evaluates the environment has been developed by Kochen (1960); it will be discussed in Chapter 9. A model of memory, in which a stochastically chosen sample of presented instances was retained in memory and used to develop a new answer when the old one was inadequate, was proposed by Hunt (1960) and used in some experiments with the simulation model. However, it involves completely veridical storage of any instance contained in the sample, which seems to be an unreasonable assumption. A model of memory based on Shepard's (1961) theory of the recognition process seems more suited to our knowledge of memory in concept learning. Feigenbaum (1961), in a theoretical study of verbal learning, has proposed that memory itself be represented as a discrimination net. Perhaps the process of developing a decision net to represent a concept could be made a continuous one in which the net was modified when proven inadequate.

If the problem of representing memory in concept learning is still a topic of conjecture, the problem of representing transfer is even more nebulous. There are at least three ways in which an interproblem transfer could be achieved: by the development of new tests for "shortcutting" the construction of a decision tree, by storing information about the types of solutions obtained on previous problems, and by modification of response strengths on which random choices would be based. Any or all of these could be included in a single model. To date, most studies of transfer have stressed the last, and least rational, factor. The fact that a high level of mastery of the first problem is necessary for effective transfer to a second concept-learning problem (Morriset and Hovland, 1959) suggests that a cognitive factor may be involved as well. As in other fields where complex interactions are found, computer program models seem especially useful as multiprocess theories of transfer.

## 8    A look forward

Hovland's (1952) information analysis of concept learning provided a description of the problem. The development of subsequently more complex models of the process has provided us with measures of problem difficulty. They have also stressed the intimate connection between perception and concept learning which had often been ignored by researchers primarily interested in concept attainment as a special type of learning.

Our main conclusion is that a useful model of concept learning can be built by programming a procedure for constructing a decision tree. This conclusion, which was not anticipated when the work began, is particularly encouraging because it suggests a compatibility between our approach and those of Feigenbaum and Banerji, who independently arrived at the same conclusion for other fields. The particular tree-growing procedure used is not a blind one. It makes use of tests on its own processes to achieve a maximally efficient tree. Such feedback control in answer development appears to be a suitable description (although one that has not yet been proven fruitful) for a wide variety of actions normally considered to be intelligent behavior.

The concept-learning models that will develop from such an approach will, hopefully, generate a great deal of research. Today, the most promising line seems to involve the relation between problem difficulty measures obtained from humans and measures describing trees which are developed from the same problem by different tree-construction methods. There are other possible lines of research, however, which are equally fascinating. Adequate representations of memory and transfer are two such projects.

Even if the decision tree representation were proven inadequate, it seems that its a priori believability is such that the disproof would be interesting. At present, very little data is available on which the position can be supported or attacked. Final evaluation will, of course, depend on the production of such data.

### REFERENCES

Amarel, S., 1960. An approach to automatic theory information. Paper presented at Illinois Symposium on Self Organizing Systems.

Banerji, R. B., 1960. An information processing program for object recognition. *General Systems*, Vol. V, Society for General Systems Research, Ann Arbor, Michigan.

Bruner, J. S., J. J. Goodnow, and G. A. Austin, 1956. *A study of thinking*. New York: Wiley.

Feigenbaum, E. A., 1959. An information processing theory of verbal learning. *Rand Corp. Tech. Rep.*, p. 1817.

Feigenbaum, E. A., 1961. The simulation of verbal learning behavior. *Proc. Western Joint Computer Conf.*, 121–132.

Goss, A. E., 1961. Verbal mediating responses and concept formation. *Psychol. Rev.*, **68**, 248–274.

Hovland, C. I., 1952. A "communication analysis" of concept learning. *Psychol. Rev.*, **59**, 461–472.

Hovland, C. I. and E. B. Hunt, 1960. The computer simulation of concept attainment. *Behavioral Sci.*, **5**, 265–267.

Hull, C. L., 1943. *Principles of behavior*. New York: Appleton.

Hunt, E. B., 1960. An experimental analysis and computer simulation of the role of memory in concept learning. Unpublished doctoral dissertation, Yale University.

Hunt, E. B., 1962. The development of decision trees in concept learning I: Model and Basic Results. *Western Management Science Institute Working Paper 6*. University of California at Los Angeles.

Hunt, E. B. and C. I. Hovland, 1960. Order of consideration of different types of concepts. *J. exp. Psychol.*, **59**, 220–225.

Hunt, E. B. and C. I. Hovland, 1961. Programming a model of human concept formulation. *Proc. Western Joint Computer Conf.*, 145–155.

Kendler, H. and T. S. Kendler, 1962. Horizontal and vertical processes in problem solving. *Psychol. Rev.*, **69**, 1–16.

Kiseda, J. R., H. Peterson, W. Seelbach, and M. Teig, 1961. A magnetic associative memory. *IBM J. Res. Develpm.*, **5**, 106–122.

Kochen, M., 1960. Experimental study of "hypothesis formation" by computer. *Proc. 1960 London Sympos. on Information Theory*.

Luce, R. D. and H. Raiffa, 1957. *Games and decisions*. New York: Wiley.

Maltzman, I., 1955. Thinking: from a behavioristic point of view. *Psychol. Rev.*, **62**, 275–286.

McCarthy, J., 1960. Recursive functions of symbolic expressions and their computation by machine. *Communications of the Association for Computing Machinery*, **3**, 184–195.

Minsky, M., 1961. Steps toward artificial intelligence. *Proc. Inst. of Radio Engrs.*, **49**, 8–30.

Morrisett, L., and C. I. Hovland, 1959. A comparison of three varieties of training in human problem solving. *J. exp. Psychol.*, **58**, 52–55.

Newell, A., J. C. Shaw, and H. Simon, 1959. A variety of intelligent learning in a general problem solver. *Rand Corp. Tech. Report*.

Osgood, C., 1953. *Method and theory in experimental psychology*. New York: Oxford University Press.

Riordan, J., 1960. The enumeration of trees by height and diameter. *IBM J. Res. Develpm.*, **4**, 473–478.

Shepard, R. N., 1961. Application of a trace model to the retention of information in a recognition task. *Psychometrika*, **26**, 185–203.

Shepard, R. N., C. T. Hovland, and H. Jenkins, 1961. Learning and memorization of classifications. *Psychol. Monogr.*, **75** (while No. 517).

Wallach, M. A., 1959. The influence of classification requirements on gradients of response. *Psychol. Monogr.*, **73** (whole No. 478).

Wells, H. H., 1962. Transfer and stimulus effects in disjunctive concept learning. Unpublished doctoral dissertation, Yale University.

Wertheimer, M., 1959. *Productive thinking* (rev. ed.). New York: Harper.

FOOTNOTES

1. This leads to a perverse interpretation of "trees." The root is the highest point of the tree.
2. The particular example is a modified version of one given by Banerji (1960).
3. Such promises are not entirely unreasonable. They may be "made" by theoretical knowledge. For instance, today we seek an explanation for peculiar rock formations in terms of water and wind erosion, glacial history, and soil composition. We know that these are possibly relevant dimensions, and not the social history associated with a particular spot. But an intelligent thirteenth-century monk might seek an explanation of the same phenomenon in terms of the names and acts of saints who had passed that way.
4. This pilot study was carried out by the author in collaboration with Dr. H. H. Wells. The disjunctive concepts were equivalent to inclusive disjunction, exclusive disjunction, implication, and biconditional connections between relevant elements (see Chapter 2). Additional studies confirming the results have been performed by the author and Miss Janet Kreuter.
5. The combination of a counting operation—conditional focusing—with the strictly set theoretical operation of intersection, is interesting. These operations are mathematically different, and would be hard to put in the same model. In simulation and in human behavior this problem does not arise.
6. In fact, Wertheimer's argument parallels in logic and antedates in time Minsky's (1961) and Newell, Shaw, and Simon's (1959) plan for intelligent learning. Wertheimer's publication is posthumous; his argument was presented in the 1930s.

# 9

# Concept formation by
# artificial intelligence

## 1  *Goals*

This chapter will discuss some information-processing systems for discovering concepts. These systems are blueprints for constructable devices which could, given certain information about the environment, develop concepts. Since this is usually conceived of as intelligent behavior, and since such devices are potentially mechanizable, it seems appropriate to call them "artificial intelligences." However this term should not be given any meaning beyond the limited one intended. Devices for solving particular problems are being described; no claim is being made that they represent the essence of intellectual behavior. The devices are designed to handle well-defined data. There is no claim that they handle it in either the only or the best possible way.

Why build such devices? There are three reasons. The builder may have a problem which he wishes to solve. To the extent that the problem is limited, his interests are limited. If we were concerned with medical diagnosis, we might build a data-processing machine which worked only for medical data. Its lack of generality would not be of any particular concern. Such limited problems are rare, especially if they involve the learning of unknown classifications. Even if our ultimate interest is in the solution of a single, specific problem, it may be necessary either to solve a general problem, of which the particular problem is an example, or at least to find out a good deal about the requirements that the characteristics of the general problem place on the specific problem-solving device. For instance, our major interest is in concept learning, not in the learning of a particular concept. No clear dividing line can be placed between research efforts motivated by either consideration. Both approaches emphasize problem characteristics, stressing what there is about the problem that requires particular information processing capabilities in the problem solver. Of course, they may differ in the features of the problem which are stressed.

Some workers in artificial intelligence research begin with an interest in the problem solver. Given a particular set of principles on which an information-processing mechanism has been designed, what is the range of problems to which this mechanism can be applied? Here we enter the realm of Amarel's (1960) "experimental engineering"; we first build a device and then test its capabilities. Contrast this procedure to the problem-oriented approach, where the first analysis is made to determine what capacities must be built into the device if it is to perform its functions well. Then compare the two approaches to that of the biological scientist, who begins with an organism and must infer both its capacities and its design principle from observation of its performance.

In concept learning we shall see that these three approaches often meet.

## 2    Pandemonia

Several systems for the recognition of patterns have been designed. Most of the research has been concerned with visual pattern recognition. This concern is primarily a heuristic aid; it is easy to talk about visual pattern recognition. The problem is not that limited. We can think of the decision to apply a particular mathematical formula, or the decision to call a thing by a certain name, as problems in pattern recognition. To recast such problems as visual pattern recognition all we have to do is think of a matrix in which the value of each entry corresponds to the value of an attribute of the situation or object to be classified. Because of the formal similarity between pattern recognition and other classification problems, some investigators have maintained that pattern recognition and concept learning are controlled by the same underlying processes.

This raises separate questions. Can a device that was designed as a pattern recognizer be considered a concept learner? Are pattern recognizers good concept learners? Are models of human pattern recognition also models of human concept learning? The first two questions are appropriate in the study of artificial intelligence, whereas the last is more of a question for psychology. The answer to the first question is clearly "yes." Answers to the second and third questions can only be obtained by empirical research.[1]

Many different pattern recognition schemes have been proposed. Some of the techniques used are highly specific to particular problems. Others are more general, but still concerned with the detection of a unitary pattern over a specific class of transformations of the input data. The problem of designing a machine to recognize a square no matter where the square is located on the input matrix is an example of recognizing invariance over specific transformations. We cannot possibly discuss all the pattern recognizers that have been designed. Instead we shall discuss a basic principle of pattern recognizers with learning capacities and then give some examples of how the plan is modified.

A good pattern recognizer ought to be able to learn by example. Furthermore, it ought to be able to recognize patterns in the presence of conflicting and only partially valid cues. In other words, it should be able to make statistical discriminations. This requirement has led to a method for designing pattern recognizers that Selfridge (1959) has described as the *Pandemonium* scheme. The name "Pandemonium" came from Selfridge's description of the recognition process. He suggested that instead of responding on the basis of a single, accurate, and perhaps complex test (such as passing the description of an item through a decision tree), pattern recognizers ought to classify objects on the basis of data obtained from many simple, error-prone tests. Selfridge likened the simple, error-prone tests to "demons," all shouting an answer. Although the individual demons might speak softly and give conflicting cries, enough demons shouting the same word could give rise to a mighty roar. Hence, Pandemonium.

A Pandemonium pattern recognizer need not have a learning capability. Special purpose Pandemonia with fixed tests have been built (Selfridge and Neisser, 1960). They consist of a preprocessing form, which puts the input stimuli into some standardized description, and a set of demons with preassigned weights. Such devices have little interest in the study of concept learning. On the other hand, a learning Pandemonium may be constructed. When patterns are learned for later recognition, we begin to approach concept learning.

A learning Pandemonium begins with a standardized stimulus description which may not be changed by the program, and a set of demons, which compute tests on the standardized stimulus. Each test results in a decision and a weight. Roughly speaking, the decision represents the confidence the testing demon has in its own computation; the weight represents the confidence the overall system has in the demon's opinion. Every time an object is presented, each demon computes a real number, based on the description of the object, which will be used as part of an abstract description from which the object's class membership is to be predicted. Symbolically, let $x_{ij}$ be an estimate of the probability that the input stimulus is in the $i$th class, computed on the basis of the $j$th test. This is combined, multiplicatively, with another number $\lambda_{ij}$ which represents the weight assigned to the $j$th test in determining the $i$th classification. A classification is decided on by finding which of the set of classes $\{C_i\}$ has the largest associated weight $w_i$ where

$$(9.2.1) \qquad\qquad w_i = \sum_j x_{ij} \cdot \lambda_{ij}$$

Learning can be introduced in three ways: alteration of the $\{x_{ij}\}$, alteration of the $\{\lambda_{ij}\}$, and change in the number and type of tests. The first type of learning is the simplest. Each test is assumed to have a finite set of possible results. Associated with each test is a memory device (it need not be complete) that counts the number of times each of the finite set of possible outcomes of that test has been associated with the stimulus patterns from a given class. This record can be used to assign an $x_{ij}$ to a particular stimulus. A good example is Gold's (1959) use of symbol length in an automatic detection device for receiving Morse code. In handsent Morse code the length of the symbol is a reasonable, but not infallible, clue as to whether the transmitter sent a dot or a dash. The accuracy of this cue varies with the operator. Gold's device stores a frequency count of symbols of different length which were previously identified as dots or dashes. The symbol length test of this device can then adjust its decisions to a particular operator after it has received messages from him.

A more interesting type of learning is the readjustment of the overall confidence weights, the $\lambda$'s. Given the set $\{x_{ij}\}$, how do we find the best $\{\lambda_{ij}\}$? Selfridge suggested that a pattern-recognition device should contain a provision for making tentative, small random changes in the weights, then determining whether or not the change resulted in better discrimination. The third type of learning—creating new tests —can be considered as a special case of the second type. Since the rules for creating new tests must be specified by the system designer, all possible tests are really in the system, but some have weights equal to zero at the beginning of the problem. All that the rules for creating new tests do is increase these weights. Of course, they do specify a particular way in which the weights will be changed. This is crucial to the performance of any Pandemonium system.

Although not labeled specically as a Pandemonium, a pattern recognizer developed by Uhr and Vossler (1961a) is an excellent example of how powerful and general Pandemonia can be. Uhr and Vossler's system receives as input patterns represented by a $20 \times 20$ matrix of ones and zeroes. (For example, handwritten letters could be superimposed on a 20 × 20 matrix, in which the entry would be a one if a line passed over a square of the grid and would be zero otherwise.) Uhr and Vossler programmed a digital computer to develop an abstract description of such stimuli by applying *operators* to local regions of the original 20 × 20 matrix. These operators were actually 5 × 5 sub-matrices which could be matched to local regions of the larger matrix. The original stimulus could then be described in terms of which operators fit, and where. To see how this was done, we shall go over the recognition procedure for a single pattern.

First the input pattern is transformed to the standard input form of a 20 × 20 binary matrix. This is completely automatic, and is not under the control of the program. The input pattern is then "normalized" by drawing a rectangular mask around all the one entries in the 20 × 20 matrix. Thus the mask is placed around the borders of the figure to be classified. Further operations will be confined to the area inside this rectangle, so the same pattern will have the same abstract description no matter where it falls on the original matrix. The large matrix can be thought of as a retina. Insofar as Uhr and Vossler's system is concerned, any pattern is identical to itself over spatial transformation on the retina.

To obtain the abstract description, each of the currently active operators (5 x 5 matrices) is fitted, systematically, to all positions inside the rectangular mask. The 5 × 5 matrices are trinary matrices; their entries may be zero, one, or X. A local region of the original matrix fits an operator if all the zeroes and ones of the operator can be superimposed on zeroes and ones in the local region of the larger matrix. Figure 9-1 gives an example; the indicated operator can be fitted to the circled local region of the larger matrix. A record is kept of all operators which can be fitted to the input matrix, and the position at which they were fitted. This record provides the abstract description. A rough statistical method is used to classify the pattern on the basis of the abstract description. The average abstract description for each possible class of patterns is also kept, and the pattern being presented at time $t$ is classified as being a member of that class whose average abstract description most resembles the current pattern.

Uhr and Vossler's system can both "learn" and "be educated." Education is achieved by changing the abstract description of a typical pattern as the pattern recognizer acquires more and more experience about its environment. This is equivalent to changing the values of the $\{x_{ij}\}$ in a Pandemonium. The pattern recognizer can learn in the sense that it can change its operators. There are $3^{25}$ possible operators. Only forty or less are used at any one time. If useful operators are known, they can be preprogrammed. Alternately, they can be generated at random and their usefulness observed. But the most interesting way in which operators are generated is by imitation. Uhr and Vossler included in their program a routine for generating an operator by imitating the segments of a figure border which pass through a local region of the input matrix. This procedure should result in much more rapid selection of good operators, since all the discrim-

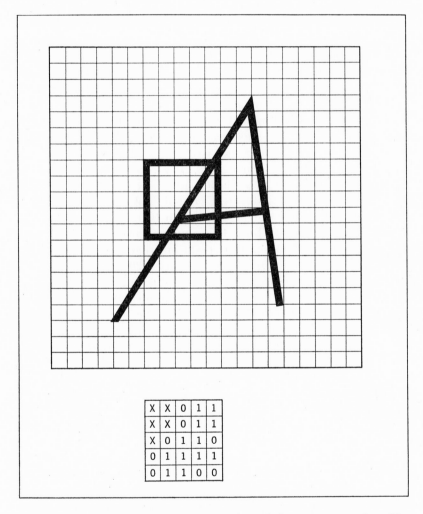

Figure 9-1. Template matching in Uhr and Vossler's pattern recognizer. The $5 \times 5$ matrix at the bottom may be superimposed on the indicated local region of the larger matrix.

inating operators must, by definition, be included in the set of operators which can be constructed by imitation. (That is, if a particular attribute is relevant to a description, there must be some objects which have this attribute!) Since the set of operators which can be constructed by imitation is normally smaller than the set of all possible operators (assuming that the problem is solvable), the search for good operators is simplified.

Uhr and Vossler's pattern recognizer has proven to be an excellent performer. Uhr, Vossler, and Uleman (1962) found that it can even recognize some patterns better than humans can. They "showed" the system a set of visual "nonsense" patterns which had been partitioned into several classes. The system was forced to give the same response to each pattern within a given class. In fact, the partition had been chosen so that there were varying amounts of intra-class similarity. This measure had been obtained in psychological experiments by other workers. After having had its responses forced the first time the patterns were shown, the system was required to make a free response the second time. Wrong responses were corrected. The patterns were then shown a third and fourth time. The experiment was repeated using humans instead of an artificial pattern recognition system. During the experiments with humans, Uhr et al. took precautions to make sure that the computer system did not do better for trivial reasons. They exposed the stimuli for a long time and made certain that the subject understood the task. They point out that the machine had to respond to the projection of the patterns on a $20 \times 20$ grid, and that the human subjects could make at least this fine a resolution of a visual stimulus. Even so, the computer program learned to assign the responses correctly in fewer trials than did the best human subject. The computer was also more accurate in generalizing its responses to new patterns constructed by the same rules used to construct patterns in each class, but not shown in the original set.

Uhr and Vossler (1961b) made one of the severest practical tests of a pattern recognizer known to this author. Their system had originally been developed to recognize printed letters. They used it to recognize speech spectrograms of spoken digits. Speech spectrograms are extremely complicated visual diagrams of vocal output, in which the amplitude-frequency distribution is portrayed. Although a trained person can "tell what the man said" when he looks at a speech spectrogram, they are unintelligible to the naive subject. By using its facility to abstract operators that imitated parts of the spectrograms shown it, Uhr and Vossler's pattern recognizer not only learned to recognize five spoken digits, it was able to recognize the digits when they were spoken by a person other than the one who had produced the spectrograms on which the machine had been trained.

The Uhr and Vossler technique could be used to develop a description of objects to be categorized by a tree-growing system. We could regard the operators as dimensions, and the location to which they were fitted as values, or vice versa. In either case, we would have an automaton capable of developing templates, fitting them, and using the resulting fit to establish a description. The reader may recall that in Chapter 4 we put forward evidence to support such a model as a description of human perception. A combination of the Uhr and Vossler system, as a model of perception, and the tree-growing procedure, as a model of cognition, seems to be a logical design for the next step in understanding concept learning. The combined system would have the capability of solving any discrimination problem that could be represented by the information on the $20 \times 20$ input matrix, regardless of the logical form of the answer. The basic Pandemonium model does not have this capability; it finds its power in the ability to try many descriptions of the objects in front of it, hoping that some description will lead to a simple concept.

Pandemonia make their ultimate discrimination on the basis of a linear weighting of an abstract description. The final result of the description process is a set of numbers to be used in a crude linear discrimination. There are more sophisticated analystic techniques by which statistical discriminations can be made (Rao, 1952). Pandemonia cannot construct discriminations more powerful than those constructed by the analytic use of statistical information. Of course, analytical statistical methods do not provide any techniques for altering tests, they operate only on the weight of known tests. Pandemonia may require much less computer storage space or computing time than programs using the analytic techniques. Also, Pandemonia do not require assumptions about the distribution of test scores. Thus Pandemonia provide an alternate to statistical discrimination techniques when the latter are not practical.

A limitation of Pandemonium-type devices that use statistical discrimination is their apparent inability to handle classification problems in which the classification is based on the exclusive disjunction of the result of two of the tests. As an example, consider a classification of colored patterns as red or star, but not both. A test for figure will give a higher $x_{ij}$ for star than not star, a test for color will do the same for red and not red. So long as additive combinations of the subtests are used, patterns that contain red stars will be classified incorrectly. This error can be avoided within the Pandemonium paradigm only by introducing a new, second-order test whose result depends on a logical combination of the first-order test results. Although this has been, and can be, done (it is in Uhr and Vossler's system), it reduces the attractive simplicity of the paradigm.

## 3    Perceptrons

Rosenblatt (1958*a,b*, 1961) developed a combination of brain model and artificial intelligence system based on reasonable biological assumptions, the *Perceptron*. Block (1961) pointed out that explorations of perceptron behavior cannot prove that this system is an accurate brain model. Such explorations may show that a perceptron is a plausible model. As there are several perceptrons, and as their biological plausibility is not of concern, we cannot attempt a complete review. Instead, we shall present the basic idea of a perceptron and an argument that the perceptron, like Pandemonium, is essentially a correlator. As such it is not believed to be an adequate device for studying the operation of symbol manipulating machines. Its utility as a model of neurological organization or as a device for studying principles of organization within random nets, both of which may be considerable, are separate questions.

A perceptron consists of a network of three types of randomly connected elements which are supposed to represent idealized neurones. Although spatial localization is *not* implied, it is easiest to think of the elements as being located in separate areas, as illustrated in Figure 9-2. The first elements are the sensory elements, which receive signals from outside the system. Projection of a pattern on the retina causes some of the sensory elements to fire. The sensory elements, if excited beyond their threshold, fire with constant strength and variable delay. Each sensory element is randomly connected to some units in the association area. The association elements are the abstract describers of the perceptron. According to Rosenblatt they may be plausible models of the

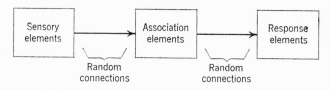

Figure 9-2. A simple perceptron.

elements found in the association area of the mammalian brain. Each association unit can receive either excitatory or inhibitory signals from its *source set,* the set of elements from which it receives signals. A particular member of the source set sends a signal to the receiving unit; this may be either positive (excitatory) or negative (inhibitory). If the sum of the signals received by an association element exceeds a given threshold value, it fires. In most perceptrons subsets of randomly chosen association elements provide source sets for response elements. In cross-coupled and series-coupled perceptrons (Rosenblatt, 1960; Block, Knight, and Rosenblatt, 1961), association elements may send signals to other association elements. In all perceptrons one association element may send signals of different weights to different response elements.

When the input to a response element exceeds a certain threshold, the element fires. This has the effect of inhibiting all association elements not in the source set of the response element. Firing of a response element is assumed to be in one:one correspondence to an overt response. The principal dependent variable of a perceptron study is alteration in the probabilities of firing of response units when members of certain classes of stimuli are projected on the retina. Thus the perceptron "learns a discrimination" when it contains a response unit which will fire whenever a member of the denotation of a particular name is presented to it. It never "learns a concept," as we defined the phrase in Chapters 1 and 2, because it contains no mechanism for explicitly stating a set of objects defined by a descriptive statement which is equivalent to the denotation of the name.[2]

Rosenblatt (1961) has pointed out the strength and weakness of a random net that can organize itself to learn a discrimination. He showed that a perceptron can, in principle, learn to mimic the behavior of any finite state Turing machine. This is essentially a statement that the perceptron could imitate any artificial intelligence device, so (as Rosenblatt does) we should examine the power and generality of the claim.

In Chapter 7 problem solving was described as the process of mapping from input to the appropriate output. Suppose that there existed a problem-solving machine that subdivided the universe of $n$ possible inputs into those for which each of the $m$ possible responses was (or was not) appropriate. In effect, it would be making $m$ discriminations between stimuli. A perceptron could organize itself to make each of these discriminations. (How this is done will be discussed shortly.) Each of the $n$ possible stimuli would be input and the appropriate response forced as output. Eventually the system would readjust its association element weights so that it would give the correct response without forcing. But, it would not have mimicked the internal logic of the original problem solver. In particular, it could not generalize. If only $n - 1$ training stimuli were used, a perceptron might give a correct response to each of them and an erroneous response to the $n$th stimulus. In a loose analogy, we could say that perceptrons are models of rote memory without understanding.

Sometimes the perceptron would generalize correctly. What happens depends on the nature of the problem and, to a lesser extent, the complexity of the particular perceptrons. Perceptrons "learn" by the adjustment of the output weights of association elements, which corresponds to adjustment of the $\lambda$'s in a Pandemonium paradigm. Indeed, the perceptron can be thought of as a specialized Pandemonium. Firing (or not firing) of an association element when an image is projected on the retina corresponds to the computation of a test on the sensory image, weighting the output from an association element corresponds to weighting this test as appropriate for each response class.

The favored procedure for readjustment of weights is the "gamma system." Here the total strength of a signal which can be produced by a source set of association elements remains constant. (The total signal is, of course, much greater than the threshold for the responding element.) If the responding element fires in response to signals received from a subset of its source set (which, in turn, will have been fired as the result of signals received from the retina), all active units in the source set will have their output signals increased at the expense of the inactive units. Intuitively we can see that, as a result, association elements that are fired by stimulus elements that, in turn, are fired by selected projections of the stimuli on the retina will eventually gain sufficient strength to fire the response elements even if other association elements in the source set do not fire.

In the original perceptron report (Rosenblatt, 1958a) three major results were reported which are applicable to the simple gamma system perceptron of Figure 9-2 with inhibitory and excitatory connections. The results are as follows:

1. A perceptron can exhibit spatial generalization. If the spatial representation of stimuli on the retina contains sufficient information on which discrimination between classes of stimuli can be made, the perceptron will learn to make this discrimination. In particular, it can extend the discrimination to new instances.

2. If random patterns are presented in a learning series, each pattern

randomly coupled to a particular response, the greatest probability of a particular response in a second presentation series will occur when the stimulus previously presented with this response is re-exposed. This is the basis for the mimicking capability described earlier.

3. In the learning of a class discrimination (case 1) the perceptron's performance becomes poorer (i.e., it takes longer to learn the discrimination) as the number of classes is increased. In case 2, performance becomes poorer as the number of patterns is increased. With each of these increases, the perceptron is required to rely on finer and finer discriminations between areas on the retina.

Simple perceptrons can learn an exclusive disjunction, to respond when either a subset $S_1$ or $S_2$ of stimulus elements are firing, and not to respond when they are both firing. Inhibitory connections must be present. The strongest bias toward acquisition of greater response strength will be found in the association units that are stimulated by $S_1$ and inhibited by $S_2$ or vice versa. This result suggests the utility of including negative weights in certain Pandemonia devices.

More complex perceptrons have exhibited more interesting behavior. The "four-layer series coupled perceptron," which has two sets of association elements connected in series, is even able to learn to assign the same response to all patterns that appear in temporal contiguity (Block, 1961). The cross-coupled perceptron, which has a single set of association elements—any given element connecting both to response elements *and* other association elements—is capable of learning to apply the same response to a given pattern and to a spatial transformation of it (Rosenblatt, 1960).[2] In both these perceptrons as in other amplifications, additional performance is gained at the cost of additional complexity. The result has been a decrease in the conceptual attractiveness of the perceptron as a model of brain functioning.

How does the perceptron function as a concept learner? We reiterate the basic thesis that it is a correlator and does not learn concepts. Instead, it develops weights for error-prone tests and becomes a probabilistic discriminator. If we consider a perceptron as a Pandemonium device, the result of the test is established by the initial random connection between sensory and association elements (each association element is, therefore, a "demon"), and the value of each test is established by the gamma system rule for recomputing output signals for association elements. Provided that the retinal projection itself contains sufficient information to discriminate between stimuli for which a response is or is not appropriate, a perceptron is bound to learn any discrimination, eventually.

In the more complex perceptrons the direct retinal projection of the stimulus alone need not contain sufficient information on which to base the discrimination. What the more complex perceptrons do is create, within the association area, a "third dimension" for the retina which contains a (somewhat fuzzy) projection of the stimulus being presented, as it would appear under a particular transformation. This information can be utilized to make the discrimination. Different types of perceptrons are capable of making different types of transformations from the retina to this "third dimension." There seems to be no theoretical limit to the complexity of the discriminations which can be learned.

There are severe practical limits, however. It seems doubtful that the perceptron (or for that matter, any randomly connected net) could be a practical device for discriminations. Either the stimulus must be preprocessed to produce a standard form [e.g., as in Uhr and Vossler (1961a)], which reduces the amount of randomness within the system, or the random system must produce such a preprocessor, by random trial. In the latter case, excessively long times and excessively large amounts of machinery will be required to produce the answer to simple problems. Green (1961) concluded that at present no random network can be developed to be a practical discriminator. He also doubted that random nets were reasonable biological models. (A doubt in which we concur, although it is not central to the topic of this discussion.)

What conclusions can we drawn concerning random self-adjusting pattern recognizers? In understanding the types of mechanism we shall require for the development of concepts, they are probably of very little help (but see footnote 1). As practical devices for using names, especially when we suspect that we cannot find an adequate description upon which to base a nonprobabilistic concept, they may help. They will be most practical in situations in which we already have a large number of discriminatory measures of low validity and, for some reason, are not able to develop the best weighting scheme for combining these measures by using an analytic method. When the tests themselves must be developed, discrimination based on random or semi-random adjustment of test weights may be excessively time consuming. In such a situation it might also be the only alternative. Some consideration should be given, however, to an alternate description of the stimuli or to abandonment of the problem as not practically solvable.

To develop nonprobabilistic concepts we need either an algorithm or an analyzable heuristic method of manipulating nonprobabilistic statements. Such systems have been proposed.

# 4 An algorithm for educated guesses

Kochen (1960, 1961) has developed an artificial intelligence system which guesses the correct answer to a concept-learning problem before sufficient information has been presented. Unlike the research described in the previous chapter, Kochen did not try to simulate human processes; he tried to develop an efficient concept learner. Some of the techniques used in Kochen's system could not be the same as those used by humans.

Kochen's system is concerned with the solution of a concept-learning problem *after* the description of objects and categorization into positive and negative sets have been decided. Thus the function of his algorithms is identical to the function of the tree-growing mechanisms in Hunt and Hovland's (1961) simulation study. No attempt is made to find new ways of describing stimuli.

Kochen represented objects by "words" of $n$ binary digits. Each digit specifies the applicability or inapplicability of a particular descriptive statement to the object. No use was made of the possible structure of stimuli into dimensions and values. If there are $d$ dimensions, with $v_i$ values in the $i$th dimensions, each object is represented by a word of binary digits of length $n$, where

$$(9.4.1) \qquad\qquad n = \prod_{i=1}^{d} v_i$$

The same object could be described in Hovland's (1952) terms by $d$ nonbinary digits. For example, in describing a particular fiber in an American flag, Hovland would use a single symbol, red, whereas Kochen would use three symbols for "it is not white," "it is not blue," and "it is red." In addition, an extra bit would be attached to indicate that the particular object was or was not a positive instance of the class to be defined.

There are $2^n$ possible $n$ digit binary words. These words define the universe. The universe itself can be divided into $2^{2^n}$ different subsets or potential denotations of names, including the empty set. Any one of these sets can be specified by the intersection and/or union of the sets of objects to which particular descriptive statements may be applied. This specification corresponds to the definition of sets of objects by descriptions and descriptive statements, as presented in

Chapter 2. To express the set defined by the union of $j$ descriptive statements, $j < n$, Kochen introduced "trit words" of length $n$ as the concepts of sets of objects. As in Uhr and Vossler's system, a trit word contains $n$ *trinary* digits each taking value zero, one, or $x$. A trit word may be used to define a set of binary words that agree with the trinary word in the position of ones and zeroes, disregarding all digits where the trinary value is $x$. For example, if $n$ is three, the trit word OOX defines the set of binary words {001, 000}. For fixed $n$, there are $3^n$ trit words. Each of these represents a possible conjunctive concept, since a conjunctive concept requires the joint applicability of all relevant descriptive statements (i.e., a match on all non-$x$ trinary digits).

Disjunctive concepts can be represented by the union of two or more sets defined by trit words. For instance, the Shepard, Hovland, and Jenkins' (1961) "Type II" concept with positive instances {001, 000, 110, 111} would be represented by the expression OOX$\cup$11X.

Suppose that objects (binary words) are chosen at random, with equal probability, and presented to a concept-learning device. Each time an object word is presented, the experimenter indicates whether it is or is not a positive instance. (We shall use $+$ after a binary word to indicate positive instances, $-$ to indicate negative instances.) Is there a way to categorize the types of information contained in each identification? How should we measure the performance of the concept-learning device in these circumstances?

At the beginning of a concept-learning problem, before any positive or negative instances are shown, the learner "knows" that the correct concept is one of a finite set of possible concepts. After the first instance is shown, the size of this set will be reduced. Subsequent instances may or may not result in still further reduction. For instance, the series of two, three-digit binary words, (001+, 000+), indicates, without reference to any other words, that the correct concept is a member of the set of trinary words, {OOX, OXX, XOX}. If the word 101$-$ should be added to the series, the set of plausible concepts would be reduced to {OOX, OXX}. The third word would transmit information. (In Watanabe's (1960) analysis, it would be a logical refutation of the hypothesis XOX.) On the other hand, suppose the original series were increased to the series (001+, 000+, 111$-$). No members of the original set of possible concepts would be refuted, and the third instance would transmit no new information beyond that transmitted by the first two instances. Kochen called the addition of a noninformation transmitting instance a redundancy. He distinguished two types of redundancies; primary redundancies, in which a previously observed object was repeated (e.g., 000+, 001+, 000+), and secondary redundancies, in which a new object was shown but no new hypotheses were refuted.

For new information to be transmitted, the new member of a series of instances must be inconsistent with at least one hypothesis that could explain the class membership of previous instances. An example of information transmission was given in the preceding paragraph. In some cases the new instance may be inconsistent with all previously plausible hypotheses which contained only one trit word. Kochen distinguished between primary and secondary (logical) inconsistencies. A primary inconsistency occurs if two identical objects are assigned to different classes (e.g., 000+, 001−, 000−) at different times. The existence of a primary inconsistency is sufficient evidence that either the $n$ dimensional binary word is not based on a relevant description or that classification is (partly) at random. In the latter case there is no concept to be learned. A secondary inconsistency occurs if a new instance is added to the series and if its class membership refutes all previously plausible hypotheses containing only one trit word. For instance, in the series (010+, 011−, 110+) the hypotheses X10 and XXO are compatible with observed class memberships. If the object 111+ is added to the series, both these hypotheses are refuted.

Let $t$ be the number of object words presented. If no primary redundancies are permitted, $t$ can take any value between 1 and $2^n$ at the appropriate point in the experiment. When objects are presented at random (subject to the restriction on redundancy) the value of $t$ is a measure of the average amount of information given the concept learner. It can be related to the probability that a particular learner will have achieved a certain concept, or reached some other point in hypothesis development. In applied problems $t$ may be interpreted as the number of patterns that must be shown to a particular machine before it can recognize patterns on its own or, perhaps, the number of cases a given medical student must see before he reaches an acceptable level of diagnostic skill.

To use $t$ we must relate it to the learner's progress toward a solution. Kochen used several measures of this progress; a partial list is given in Table 9-1. Notice particularly the two measures $N_o$ and $N_L$. The point at which the series of binary digit words has reduced the set of plausible hypotheses to one is represented by $N_L$. In the series (001+, 000+, 111−, 011+) $N_L$ occurs at $t = 4$, at $t = 5$ in the series (001+, 000+, 010−, 111−, 100−), and at $t = 2$ in the series (000+, 011+). However, at any point in the experiment, the concept learner could guess (or, select as a trial hypothesis) a particular member of the set of possibly correct concepts. If the correct concept were to be selected, it would never be changed. An efficient concept-learning strategy would let the learner do this. For instance, one of Bruner, Goodnow, and Austin's (1956) "wholist" subjects would have guessed the answer to the first example (above) to be OOX at $t = 2$, which is correct. Kochen symbolized the point at which the correct answer was first offered as $N_o$. In efficient concept learning $N_o$ should be smaller than $N_L$.

The point of occurrence of $N_o$ can be known only to the experimenter, not to the concept learner. The same is true of any distance function $d$, which measures discrepancies between the current and correct concept. In practical situations a concept learner would like to have a measure of the confidence that he ought to have in his current hypothesis, even though he cannot prove that it is correct on the basis of the information available to him. Watanabe's measure $H(q)$ represents one such index. Kochen used an alternate one. Let $c_1(t)$ be the number of times that the current hypothesis has been confirmed by the occurrence of positive instances, let $c_2(t)$ be the number of times it has been confirmed by negative instances. Let $p(t)$ be the best estimate of the probability of choosing a positive instance at random. A reasonable estimate of confidence in the current hypothesis is

$$(9.4.2) \qquad w(t) = \frac{t}{t+1} \cdot \{ p(t)c_2(t) + [1 - p(t)]c_1(t) \}$$

This function satisfies Polya's (1954) requirement for an index of plausibility. It responds strongly to confirmation by unusual events, since the confirming power of a particular type of instance is weighted by the probability that that instance will *not* occur. Hypotheses that occur after an evaluation of a large body of evidence are given greater weight than early hypotheses; this is insured by introducing the factor $[t/(t + 1)]$.[3]

At first, Kochen (1960) considered the performance of several information processing systems which guessed answers to conjunctive concept-learning problems. A single trit word would be chosen by the experimenter as the concept. A series of randomly chosen object words consistent with the concept would then be presented. After each presentation the information-processing mechanism produced an hypothesis (i.e., a tentative trit word) and computed a weight function for it.

For moderately sized problems, and for concept learners using somewhat complex strategies, $N_o$ and $N_L$ are difficult to calculate on the assumption of random selection of objects. Kochen estimated them for different problems and concept learners by the Monte Carlo technique. He realized several information processing systems as digital computer programs and observed the solution they reached on a series of concept-learning problems.

*Table 9-1 Some of the measures of performance used in Kochen's hypothesis development system*

| | |
|---|---|
| $p(t)$ | An estimate of the frequency of $+$ words, based on the observed sequence. |
| $B$ | The correct hypothesis, either a single trit word or a union of trit words. |
| $N_o$ | The smallest $t$ (serial order of presentation of object words) after which the hypothesis, as represented in the machine, is equivalent to $B$. This hypothesis may be only one of several logically possible hypotheses. |
| $N_L$ | The smallest $t$ at which only one possible hypothesis can be entertained (i.e., the point at which sufficient information has been presented to solve the problem on a logical basis). |
| $d_X$ | The number of digit positions which are $X$ in $B$ and labeled as constants (0 or 1) in the current hypothesis, assuming that both the current hypothesis and $B$ are expressed by a single trit word. |
| $d_c$ | The number of constants (0 or 1) in $B$ which are labeled as $X$ or as the complement of the correct value (1 or 0) in the current hypothesis, under the same assumption. |
| $d$ | A distance function, a function of $B$ and the current hypothesis which represents the extent to which they are different. (Several such functions are possible.) |

Several systems were tried; for details the original report should be consulted. The final three versions were fairly similar to each other. They began by assuming, as an initial hypothesis, that all trits in the concept have the value $X$. This assumption led to the prediction that all instances are positive. When this (or any other) hypothesis was refuted, all presented instances were scanned to determine as many trits as possible which could be *logically fixed*. Logical fixing occurred every time a new instance was presented, using the rules of implication which are valid for conjunctive concepts.[4] Unless $N_L$ has been reached there will always remain a set of trit positions that cannot be logically fixed. The correct values of these positions are guessed whenever the current hypothesis is revoked.

If the hypothesis was refuted by a negative instance, and if it did not provide information that could be used to alter the hypothesis on a logical basis, a trit provisionally set at $X$ in the hypothesis would be set at the complement of the value of that bit position on the infirming negative instance. If no single trit position could be found that, when altered in this manner, did not result in an inconsistent hypothesis, pairs, triples, etc. of bit positions were tried. (In practice, this was seldom necessary.) If there was no trit digit position provisionally set at $X$, a position(s) *provisionally* set at a constant (0 or 1) in the hypothesis, was reversed.

If the hypothesis in force was refuted by a positive instance, and if the new instance did not provide for a new logical fixing, a provisional non-$X$ trit in the current hypothesis was found that, when replaced by an $X$, created an hypothesis which included the refuting instance in the set it defined. If no such single digit could be found, doubles, triples, etc. were tried, and the "assumed" denotation (the set defined by the current hypothesis) was expanded.

In the final system for learning conjunctive concepts ($S_6$) an additional ramification was introduced. Following revision of the hypothesis some digit positions remained which were not logically fixed. Since any hypothesis predicts that there will be $2^k$ positive instances, where $k$ is the number of irrelevant trit positions in the answer, out of a total of $2^n$ possible instances, an attempt was made to select, randomly, a certain number unfixed and fixed digits as provisional $X$'s so that the observed frequency of positive instances agreed with that predicted by the hypothesis. System $S_6$ tried to match observed and predicted frequencies of positive instances, thus taking advantage of Watanabe's (1960) rule that inductive procedures should favor the hypothesis that approximates the data the closest, even though other hypotheses may not be logically refuted.

Kochen investigated the performance of his information-processing systems with $n$ varying between 3 and 14 and $k$ varying between 0 and 12. (Not all possible problems were investigated.) Three important empirical observations were made. The point at which the correct concept was guessed, $N_o$, occurred considerably before $N_L$, the point at which the current hypothesis could be proven to be correct. (In some cases $N_o$ occurred within less than thirty object presentations although $N_L$ never occurred within the time limits of the experiment.) Furthermore, the point at which $N_o$ occurred was approximately the same so long as at least the last twenty object words presented were retained in the system's memory. This modification is extremely important because it greatly reduces the computing time required in the logical checking phase. For some problems, limitless memory would require centuries of computing time on a high-speed computer.[5] Introducing a limit on memory size may pare the time required for the same problems to a matter of hours without appreciably reducing performance.

Kochen's most interesting conclusion concerns the performance of the weight function. On the conjunctive problems discussed above it was found that a sizable first difference in the weight function [i.e., a sudden increase in $w(t)$] was associated with a large decrease in the distance between the current hypothesis and the correct answer. Define $N_1$ as the smallest $t$ such that $w(t)$ plus the number of trit words that are logically fixed is three if $t$ is two, two if $t$ is three, and one otherwise. $N_o$ was always less than $2N_1$, provided that at least twenty-five words were kept in memory. Since $N_1$ may be calculated entirely from information available to the concept learner, it can be used by him (it) to estimate the point at which his unproven hypothesis is the correct answer.

The foregoing results hold only if the correct concept can be expressed by a single trit word. If the correct concept is a disjunction, this requirement will not be satisfied. Kochen (1961) has proposed an as yet untested system for handling such problems. This system uses an additional procedure to revise its hypotheses, if the previously described ones do not work. This procedure is somewhat similar to the "keeping track" focusing problem described in Chapter 6.

If a positive instance is logically inconsistent with any single trit word in the current hypothesis, a new conjunction must be added to expand the hypothesis to include the offending item. This can be done by forming a new conjunction by the same procedure as before except that the only object words used in the formation of the new conjunction are those which are consistent with the refuting instance. At any one time then, the hypothesis will consist of a logical sum of trit words, each of which provides a conjunctive hypothesis consistent with a subset of the object words presented.

If a negative instance is logically inconsistent with the current answer (i.e., no modification of a single trit word in the current answer can be found which will result in an hypothesis that excludes this instance from the set of positive instances), all trit words in the hypothesis that include this object word as a positive instance must be split so that they reject it. Kochen modified his answer by creating two new trit words from the erroneous words of the current answer. Each of the new trit words was identical to the original trit word except that one randomly chosen X in the original word was replaced by the *complement* of the value of that digit position in the refuting object word. A different digit was selected for each of the two new trit words. If only one trit word could be created, this was done. The union of the set defined by the two new trit words was different from the set defined by the original word in that it did not include the inconsistent negative instance. In the unlikely event that there was no

$X$ in any original trit word, all words including the negative instance in their denotation were dropped from the answer.

Only preliminary results have been reported for this system. In a personal communication, Kochen has stated that the disjunctive system will solve concept-learning problems, reaching $N_o$ before $N_L$. The importance of memory capacity to this system is not known, although it can be conjectured that $N_o$ will be much more dependent on the size of storage for previous object words than it was in the conjunctive concept learning system. Finally, and perhaps most discouraging, the correlation between $N_o$ and $N_1$ does not hold in the disjunctive system, indicating that $w(t)$ does not provide a good confidence index for disjunctive concept-learning problems.

As a practical design for concept-learning mechanisms, Kochen's systems are worth investigation. In particular, they attack the problem of continual modification of the current hypothesis in the light of new information, and do so in an efficient manner. Even so, $N_o$ is evidently an exponential function of $n$ (and a negative exponential function of the number of $X$'s) for conjunctive and probably disjunctive problems. This suggests that there will be limitations on the size of the problems that can be handled with current machinery. It would be particularly enlightening to compare Kochen's techniques with a modified decision tree system, handling the same problem with a known relevant description of objects. If the description is known, either technique should provide more rapid discovery of the correct concept than an artificial intelligence system based on random nets.

Once again, comparison of the systems for solving conjunctive and disjunctive concepts stresses the fact that different information-processing procedures are required to solve conjunctive problems.

Although he was not primarily interested in simulation of human processes, Kochen (1960) did conduct an experiment in which human subjects solved some conjunctive problems that had been presented to his concept-learning systems. Subjects were required to state their current hypothesis and their confidence in it. Records of previously presented instances were always available. Although Kochen reported wide individual differences, the humans did not do markedly better at guessing the correct answer than did the artificial intelligence systems. Kochen interpreted this as evidence that his problem situation did not elicit the human ability to make rapid and accurate inferences on the basis of few cues, which ability "is not believed to be shared by present computers." It appears to this author that an equally reasonable conclusion is that if we really understood the stimuli to which humans are responding, and the responses they can make, we would find that humans have no information-processing capability that cannot be represented by a machine. Whether it can be practically represented by existing hardware is another question.

## 5    A heuristic system that learns to learn

Kochen's techniques for guessing hypotheses are fixed algorithms. Exactly the same procedure for discovering the answer is followed on every problem. The system will never cease processing information unless it is terminated by outside intervention. Otherwise it will always find a solution (when $N_L$ is reached), even though centuries of computing time might be required. The amount of time required to solve a particular problem is entirely a function of that problem and does not depend on previous problems solved. Any "learning to learn" must be done by the experimenter, who can create a new information-processing system after observing the performance of the old one. We can conceive of problem situations in which these characteristics would be fatal. Perhaps the chief advantages of humans over machines as solvers of well-defined problems are related to the ability of humans to take advantage of past experience. This can be very helpful if it is combined with the human tendency to cease trying to solve a problem that is too complex, given the present solution methods. The problem may be put aside until, as a result of future experience, new problem-solving methods are developed.[6] Are these advantages necessarily reserved to biological problem solvers?

They are not. Amarel (1960) has designed an artificial intelligence system that learns to produce the operations of the propositional calculus. The system learns in the sense that it creates, by induction, machine routines equivalent to sixteen basic operators. Once a particular operator is learned (i.e., available to the system) it can be used to facilitate further learning of other operators. The system is heuristic rather than algorithmic. It contains features for self-termination and/or reordering of its attack on a problem by monitoring the computing effort being expended. Like Kochen's, Amarel's information processor has the capability of guessing a correct answer before this answer can be proven from the available evidence. Although Amarel's present results are preliminary, his proposal is of sufficient general interest to warrant discussion.

Consistent with our previous definition of a concept, we can say that a class, or name, indicates that for all objects within the denotation of the name there are only certain combinations of relevant descriptive elements. Therefore, if we know the name of the class to which the object belongs and some of its descriptive elements, we should be able to predict what certain other elements are. Suppose we divide the set of relevant descriptive elements into two subsets, corresponding to dimensions whose values are known and unknown. If we know the name of the class to which an object belongs, and understand the concept of that name, we should be able to predict the values of the unknown dimensions from values of the known dimensions. In psychological terms, we "go beyond the information given" (Bruner, 1956), assuming particular statements because we have observed others. This is a psychological definition of the use of a concept. In mathematical terms, we should be able to produce a mapping from a point in a set defined by combinations of values on the known dimensions to a point in a set defined by combinations of values on the unknown dimensions. Amarel maintained that having a machine theory of a concept was equivalent to having an information-processing routine that produced this mapping. He then asked what sort of self-organizing system could organize such a routine if it were permitted to observe instances of the mappings permissible within a certain class.

Without reference to any particular concept, some requirements can be placed on such a system. It must contain, initially, certain primitive information-processing routines, or "building blocks," which, when combined in some manner, can realize the mapping. Although it would be possible to try random combinations of primitive routines, a more efficient procedure is desirable. This can only be achieved if the system has some way of describing the characteristics of its building blocks and of the situation facing it. If it faces a situation in which a mapping of the combination of two sets into a single set is to be achieved, it should not attempt to use primitive routines which map single sets into other single sets. In other words, the self-organizing system must be able to construct a plan. The plan is a specification of the type of subprocesses that will be needed at different points in the mapping to be realized. Once the plan is constructed it can be filled in by trying different combinations of blocks of the appropriate type. In making choices of which of the eligible blocks to try first, the system might make use of its previous experience.

The idea of planning is not unique to Amarel's system. The overall design of the concept learner proposed by Hunt and Hovland (1961) is a plan: input different categorizations and descriptions; use the combined result to construct a decision tree. Newell, Shaw, and Simon (1959) have designed a "general problem solver" for solving deductive logic problems which operates by creating and trying out different plans. Several authors (Polya, 1954; Johnson, 1955; Miller, Galanter, and Pribram, 1960; Wertheimer, 1959) have suggested that plans, as described here, are necessary descriptions of human thought processes. Amarel's contribution is in applying the technique of automatic plan construction explicitly to inductive problems.

Plans make use of the building blocks available to them at the time that they are created. Previous, successful plans may be stored in memory for use as building blocks in later plans. Thus, as the system learns concepts in an environment, it will be able to solve, in less and less time, progressively more complex problems. Amarel points out that a machine that benefited from its experience in this way would increase its intellectual capacity essentially in the way that Piaget (1957) alleges humans do. Increased experience could be equated with the availability of more powerful operators and, hence, greater problem-solving ability. Such a machine would be extremely sensitive to the order in which problems were presented to it, since this would determine the point at which particular operators were developed.

Learning should be progressive within as well as across problems. Amarel considered only the situation in which the system encounters positive instances (mappings) of a particular class. The system should not wait until all possible instances are presented. Beginning with the first instance, it should produce a routine equivalent to the mapping between relevant descriptive elements specified on that instance. When the second positive instance is observed, the routine just produced should be attempted. If it works, well and good. If the routine can produce the first mapping between relevant elements but not the second, the system must produce a new routine that covers both cases. Presumably the correct information processing routine (i.e., the filled-in plan) which is adequate for all mappings included in the class will be discovered before the entire class is presented.

Amarel has not considered the problem of discovering which elements are relevant. He has assumed that each object to be classified is represented only by a subset of relevant descriptive elements drawn from the set of elements from which a mapping begins, and a subset of elements drawn from the set of elements to which the mapping is to be completed.

In spite of the limitation just noted, which is somewhat surprising since the discovery of relevant elements comprises a major portion of the processing time in the concept-learning systems designed by Kochen and Hunt and Hovland, Amarel's inductive reasoning system can be applied to a basic, inductive problem. By hand simulation techniques, an information-processing system "M," has been designed which produces operations equivalent to the sixteen operators of two valued propositional calculus. The system does this by induction, using as its data observations of mappings between compound and simple functions. *In principle,* an information processing system which can produce these sixteen operations could then use them as building blocks to produce any other formula of the propositional calculus. Thus the system should be able to solve any concept-learning problem in which the concept can be expressed in the notation presented in Chapter 2. Whether such a system can be realized as a practical concept learner, operating within reasonable time and hardware limitations, is unknown.

To understand Amarel's M system, a brief explanation of his problem is in order. There are four possible combinations of two binary arguments. These define the set [(0,0), (0,1), (1,0), (1,1)]. There are sixteen possible mappings of this set into the set (0,1). For instance, the mapping corresponding to the propositional calculus operation of conjunction is:

$$
\begin{array}{ccc}
0,0 & \ldots\ldots\ldots\ldots & 0 \\
0,1 & \ldots\ldots\ldots\ldots & 0 \\
1,0 & \ldots\ldots\ldots\ldots & 0 \\
1,1 & \ldots\ldots\ldots\ldots & 1 \\
\end{array}
$$

The reader will recognize that this is one way of stating the truth table definition of conjunction, as given in Chapter 2. Other simple examples of mapping are $T$, in which the value is always 1, or $F$, in which the value is always 0, regardless of the argument. Each of the sixteen mappings defines a function $(f_1 \ldots f_{16})$. The final goal of M is to produce an information-processing routine equivalent to each of these sixteen functions.

To avoid a trivial problem, Amarel did not use the sixteen basic mappings as his observable data. Instead he used as examples of a class functions whose arguments are functions. Unfortunately for exposition, the details of this become rather involved. We shall attempt to explain by example and intuitive reasoning.

Let the arguments of the "basic" functions, which are to determine the value of the arguments of the function to be learned, be fixed. Now, take a given function to be learned and two basic functions to determine its arguments. The final value of the function to be learned will be a member of the set 0,1. Furthermore, for all four possible values of the arguments of the basic functions, the mapping between the set $(0,1)^2$ and the set $(0,1)$ will be identical to the mapping produced by one of the sixteen possible basic functions. As an example, consider the function "conjunction" when its arguments are determined by the values of the arguments "conjunction" and "$T$." If the arguments of the basic functions are (0,0), the value of "conjunction" is 0 and the value of $T$ is 1. Keeping the arguments fixed at (0,0), we find that the value of CONJUNCTION [conjunction (0,0), $T$ (0,0)] is the same as the value of conjunction (0,1), or 0. In fact, this identity holds for all members of the set of arguments, (0,1) $^2$. Thus we can say that the mapping CONJUNCTION maps the point defined by the pair (conjunction, $T$), in, the set of pairs of possible functions (or arguments of functions of functions) $\partial^2$, into the point, conjunction, in the set $\partial$ of possible functions. In fact, CONJUNCTION establishes a mapping of each pair in $\partial^2$ into a member of $\partial$, the set of sixteen functions. Each of the other fifteen functions, when its arguments are established by the value of pairs of functions, establishes a similar (but distinct) mapping.

The objects that Amarel uses as data for his inductive system are pairs, an element of $\partial^2$ and an element of $\partial$, together with the name of a function which contains this pair as an example of its mapping. A particular pair may be in several mappings, so the name must be specified, and only positive instances should be considered at any one time.

The primitive routines of M can be classified by the way in which they manipulate elements of $\partial$: combinatorial operations on sets (union, intersection, etc.), all possible mappings from one point in $\partial$ to another point in $\partial$, and certain special relations between points in $\partial$ and specified subsets of point in $\partial$.[8] This is the logical classification of the original primitive routines. The system actually categorizes its basic operations by their performance characteristics, routines that create one set from many sets (e.g., union of sets), routines that produce one set from two sets (e.g., intersection of sets), routines that produce a point set from an element of the set $\partial$, routines for producing a set, not necessarily a point set, from an element, and routines that produce many sets from one set.

When an input pair is presented, the system is faced with the problem of producing an information-processing routine which goes from an element in $\partial^2$ to a point in $\partial$. If such a routine is not available, the system plans one. For instance, the last step of the desired routine must be a primitive which produces, as its value, a point in $\partial$. Choosing such a routine specifies the required value of the next to last primitive routine(s); it (they, if they are in parallel) must produce the values that can be used as arguments for the last primitive routine. This process is continued, choosing a primitive routine at each step from the set of routines with the proper characteristics, until routines are selected which can use the element of $\partial^2$ which is contained in the original input statement as arguments. At this point a complete mapping routine will have been developed. This is added to the list of primitive routines, thus increasing the power of the system.

Each step in building such a routine involves searches among possible candidates for producing the appropriate value. Notice, also, that there may be more than one category of primitive routine which will produce the desired value, since primitive routines in different categories may produce the same value type but differ in the argument they require. For instance, the operations of taking the union or the intersection of a set both produce a set. The operation of union is a function with $n$ arguments, the operation of intersection requires two arguments. To guide in selecting operations to be assembled into routines, Amarel proposed that M record association numbers, similar to the habit strength indices found in some psychological models of learning (see Chapter 3). The function of these numbers would be to guide the selection of the next operation, given that particular operations had already been selected. The association numbers would be, essentially, a record of the frequency with which primitive routine $a$, followed by primitive routine $b$, had been part of a successful problem-solving routine. This record would be used to determine the probability of trying $b$ as the next step in a tentative routine, given that $a$ had already been selected.

The use of association numbers provides Amarel with a very flexible concept learner. It could monitor its attempted solutions, terminating them if they reached a certain level of complexity without producing an answer to the problem at hand. If one combination of primitive routines failed to produce an answer, the system could try another. Whenever either a category or a primitive routine participated in the development of a successful routine, the appropriate association strength indices would be incremented. If a routine were terminated before completion because of undue complexity, all the association indices of its subunits would be decremented. Within this general scheme there are many ways to alter association strength. The effect different plans would have on the behavior of the system has not been reported.

In so far as it can be evaluated from the hand simulations reported, M is capable of developing internal information processing-routines that are equivalent to some of the sixteen mappings in the set $\partial$. There is no reason to believe that it cannot learn them all. We do not know, however, what the effect of learning them in different orders will be.

Clearly, there will be some effect, but its size is unknown. Perhaps more important, we do not have an adequate estimate of the relation between problem complexity, the performance of this information-processing system, and practical limitations imposed by present-day hardware. Intuitively the system is an attractive one. It provides for both rote learning (via association indices) and learning by planning, reminiscent of Wertheimer's bad and good thinking. It is certainly a worthwhile model of the general process of concept learning. It may require better machinery than we have today before it can be realized as a practical problem solver. This suspicion is fortified by our earlier observation that it has no provision for handling or eliminating irrelevant information.


## 6    Summary

Commenting on the "state of the art" in artificial intelligence, Ashby (1961) said that although the 1950s were a period of ferment and excitement, the 1960s will probably be a period of elaboration and development of ideas. This is what is needed in the field of automatic induction. We have four candidates for designation as the design principle of automatic induction: random nets, decision trees, "guessing" algorithms, and planning. All have their place no doubt; their potentiality for solving particular types of problems and the effect of combining them into a single device is not well known.

Random nets and randomly adjusting devices that are not based on neural networks (e.g., Pandemonium) are not really concept-learning devices, since they contain little provision for stating the logic behind their operation. However, random search techniques might be included within a program designed to operate on a more restricted logical basis in order to increase its flexibility.

Kochen's work and the decision tree technique portrayed in the previous chapter are different attacks on the same problem. An experimental engineering approach is needed; by experimenting with different types of problems it may be possible to state when a concept-learning mechanism should be designed on one principle or the other.

Amarel's work is directed at finding the relations between elements that are known to be relevant. In many practical situations this information is not available. Before Amarel's system could be used as a practical concept learner (and it must be remembered that it was not intended as such), it would have to include a rapid method for determining relevancy of a descriptive element. In some ways, however,

Amarel's proposal represents the most advanced concept learner. Amarel's system has a great many implications for the simulation of human behavior.

This chapter has probably raised more questions than it has answered. In the next chapter some tentative answers will be suggested. They may be completely wrong. Research on artificial intelligence is developing rapidly. The work that has been discussed appears to this author to represent probable lines of investigation that will pay off, in terms of a practical artificial intelligence, in the next few years. Such a device will probably be an extremely limited one. In particular, it will most certainly be able to operate only within a clearly defined set of inputs and outputs. Even so, it may develop concepts about important data that are unknown today.

REFERENCES

Amarel, S., 1960. An approach to automatic theory formulation. Paper given at Illinois Symposium on Principles of Self Organization.

Ashby, W. R., 1961. What is an intelligent machine? *Proc. Western Joint Computer Conf.,* 275–280.

Block, H. D., 1961. Analysis of perceptrons. *Proc. Western Joint Computer Conf.,* 281–289.

Block, H. D., B. W. Knight, Jr., and F. Rosenblatt, 1961. Analysis of a four-layer, series-coupled perceptron. Cognition systems research project, Cornell University, Rep. No. 1.

Bruner, J. S., 1956. Going beyond the information given. In *Contemporary approaches to cognition.* Cambridge: Harvard University Press.

Bruner, J. S., J. J. Goodnow, and G. A. Austin, 1956. *A study of thinking.* New York: Wiley.

Gold, B., 1959. Machine recognition of hand sent morse code. *I. R. E. Trans. Prof. Group on Information Theory,* IT-5, 17–24.

Green, B. F., Jr., 1961. Computer models of cognition. *Psychometrika,* **26**, 85–96.

Hovland, C. I., 1952. A "communication analysis" of concept learning. *Psychol. Review,* 59, 461–472.

Hunt, E. B. and C. I. Hovland, 1960. Programming a model of human concept formulation. *Proc. Western Joint Computer Conf.,* 145–155.

Johnson, D. M., 1955. *Psychology of thought and judgment.* New York: Harper.

Kochen, M., 1961. An experimental program for the selection of "disjunctive hypotheses." *Proc. Western Joint Computer Conf.,* 571–578.

Kochen, M., 1960. Experimental study of "hypothesis formation" by computer. *Proc. 1960 London Sympos. on Information Theory.* (Also reprinted as an International Business Machines Technical Report.)

Miller, G. A., E. Galanter, and K. Pribram, 1960. *Plans and the structure of behavior.* New York: Holt.

Newell, A., J. C. Shaw, and H. A. Simon, 1959. Report on a general problem solving program. *Proc. International Conf. on Information Processing*, Paris: UNESCO, 256–264.

Piaget, J., 1957. *Logic and psychology*. New York: Basic Books.

Polya, G., 1954. *Patterns of plausible inference*. Princeton: Princeton University Press.

Rao, C. R., 1952. *Advanced statistical methods in biometric research*. New York: Wiley.

Rosenblatt, F., 1958a. The perceptron: a theory of statistical separability in cognitive systems. Cornell Aeronautics Laboratory Report VG-1196-G-1.

Rosenblatt, F., 1958b. The perceptron, a probabilistic model for information storage in the brain. *Psychol. Review*, 65, 386–468.

Rosenblatt, F., 1961. Principles of Neurodynamics. Cornell Aeronautics Laboratory Report 1196-G-8.

Rosenblatt, F., 1960. Stimulus generalization over transformation groups. In Yovits & Cameron (eds.), *Self organizing systems*. London: Pergamon Press.

Selfridge, O., 1959. Pandemonium, a paradigm for learning. *Proc. Sympos. on the Mechanization of Thought Processes*. London: H. M. Stationery Office.

Selfridge, O. and U. Neisser, 1960. Pattern recognition. *Sci. American*, 203, 60–79.

Shepard, R. N., C. I. Hovland, and H. Jenkins, 1961. Learning and memorization of classifications. *Psychol. Monogr.*, 75 (13, whole No. 517).

Uhr, L. and C. Vossler, 1961a. A pattern recognition program that generates, evaluates, and adjusts its own operators. *Proc. Western Joint Computer Conf.*, 555–570.

Uhr, L., and C. Vossler, 1961b. Recognition of speech by a computer program that was written to simulate a model for human visual pattern perception. *J. Acoustical Soc. Amer.*, 33, 1426.

Uhr, L., C. Vossler, and J. Uleman, 1962. Pattern recognitions over distortions, by human subjects and a computer model of human form perception. *J. exp. Psychol.*, 63, 227–234.

Watanabe, S., 1960. Information theoretic aspects of inductive and deductive inference. *IBM J. Res. Development*, 4, 208–231.

Wertheimer, M., 1959. *Productive thinking*. (rev. ed.). New York: Harper.

FOOTNOTES

1. In a personal communication, Dr. Leonard Uhr, of the University of Michigan, has suggested that, although there may be some differences, it is a mistake to think of concept learning as being basically different from the process of perception. Bruner (1956) and the present author feel that there is a difference, that concept learning is more of a conscious, analytic process. It is hoped that future work in which specific (computerized) models of conception and perception are compared will settle the question.

2. Interestingly, it does this by observing instances of the *inverse* of the transformation, applied to other patterns.

3. In Kochen's first (1960) article an additional term $l\ (t)$—the number of trits which could be fixed with logical precision on the assumption (which was always true) that the correct concept was a conjunctive one—was added to the right-

hand side of equation 9.4.2. This cannot be done if disjunctive answers are allow-able, because there may be several ways to express a satisfactory disjunctive concept (Kochen, 1961, p. 575).

4. Any digit position in the bit words that varies over positive instances must be an X in the correct trit word. Any bit position that represents the *only* dif-ference between a positive and a negative word must have as its value in the correct trit word the value contained in the appropriate positive bit word. Any digit position that is constant over all positive bit words but does not represent the only difference in a positive-negative pair may be 0, 1, or X in the correct trit word.

5. This estimate is based on Monte Carlo runs using an IBM 704 with a machine language program. No projected computer would appreciably reduce the esti-mate. The time saved was in the logical checking phase.

6. As an illustration, take the problem of determining the optimal size of a tin can. This is a very difficult problem until the differential calculus is mastered.

7. More specifically, from a point in $\partial$ to a set defined as the set consisting of a set of size one containing a point in $\partial$. For any $f_i$, $f_j$, there exists a mapping of $f_i \rightarrow \{f_j\}$ as an original building block.

8. These are based on a lattice theoretical definition of the operations of two valued propositional calculus.

# 10

# The near future

Concept learning has been presented as a topic for logical analysis, a behavior to be explained by psychology, and as a desired capability of intelligent automata. When stated together in a single sentence, it seems obvious that many common problems face researchers in each area. They should be able to support each other. However, in a selected review of research that has actually been done, we found that they cannot. More often than not, the empirical work on logic, psychology, and artical intelligence aspects of concept learning has been carried out without any cross reference. Fragmentation of effort has not helped advance our knowledge of the underlying process.

Perhaps psychologists have been the most guilty of ignoring the related work in engineering and logic. This may be due to historical accident. Concept learning entered into modern experimental psychology as a derived problem. It was regarded as a complex case of discrimination, a phenomenon to be derived from more basic laws. Making the wish father of the thought, psychologists leaned toward an operational definition of concept learning which was not based on the use of concepts in logic. Since some language like symbolic logic is probably necessary for the accurate statement of a scientific problem, the use of an operational definition of a phenomenon that differs markedly from its logical definition appears unwise.

Of course, it would be possible to define concept-learning research in accordance with the definitions of symbolic logic and still treat it as a phenomenon to be derived. If concept learning were of no importance in itself, this strategy might be recommended as an interesting exercise to demonstrate the generality of a learning theory. But concept learning is important. It represents the essence of the peculiarly human ability to use names. There is much to recommend the counsel that we attack a research problem in the manner that will permit its most rapid solution, rather than its solution along preconceived lines. Consider an analogy to the use of knowledge about automobiles. Ultimately, the behavior of an automobile can be explained in terms of attractions between subatomic particles. Probably no one has ever tried to derive theorems about the behavior of automobiles on highways from postulates about the construction of the nucleus of the atom. No one should. There would be no point to it. The theorems themselves are important. They can be constructed using higher order postulates. Is it true that the researcher who attempts to derive theorems about how humans learn to use names from a basic theory of stimulus-response connections is in the same position as the man with the nuclear physics theory of highway behavior? Concept learning can be thought of as a technique for solving an inductive problem in symbolic logic through the use of information-processing routines. Such an analysis can and should be no less rigorous than any mathematical theory of learning.

Evidently some psychologists have adopted this attitude. The frequently cited research effort by Bruner, Goodnow, and Austin (1956), although certainly not composed of studies in symbolic logic, was oriented toward finding information-processing routines used by humans for solving problems that were statable within a formal logic system. Great interest has been displayed in work by Newell and his associates on the construction of information-processing models to simulate human deductive reasoning. The prototype problem in this research is the derivation of symbolic logic theorems. Many of the techniques developed during this work could be, and are being, extended to analysis of inductive reasoning.

The principal technique was the computer model. At the present time its chief contribution to psychology has been the construction of a new theory-building device. Psychologists can now construct models using set-theoretic statements and decision tree structures that were formerly just not computable. Because of their very newness, these techniques are not well understood by psychologists or by mathematicians and logicians. Perhaps this is why information-processing models have, so far, made little substantive contribution. When difference equations (to name a technique which, when applied, resulted in substantial immediate empirical work) were introduced in psychology, it was a matter of indicating to the scientist that the mathematician had a well-developed tool that might be applicable to a particular problem. When information-processing systems were introduced, it was suggested that mathematicians and logicians had *under development* a tool that might be useful. Thanks, in part, to psychologists who have been interested, and more to highly motivated information processing experts, the new tool has been developed rapidly. In the next few years we can expect to see a large number of experimental tests of information-processing simulation models. This should be especially true in the concept-learning field, where intensive research is being carried on to develop the very tools—induction algorithms, means-end analyses, planning heuristics, and decision trees —that the psychologist will need to build his models. We should demand, however, that as the tools are better developed the tests of simulation models become more and more precise. It may well be that our conventional techniques for testing scientific models will not be applicable. This does not excuse us from making and justifying some test. Research on the appropriate procedure for evaluating information processing models of inductive reasoning will be required. This is, in itself, such a large and poorly understood topic that it has not been discussed here.

Many of the techniques that are attractive to the psychologist were originally developed to aid in the search for an artificial intelligence system that can perform inductive reasoning. The problems facing an engineer who attempts to design such a system are somewhat different from the problems facing a psychologist attempting to create a simulation model. The psychologist must account for the known behavior of a given organism of unknown design. The engineer must determine whether (a) a problem solver with certain capabilities can be created from a known design principle or (b) given a problem, how an optimal problem solver should be constructed. To accomplish either of these tasks the system designer must understand the design principles that are available to him. To date, most of the work in designing artificial intelligence systems of inductive reasoning has been pointed toward a better understanding of some of the design principles that have been suggested. This work is by no means completed. In the next few years we can hope for important developments which should increase our knowledge of how to proceed in designing a system, given a problem, and in predicting the performance of a given system over various problems.

In all probability, analytic techniques will not provide all the information that we need about the mechanization of inductive thought processes. Experimentation will be necessary. (Kochen's work is an excellent example of this type of research.) We appear to be handicapped in an experimental program because present-day general purpose computers were really designed with an entirely different purpose in mind, the solution of complex mathematical equations. A digital computer can be made to perform operations on sets, but it is an expensive and time-consuming operation. New computer languages will help, but they do not represent a final answer. At some point before we begin to design useful artificial inductive reasoners, and certainly before we begin to solve a great many real world problems by using them, we shall need more suitable computer hardware. But until we have more experience with preliminary models of inductive reasoning we shall not be able to say what the basic operations of the desired computing devices should be. Therefore, the fact that present-day digital computers are not the optimal vehicles for the construction of concept-learning models should not deter the construction of prototype models. We need to experiment with a wide range of possible concept-learning models before we can place production orders for inductive automata.

The preceding reservations concerning present-day computers should not be interpreted as a withdrawal of support. The author believes that an interesting concept will be formed by an inductive automaton within the near future. Perhaps we can guess what the problem that is solved will look like. It will probably be a problem for which some sort of existence proof is known, one that specifies some very large set of descriptive elements within which the correct concept must lie. In other words, the problem will have to be one that involves a finite set of elements from which the concept can be constructed. After all, the computer can only recombine the knowledge we give it. If we do not provide it with a vital element, it can never find the correct combination. Second, the problem will probably have as its answer an extremely complex disjunction. Otherwise a human would have already solved it!

The ultimate in concept-learning automata is the inductive reasoner that redesigns itself. Although investigation of different techniques of artificial "learning to learn" should be continued, it seems that this device is still some distance away. On the other hand, there is a tremendous potential in research on the design of complex man-machine systems that reorder themselves. These systems could utilize the combination of the (as yet unknown) heuristic techniques available in the human to evaluate the results of unfinished computer calculations of great complexity. In the near future, say the next 5 years, it can be anticipated that most practical inductive reasoning systems will be of this type. If our sole interest is in the solution of a particular problem, there is no objection to including a human being as one of the components of a problem-solving device. He is still the best concept learner available, and will be for some time.

REFERENCES

Bruner, J. S., J. J. Goodnow, and G. A. Austin, 1956. *A study of thinking.* New York: Wiley.

# Author Index

# Subject Index

283